REVIEWING
BIOLOGY

By Mark A. Hall
East Hampton High School
East Hampton, New York

DRAWINGS BY EDNA F. MILLER

AMSCO SCHOOL PUBLICATIONS, INC.

45 East 17 Street ● New York 3, N. Y.

Mailing Address: Box 351, New York 3, N. Y.

PREFACE

Reviewing Biology is a concise and up-to-date text designed to provide a complete review of Biology. At the same time, this text adds real understanding, appreciation and purpose to the course. The principal features of this book are as follows:

1. *Content:* The material included in the text has been carefully selected to meet the required course of study. The relative importance of the various topics has been carefully considered. The highlights of the subject have been emphasized, the non-essentials minimized.

2. *Presentation:* The topics are arranged in logical sequence and are designed to present the science of Biology in carefully planned, easy-to-understand steps. The material on human biology not only presents the structures and functions of the human body, but also gives the student an understanding of man's place in the world of living things.

3. *Language:* The language is clear-cut and understandable. Sentence structure is simple. Since an understanding of Biology depends in large part on an understanding of biological terms, all terms are clearly defined the first time they appear in the text. Non-essential terms have been omitted.

4. *Illustrations:* In addition to numerous charts and tables, a fine collection of drawings has been prepared to supplement and clarify the text. All drawings are simple, accurate and carefully labeled in order to provide the student with an understandable and usable illustrative device.

5. *Questions:* At the end of each chapter is a large number of carefully worded questions of various types. These questions provide an abundance of material for class work, home study and review. Careful practice with these questions will enable the student to master Biology more efficiently and to prepare adequately for any examination.

6. *Appendix:* At the end of the book is a list of famous biologists, recent examinations, and a complete index to the entire text.

—M. A. H.

CONTENTS

Chapter I

MAN APPEARS AND DOMINATES THE EARTH

LIFE APPEARS ON THE EARTH

The Age of the Earth. The age of the earth has always been a puzzle to scientists. No one knows *exactly* how long ago the earth was formed. From scientific estimates, though, it seems that the earth is from two to three billion years old.

Estimating the Age of the Earth. The most accurate means of estimating the age of the earth is the *radioactivity* method, as follows: As the element uranium disintegrates, it gives off certain radiations, changes to radium and finally to the stable element lead. The time required for a certain amount of uranium to change to a certain amount of lead is known. Hence, by determining the proportion of lead to uranium in deposits of uranium ore, we have a clue to the age of the earth.

Scientists have also tried to estimate the age of the earth by determining how many years it has taken for (1) the salt in the sea to reach its present concentration, and (2) the sedimentary rock layers to reach their present thickness. However, these two methods are not considered reliable.

Life Begins. How the first living thing was formed, and when it appeared on the earth, are not definitely known. One theory suggests that life began about two billion years ago in the salty sea, probably near the shore where the water was warm and quiet. There, under the influence of sunlight, the first bit of living matter was formed by the union of certain chemical elements, including nitrogen, oxygen, hydrogen and carbon.

It is believed that the first living thing was a single-celled organism, even smaller and simpler than the well-known ameba. The first living thing must have been able to make its own food, since there was no food on earth at that time. As this first simple organism became more numerous, and more widely distributed, two groups eventually arose: simple plants and simple animals. When the water became thickly populated, some plants and animals developed structures enabling them to live on land. Plants, being the food supply for the animals, appeared on the land first.

1

Today, there are about 350,000 different kinds of plants, ranging in size from microscopic bacteria to the great Sequoia trees of California. At present, there are about 800,000 different types of animals. These range in size from microscopic forms to the great sulphur-bottom whale, weighing over 150 tons.

PREHISTORIC MAN IS DISCOVERED

The Prehistoric Period. The invention of writing, about 6,000 years ago, ushered in the *historic* period of man. The time prior to 6,000 years ago is known as the *prehistoric* period. There is evidence —although meager—that two-legged ape-like animals, standing erect and resembling man, lived on earth during the prehistoric period, perhaps a million years ago. But, without written records, the full story of their civilization is lacking.

What we know of prehistoric man and his culture has been pieced together from *remains* (bones) and *artifacts* (such as tools, weapons, pottery) unearthed by *archeologists.* These men of science dig the soil to uncover physical evidences of prehistoric life. From the remains and artifacts, other scientists, called *anthropologists,* determine man's origin, development, distribution, civilization and general culture.

Prehistoric Man. Anthropologists generally agree that ancient man made his appearance in Africa or Asia. From there, by way of ancient land bridges, he spread to other parts of the earth. The following prehistoric men are known to us through archeological discoveries:

1. *Java Man.* The skeletal remains of the Java ape-man were unearthed in Java toward the end of the 19th century. He is the oldest known prehistoric man. In appearance, he resembled both ape and man, but more closely man. Java man had a low forehead and large bony ridges overhanging the eyes. His brain was considerably larger than that of an ape, but only about two-thirds as large as the brain of modern man. Since the structure of his thigh bone was straight, Java man probably walked erect, a decidedly human characteristic. Very little is known about the culture of Java man, because his remains are so fragmentary.

2. *Peking Man.* The remains of about fifty individuals, found in a cave near Peking, China, give us information about this prehistoric species. Peking man is believed to have been on earth at about the

same time as Java man, and to have resembled him in some ways. Peking man had a larger brain than that of Java man. Peking man's use of crude stone tools and his knowledge of fire also suggest a higher intelligence. He is thought to have practiced cannibalism, for the skulls of most of these ape-like creatures were broken, their brains probably having been removed.

3. *Neanderthal Man.* The remains of this man were first found in the Neanderthal Valley, near Dusseldorf, Germany. Remains were later discovered elsewhere in Europe, and in Asia and Africa. Neanderthal man was primitive in appearance, having heavy bones that emphasized a short, powerful stature. Because his knees were bent, he walked slouchingly. A low forehead, heavy ridges over the eyes, a massive jaw and receding chin added to his ape-like appearance. His cranium (brain case) was larger than that of his predecessors', so he must have had a higher degree of intelligence. He used fire, and made spears and axes from flint stone. He buried tools with the dead, thus suggesting a belief in life after death.

MAN PROGRESSES THROUGH THE AGES

Cro-Magnon Man. Cro-Magnon man is the first known representative of *Homo sapiens*, the species to which modern man belongs. His remains were discovered in a cave near Cro-Magnon, France. He was tall and had a well developed head. His large brain indicates a high degree of intelligence. Cro-Magnon man was able to make carefully wrought tools and weapons. Artistic sketches on the walls of his caves give evidence of his having fished and hunted to obtain food, and having used skins for clothing. Religion, and a belief in life after death, also show his culture to have been further advanced than the prehistoric men discussed previously.

The Ages of Man. The thousands of years that man has been on earth are divided broadly into three ages: the *Old Stone Age, New Stone Age* and *Age of Metals.* The Old Stone Age was the longest period. Life was exceedingly crude; man made progress only very slowly. The New Stone Age was comparatively short. Once man started to move forward, he advanced quickly. The Age of Metals, in which we now live, is about 6,000 years old, and is marked by the significant change of using metals instead of stone for the making of tools, weapons, buildings, etc.

1. *The Old Stone Age, or Paleolithic Period* (started about 30,000 years ago). Early man lived in the open, but sought the shelter of caves as protection against severe weather and wild beasts. His food consisted of wild fruits and berries, and animals which he could catch with his hands. For tools and weapons, he first used stones as he found them. Later he chipped the stones (mainly flint) in order to produce a better variety of tools, such as knives, spears, and bows and arrows. These served his needs for hunting and fishing. He also used the horns of animals to make harpoons, and bone to make needles for the sewing of clothing from animal skins. Important, too, was the discovery of fire, with which to cook his food and heat his cave. Paleolithic man showed an interest in art and religion. Pictures on the walls of his cave help give us a view of the culture of early man.

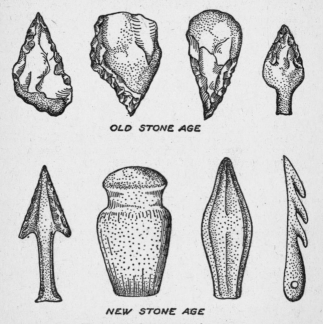

OLD STONE AGE

NEW STONE AGE

Fig. 1. Prehistoric Implements

2. *The New Stone Age, or Neolithic Period* (started about 10,000 years ago). In this period, man began to develop agriculture, growing vegetables and grain. Since the cultivation of crops necessitated his living in one place, Neolithic man built a permanent home. This was the beginning of community living. He domesticated animals, such as dogs, sheep and cattle. He was able to make superior tools and weapons by grinding and polishing stone. He also learned to make pottery and weave textiles. He invented the wheel, and then built carts and wagons. Neolithic men buried their dead and set up monuments to mark their graves.

3. *The Age of Metals.* Man's discovery of the process by which a metal can be extracted from its ore, a process called *smelting,* ushered in the Age of Metals. This period, extending from about 4,000 B.C. to the present, witnessed man's greatest progress in a comparatively short period of time. Working with metals instead of stone, man created better tools, weapons and machines. He developed art, religion, commerce, industry, science and government.

The Age of Metals is divided into the following three periods, each named for the metal dominating the age.

a. The Copper Age (started 4,000 B.C.). The first metal utilized by man was copper. Because of its softness and luster, copper was then used only for the making of ornaments. It was found unsatisfactory for the fashioning of tools, weapons and utensils, since copper does not retain its shape or keen edge.

b. The Bronze Age (started 3,000 B.C.). By mixing tin with copper, man obtained bronze, a much harder metal than pure copper. Such a mixture of metals is known as an *alloy.* Thereafter, bronze replaced copper for the making of tools and implements requiring a sharp or pointed edge.

c. The Iron Age (started 1,000 B.C.). Man made the greatest progress after he developed the process of extracting iron from its ore. Iron is harder and tougher than copper or bronze, and therefore has many additional uses. *Steel,* an alloy of iron, is produced in many varieties, according to special uses.

MAN OF TODAY

The Superiority of Modern Man. During the few thousand years that modern man has been on earth, he has developed (1) superior tools, weapons, utensils and homes from iron, steel, copper and other metals, (2) power from steam, petroleum, electricity and atomic energy to run machines, (3) better foods, (4) ways to better health, sanitation and control of disease, (5) means of protection against the elements and wild animals, (6) systems of government for the public welfare, (7) art, literature and music.

Modern man has been able to progress as rapidly as he has mainly because of his superior brain and hands. He has the capacity to think, reason, plan, do things. He is able to manipulate tools. He has learned to control his environment, and modify it to meet his needs.

Stocks and Races of Modern Man. There are over two billion men on earth today, all belonging to the same species—*Homo sapiens.* But there are many differences in the physical appearance of people. Some have a light skin, others dark or yellow. Some have woolly hair, others wavy or straight. Some have a broad nose, others narrow or medium. These characteristics and others have made it possible for anthropologists to divide modern man into three main groups, or *stocks,* which are further subdivided into *races.*

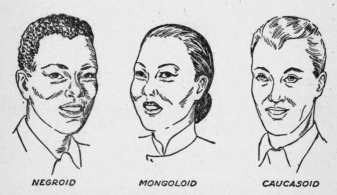

NEGROID   MONGOLOID   CAUCASOID

Fig. 2. Stocks of Modern Man

1. **Negroid Stock.** This stock is believed to have originated in Africa. The general characteristics are: dark skin, black woolly hair, black eyes, broad nose, a prominent jaw. The Negroid stock is divided into the following races:

a. Bushman Race. Native of southern Africa, small stature (under five feet), flat face, bulging abdomen, small brain, coarse yellowish skin.

b. Negro Race. Native of Africa, tall stature, powerful physique, woolly hair, flat nose, prominent lips, dark skin.

c. Pygmy Race. Native of central Africa, small stature (under five feet), small chin, broad nose, dark skin (lighter than Negro).

2. **Mongoloid Stock.** This stock is believed to have originated in Asia. The general characteristics are: yellow skin, black straight hair, black eyes, medium-wide nose, medium jaw, short stature (except the American Indian). The races of the Mongoloid stock are:

a. American Indian Race. Native of North America, tall stature, broad face, prominent cheek bones, straight black hair, little body hair, yellow-brown to coffee-brown skin.

b. Malay Race. Native of Malay peninsula, short slight stature, prominent cheek bones, large eyes, straight black hair, yellowish skin.

c. Mongol Race. Native of Mongolia, short stature, broad flat face, prominent cheek bones, narrow eyes, straight black hair, yellowish skin.

3. **Caucasoid Stock.** This stock is believed to have originated in Europe, except the Hindu race, which originated in India. The general characteristics are: light skin, dark or light hair (either straight or wavy), dark or light eyes, narrow nose, slight jaw, tall stature. There are four races of the Caucasoid stock:

a. Alpine Race. Native of central Europe, tall stature, brown hair (straight or wavy), brown eyes, narrow nose, light skin.

b. Hindu Race. Native of India, tall stature, black straight hair, black eyes, variable nose, brown skin.

c. Mediterranean Race. Native of southern Europe, medium stature, black wavy hair, black eyes, narrow nose, dark white skin.

d. Nordic Race. Native of northern Europe, tall stature, light hair (straight or wavy), blue eyes, narrow nose, light skin.

Race Superiority. The individuals belonging to a race vary greatly in their physical traits, inborn abilities, individual opportunities and learning. Accomplishment is dependent to a great extent upon climate. The greatest contributions to civilization have been made by races inhabiting climates favorable for work and for the raising of crops. Every race has produced outstanding leaders in the various fields of human endeavor. In light of scientific evidence, it is recognized that no one race is mentally superior or inferior to all other races.

Multiple-Choice Questions

Write the number preceding the word or expression that best completes the statement.

1. Life probably began in the (1) air (2) soil (3) water (4) rocks.

2. One of the places that scientists believe may have been the cradle of mankind is (1) North America (2) France (3) Asia (4) Greenland.

3. Primitive man at first used (1) bows and arrows (2) weapons made of iron (3) weapons shaped of stone (4) weapons made of bronze.

4. One term in the following group has no biological relation to the others. That term is (1) Caucasian (2) Neanderthal (3) Mongolian (4) Malayan (5) Negroid.

5. Blue eyes and light hair are characteristic of the (1) Mediterranean (2) Nordic (3) Alpine (4) Mongolian race.

Completion Questions

Write the word or expression that, when inserted in the blank, will correctly complete the statement.

1. The _____ period is so called because there are no written records of this period.

2. Peking man lived (*before, after*) _____ Cro-Magnon man.

3. The scientific name of all living men is _____.

4. _____ was the first metal used by man.

5. The characteristic color of the hair of the Mediterranean race is _____.

Essay Questions

1. *a.* State two ways by which scientists can estimate the age of the earth.

   b. State two ways in which prehistoric man differed in structure from modern man.

2. Tell whether each of the following statements is true or false, giving a reason for each answer:

   a. Animals must have existed on the land before plants appeared.

   b. Man's brain and hands give him superiority over all other organisms.

   c. The highest culture of man has been developed in the temperate zone.

   d. There is no superior race.

   e. Java man used copper-tipped spears for hunting.

3. *a.* Name two races of men and give a characteristic of each with regard to hair and eye color.

   b. Why are color and texture of hair better standards for classification than color of skin?

4. *a.* Mention three stages of culture that show that man's progress has been gradual.

   b. Name several implements or utensils of each stage, and show how they indicate that man's progress has been gradual.

5. Write a brief composition concerning one of the early stages of the culture of man, treating five of the following topics:

   a. Appearance of the people.

   b. Kind of shelter used.

   c. Type of clothing worn.

   d. Food used, with its source and preparation.

   e. Enemies most feared.

   f. Means used to modify and control the environment.

Chapter II

THE NATURE OF MODERN SCIENCE

Superstition Gives Way to Science. Lacking an understanding of his environment, early man believed in evil spirits, charms and witchcraft. Such beliefs based on fear are called *superstitions*. Even in our modern society there are superstitious people. You will at times hear a person say that walking under a ladder brings bad luck, or that handling a toad causes warts, etc. But superstition is rapidly giving way to *science*, which promotes beliefs and ideas *founded on fact.*

Modern Science. The sum of the knowledge which man has gained about himself and his surroundings is called *science*. The vastness of science makes necessary many subdivisions, some of which are the following:

Chemistry: the science of the composition and properties of matter.
Physics: the science of the behavior of matter and energy.
Geology: the science of the history and nature of the earth's crust.
Biology: the science of living things.

The Science of Biology. Biology is the study of life—of all living things, both plant and animal. Biologic principles are daily being applied for the benefit of man: in controlling disease, in improving health, in developing better foods, in conserving natural resources, etc. Consequently, industry, agriculture and the medical profession provide unlimited vocational opportunities to youths with a biologic background.

Students find that biology offers many interesting and rewarding life hobbies.

Students of biology have a better understanding of themselves and a greater appreciation of the living things surrounding them.

Branches of Biology. Biology is the most extensive of all the sciences. A few of the branches of biology which we shall meet in this course are the following:

Agriculture: crops   *Hygiene:* health
Botany: plants   *Medicine:* health and disease
Cytology: cells   *Ornithology:* bird life
Dietetics: foods   *Physiology:* life activities
Horticulture: gardening   *Zoology:* animals

The Modern Scientist. The modern scientist has a natural curiosity about life. He feels a great urge to learn the true facts of nature. He is logical, open-minded, tireless, thoroughly honest. To him the search for truth is a compelling thing. He never takes anything for granted.

The Scientific Method. The scientist solves a problem by the *scientific method*, as follows: He performs a controlled experiment. He makes careful observations. He repeats the experiment to be sure that his original findings are correct.

Performing a Scientific Experiment. In carrying out an experiment, a fairly definite pattern of activity is followed, as below.

Experiment	*Explanation*
Problem: Does light help mushrooms to grow?	This is a carefully worded statement of what is to be proved or disproved.
Materials: Two similar boxes, soil, mushroom plants.	This is a list of the materials needed to carry out the experiment.
Procedure (or Method): 1. Fill both boxes with the soil. 2. Plant half of the mushrooms (selected at random) in one box and half in the other box. 3. Keep the two boxes under exactly the same conditions of temperature, moisture, etc., but keep one box in the dark and the other in the light. 4. After one week, compare the mushrooms in the two boxes to see whether they grew better in the light or in the dark.	This is the method followed in performing the experiment. It consists of a series of carefully planned, logical steps carried out to prove or disprove the problem.

Experiment	Explanation
Observations: We see that the mushrooms kept in the light did *not* grow better than those kept in the dark.	This step consists of noting and recording everything that happened during the experiment which might have a bearing on the problem.
Conclusions: Light does not help mushrooms to grow.	This is the answer to the problem.

The Control (or Check). In the above experiment, it is significant that one group of plants was kept in the *dark*, while the other group of plants was kept in the *light*. The presence of light was the *experimental factor*—that is, the one factor whose effect was being determined. All other conditions were the same for the two plants.

The plants grown in the dark served as a *control* (or *check*). Without this check, there would be no way of determining the effect of light upon the growth of the plants.

Essay Questions

1. *a.* Describe the control in an experiment which you have studied.
   b. Why is an experiment more scientific than a simple observation?
   c. Explain why scientists repeat experiments again and again.
2. In performing an experiment, a scientist follows a definite procedure. Describe an experiment that you have performed or studied, including the following:
   a. Why it was done.
   b. How it was done.
   c. What means were used to control or check it.
   d. State the facts or the information obtained from the experiment.
   e. State the conclusion drawn from these facts.
   f. Did this experiment justify the conclusion?
   g. Give definite reasons for your answer to *f*.
3. A group of biology students performed an experiment to determine the responses of earthworms to light and sound. The experiment was conducted in a darkened room. A box was filled with moist soil. Ten earthworms were placed on the soil. A strong light was turned on the earthworms and a police whistle

was blown loudly while the light was on. Within three minutes, all the earthworms buried themselves in the soil.

Five tentative conclusions were suggested by various members of the group—conclusions apparently based on their observations. Tell whether each of these conclusions is justified and give a reason for your answer in each case.

a. The experiment showed that earthworms respond negatively to light and sound.

b. The experiment should be repeated several times, exactly as described, before conclusions may be drawn.

c. The responses of the earthworms to light and to sound should be tested separately.

d. The response of the earthworms to moist soil, without any other stimulus, should be determined first.

e. The experiment showed that earthworms are unaffected by light or by sound, since it is well known that earthworms have neither eyes nor ears.

4. A 10-year experiment on the prevention of tooth decay is being made in two cities. In one city, a little fluorine is added daily to the drinking water, for it is believed that fluorine will prevent tooth decay. In the other city, fluorine is not added to the drinking water. In both cities, the teeth of the school children will be examined regularly and records of the amount of tooth decay will be kept.

a. How will the experimenters be able to conclude whether fluorine helps prevent tooth decay?

b. State three ways in which the procedure outlined above meets the requirements of a good, scientific experiment.

5. Select five of the following statements. In each case tell why the idea is part of good scientific procedure.

a. A conclusion should be based on many facts.

b. A control or check is part of a properly performed experiment.

c. It is better for a scientist to report his findings to his fellow scientists first, before disclosing them to the general public.

d. Sometimes it is necessary to change a conclusion.

e. Apparatus used in a biological experiment must be very clean.

f. Every experiment should be so described that another person can repeat it.

g. A good scientist must be open-minded.

Chapter III

THE MICROSCOPE

Leeuwenhoek and the Microscope. The first microscope of importance was that developed in the 17th century by the Dutch lens grinder, *Anton van Leeuwenhoek*. Although his microscope was crude, Leeuwenhoek was able to probe into the wonders of a hitherto unknown world and make many astounding discoveries. He saw tiny animals in a drop of stagnant water, and observed bacteria and blood corpuscles.

Importance of the Microscope to the Biologist. The most important tool of the biologist is the microscope, for it magnifies objects too small to be seen by the naked eye. Without the microscope, modern biology would not be so far advanced. Man's knowledge of medicine, surgery and hygiene, as well as his understanding of the structures and functions of all living things, is based on facts revealed by the microscope.

Importance of the Microscope to the Biology Student. In your laboratory study of biology, you are going to make some wonderful discoveries of your own. You will see much more than Leeuwenhoek ever dreamed of, because the microscope has been greatly improved in the last three hundred years. Your discoveries will include the amazing structure of a fly's foot, the circulation of blood in the tail of a tadpole, the intricate tissues within a green leaf, etc.

The Modern Microscope. Modern microscopes are of two kinds: simple and compound. A *simple* microscope has a single magnifying lens. A *compound* microscope has a system of lenses. The figure on page 15 shows a compound microscope of the type used in school laboratories.

Parts of the Microscope:

1. *Base:* the heavy supporting structure, shaped somewhat like a horseshoe, on which the microscope rests.

2. *Inclination Joint:* a hinge which permits the upper portion of the microscope to be tilted.

3. *Mirror:* a glass reflector, usually flat on one side and concave on the other. The mirror is pivoted so that it may be turned in any direction in order to direct light up through the microscope.

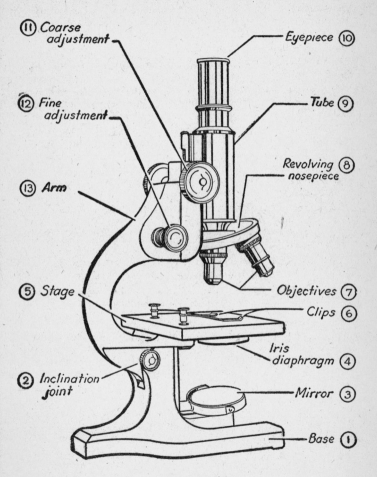

11 Coarse adjustment
12 Fine adjustment
13 Arm
5 Stage
2 Inclination joint
Eyepiece 10
Tube 9
Revolving nosepiece 8
Objectives 7
Clips 6
Iris diaphragm 4
Mirror 3
Base 1

Fig. 3. The Compound Microscope

4. *Iris Diaphragm:* an intricate circle of thin sliding leaves just above the mirror. The diaphragm may be opened and closed to control the amount of light passing through the instrument.

5. *Stage:* the platform on which the slide bearing the specimen is placed for observation.

6. *Clips:* two metal spring clips, one on each side of the hole in the stage, to hold the slide in place.

7. *Objectives:* the two lenses just above the stage. The high-power objective, which gives the greater magnification, is slightly longer than the low-power objective.

8. *Revolving Nosepiece:* the fitting on which the objectives are mounted. The nosepiece is rotated so that either the high-power or low-power objective can be used.

9. *Tube:* a hollow cylinder (barrel) through which light travels. The revolving nosepiece is at the bottom of the tube and the eyepiece is at the top.

10. *Eyepiece* (or Ocular): the topmost part which contains a combination of lenses.

11. *Coarse Adjustment:* two large wheels by means of which the tube is raised and lowered for focusing.

12. *Fine Adjustment:* two small wheels, similar to the coarse adjustment. The fine adjustment is used for finer focusing.

13. *Arm:* the supporting structure between the base and the tube. The arm is used as a handle in carrying the microscope.

Preparing the Microscope:

1. Place the microscope on a level table illuminated by indirect sunlight or by artificial light.

2. Place the microscope so that its arm is toward you.

3. Slightly tip the upper part of the microscope at the inclination joint.

4. Rotate the nosepiece so that the low-power objective is aligned with the tube. When the objective is in the correct position, a click will be heard.

5. Rotate the coarse adjustment so that the bottom of the objective is ¼" above the stage.

6. Adjust the mirror until a well-illuminated circular area is visible through the eyepiece.

7. Adjust the size of the iris diaphragm opening to regulate the intensity of the light.

Note: Always check the microscope for dirty lenses, and clean them with special lens tissue.

Preparing the Specimen:

1. Slice the specimen, if necessary, so that it is thin enough for light to pass through it.

2. Place the specimen in the middle of a clean glass slide. In a wet mount, a drop of water is placed on the specimen in order to keep it moist as well as in place.

3. Slowly lower a cover glass over the specimen, taking care not to trap air bubbles beneath the cover glass.

Note: Sometimes it is necessary to stain the specimen with dye to make the structures of the specimen more visible under the microscope.

Observing the Specimen Under Low Power:

1. Place the slide on the stage so that the specimen is centered directly below the low-power objective.

2. Look through the eyepiece, keeping *both* eyes open.

3. Slowly rotate the coarse adjustment wheel towards you to raise the tube until the specimen is sharpest. *Never* lower the tube while looking through the eyepiece.

4. Turn the fine adjustment for a sharper focus.

Note: Specimens observed through a microscope appear inverted (upside down) and reversed from right to left.

Observing the Specimen Under High Power:

1. When the low-power objective is in focus, carefully rotate the revolving nosepiece until the high-power objective is in line with the tube.

2. Slowly turn the *fine* adjustment wheel until the specimen is in sharpest focus.

3. Rotate the fine adjustment to observe various depths of the specimen.

Note: Never use the coarse adjustment with high power because of the danger of striking the cover glass with the objective lens.

Magnifying Power of the Microscope. The magnifying power of a microscope depends on the power of the lenses being used. The power is marked on the part that holds the lenses. To determine the magnifying power, multiply the power of the objective lens being used by the power of the eyepiece lens. For example, a 10-power magnification is marked 10X, a 43-power magnification is marked 43X. If a 10X-eyepiece is used with a 43X-objective, the resulting magnification is 10 times 43, or 430.

Care of the Microscope:

1. Keep the microscope covered when not in use.

2. Keep the microscope dry to prevent corrosion (rusting).

3. When carrying the microscope, grasp its arm with one hand and rest the base on the other hand. Keep the microscope in a vertical position.

4. Use the microscope only on a steady, level table.

5. To clean a lens, carefully brush off dust particles with a clean camel's hair brush, and then wipe with special lens paper.

6. Never lower the tube while looking through the microscope.

The Electron Microscope. This instrument, developed in recent years, uses a beam of electrons instead of light rays. Its magnifying power far exceeds the most powerful compound microscope. Viruses, heretofore unseen through the compound microscope, have been photographed and studied. It is hoped that the electron microscope will enable scientists to increase their knowledge of ultra-microscopic organisms for the benefit of man.

Completion Questions

1. The microscope was improved in the 17th century by _____.

2. For microscopic observation, a specimen is usually mounted on a (an) _____.

3. Near the eye of the observer is a part, called the _____, which contains a combination of lenses.

4. The part of the microscope on which the slide is placed for observation is called the _____.

5. Light is directed up into the tube of the microscope by means of the _____.

6. The combination of lenses nearest the specimen is called the _____.

7. Optical glass is easily scratched because it is very _____.
8. The electron microscope uses _____ instead of light.

Multiple-Choice Questions

1. To be observed under the microscope, a specimen must be (1) alive (2) dead (3) thick (4) thin.
2. A specimen is placed in a drop of water (1) to keep it alive (2) to keep it in place (3) to make it appear larger (4) to preserve it.
3. Specimens are more easily studied under the microscope if they have been (1) bleached (2) stained (3) preserved (4) hardened.
4. After the microscope has been adjusted for high power, one should not use the (1) diaphragm (2) ocular (3) coarse adjustment (4) fine adjustment.
5. The microscope should always be lifted and carried by the (1) tube (2) stage (3) arm and base (4) objective.
6. The image seen by means of a compound microscope is (1) upside down (2) smaller (3) black (4) bent.
7. The electron microscope is the instrument through which, for the first time, scientists can see (1) chromosomes (2) spindle fibers (3) typhoid germs (4) viruses.

Essay Questions

1. From your study of biology, give instances to illustrate the following statement: The compound microscope has been of great value in increasing our biologic knowledge.
2. Tell how the following statement might be explained: A girl looked at her finger through a microscope but she was unable to see any cells.
3. Why is a stain often added to onion cells before they are examined under a microscope?
4. *a.* Distinguish between a simple and a compound microscope.
   b. Give at least five rules for the proper care of the microscope.
   c. Explain how to prepare a microscope for use.
   d. Explain how to find the magnifying power of a microscope.

Chapter IV

THE NATURE OF LIVING THINGS

PROTOPLASM

What Is Protoplasm? All living things—whether plant or animal—are made up of a material called *protoplasm*. Protoplasm is the substance of life, present in all living cells. It is protoplasm that distinguishes living things from non-living things. Huxley, the eminent English biologist, called protoplasm the "physical basis of life."

Discovery of Protoplasm. In the middle of the 19th century, several scientists delved into the nature of living things and discovered protoplasm. The most significant contributors were the following:

Felix Dujardin, a Frenchman, first discovered that one-celled animals are made up of a living material, but he did not name it protoplasm.

Johannes Purkinje, a Czech, was the first to use the word protoplasm to describe the living matter he discovered in young animal embryos.

Hugo von Mohl, a German, was the first to name the living matter in plant cells protoplasm.

Max Schultze, another German, first demonstrated the fact that protoplasm in plants and animals is fundamentally the same substance, capable of carrying on the life functions of the organism.

The Nature of Protoplasm. Protoplasm is a semi-clear, jelly-like fluid with the consistency of raw egg white. Throughout protoplasm, undissolved particles are suspended. These particles range in size from small invisible molecules to grains of matter visible under the microscope. A mixture such as protoplasm is called a *colloid.*

Seventy to eighty per cent of most protoplasm is water. Suspended or dissolved in the water are chemical compounds: proteins, carbohydrates, salts and fatty materials. These compounds are composed of elements, mainly carbon, oxygen, hydrogen and nitrogen, and small amounts of sulfur and phosphorus.

THE LIFE FUNCTIONS

What Are the Life Functions of Protoplasm? Although we know what makes up protoplasm, no one knows just why it is alive. In the absence of a precise explanation, it is said that matter is living if it performs certain *life functions*. The life functions are the properties of protoplasm, and are described briefly below but more fully in later chapters.

1. *Nutrition.* Plants and animals require food for energy. The life functions concerned with obtaining and using food are collectively termed *nutrition*, and consist of the following processes:

a. Food-getting. The taking in of food by animals is called *inges-tion*. Green plants have no problem of food-getting, for they manu-facture their own food by photosynthesis.

b. Digestion. Food is digested, that is, broken down into soluble end products that can be used by the cells of the plant or animal.

c. Absorption. The digested food passes into the bloodstream of the animal. In the process of *circulation*, the blood (1) carries the digested food and oxygen *to* the cells in all parts of the body, and (2) carries waste products *away from* the cells. In plants, sap is the fluid medium of circulation.

d. Assimilation. Finally, the cells in the body convert the digested food into new protoplasm for the growth and repair of cells. *Growth* is the increase in the size of an organism. Growth in a multicellular organism takes place by the increase in number of cells making up the body, not merely by the increase in size of the individual cells.

2. *Respiration.* Plants and animals absorb oxygen into their cells. There, the oxygen combines with digested food in a chemical process called *oxidation*. Energy is released, and carbon dioxide and water are given off as wastes.

3. *Excretion.* The chemical changes taking place in plants and animals produce poisonous wastes which must be eliminated. Higher animals have special organs of excretion. Plants, however, excrete mainly through their leaves.

4. *Secretion.* Animals and plants produce enzymes and hormones. These are chemical secretions which help the body to function properly. Animals secrete many more substances than plants do.

5. *Motion.* Living matter can move by virtue of power *within* itself; that is, its movements do not depend on any outside force. Most animals move freely from place to place (*locomotion*). Most plants do not have the power of locomotion, but have the ability to move only very slowly, as when their leaves turn toward light.

6. *Irritability.* Living things react to external factors (*stimuli*) in their environment. Light, heat and moisture are some types of stimuli affecting the reactions of plants and animals. For example, a potted plant is moved from a dark corner of a room to a window sill; its leaves then turn *toward* the light. An earthworm, brought into contact with a bright light, moves *away from* the light.

7. *Reproduction.* All living things, both plants and animals, carry on reproduction, the process by which an organism gives rise to offspring like itself. Since every individual plant and animal will eventually die, reproduction is necessary to maintain the species (*race-preservation*). All other life functions are carried on primarily for the maintenance of the individual (*self-preservation*). Biologically, race-preservation is more essential than self-preservation.

Metabolism. Metabolism refers to all the chemical activities taking place in the body of a living thing. Metabolism is divided into two parts: anabolism and catabolism. *Anabolism* refers to the chemical activities by which protoplasm is *built up. Catabolism* refers to the chemical activities by which protoplasm is *broken down.* Anabolism includes the life functions of assimilation and growth in plants and animals. Photosynthesis is also an anabolic function, but occurs only in green plants. Catabolism in both plants and animals includes respiration, oxidation and excretion.

CELLS

What Is a Cell? Protoplasm, when viewed under a microscope, reveals itself in tiny units called *cells.* Cells carry on all the life functions of the living plant or animal. Therefore, a cell is defined as *the unit of structure and function of all living things.* The study of cells is called *cytology.*

Just as a building is made up of bricks, so a living body is made up of cells. The larger the body, the greater the number of cells. The human body, for example, contains billions of cells. On the other hand, some plants and animals, such as the spirogyra and the ameba, exist as a single cell. A single-celled plant or animal is *unicellular;* a living thing consisting of many cells is *multicellular.*

Discovery of the Cell. The invention of the microscope made possible investigations into cells. Tiny objects that previously could not be seen with the naked eye could now be viewed and studied. In the 17th century, and again in the 19th century, several scientists made historic discoveries leading to the *cell theory*. This theory states in brief that "all living things are composed of cells."

In 1665, *Robert Hooke*, an Englishman, discovered the cell. Placing a thin slice of cork under a microscope, Hooke found the cork to be composed of rows of tiny, box-like spaces. To these openings, Hooke gave the name *cells*. Although he did not realize it, Hooke saw dead cells, for cork is dead matter. The living cell content, protoplasm, had dried up and disappeared, leaving only cell walls. Today, however, the term *cell* implies a unit of living material, since every cell contains protoplasm.

In 1831, *Robert Brown*, a Scotchman, discovered a dense structure in plant cells which he named the *nucleus*.

In 1838, *Matthias Schleiden*, a German, found that plants are composed of cells.

In 1839, *Theodor Schwann*, another German, found that animals are composed of cells. Then, Schleiden and Schwann combined their individual findings in the one statement that *all plants and animals are composed of cells*. This was the beginning of the cell theory. Later scientists, working on cells, extended the scope of the cell theory, as you will find at the end of this chapter, on page 30.

During the present century, *E. B. Wilson*, an eminent American biologist, made great contributions to our knowledge of cell structure and function.

Sizes and Shapes of Cells. Cells vary widely in *size*. The largest known single cell is the egg cell (or egg "yolk") of birds. These cells can be seen by the naked eye. But by far the greater number of cells are unbelievably tiny, and are revealed to the eye only with the aid of a microscope. Bacteria, the smallest known cells, are visible only with the high power of the microscope.

Cells also show great variety in *shape*. This is due to the fact that cells form into groups in order to perform specific functions in the body. Therefore, some cells are round, others flat, still others long. But cells that function alone are usually round, because they are not subject to the pressure of surrounding cells.

The Structure of a Cell. The cell structure of all living things is fundamentally the same. Each cell, or unit of protoplasm, has two main parts: the *nucleus* and the *cytoplasm.* In addition, both animal and plant cells have a thin *cell membrane,* or boundary, surrounding the protoplasm. Plant cells, however, have an additional outer covering, called the *cell wall.*

1. *The Nucleus.* The nucleus is a dense, round body of protoplasm usually found near the center of the cell. The protoplasm of the nucleus is called *nucleoplasm.* The functions of the nucleus are to (*a*) regulate the life activities of the cell, and (*b*) control cell division. A cell which has been deprived of its nucleus soon dies.

There are three important parts of the nucleus, as shown in the figure below.

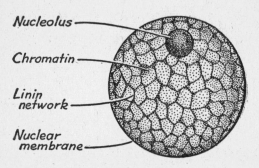

Nucleolus —

Chromatin —

Linin network —

Nuclear membrane —

Fig. 4. The Nucleus

a. Nuclear membrane—the thin covering surrounding the nucleus, separating the nucleus from the rest of the cell.

b. Nucleolus—a small round body, the function of which is unknown. Some cells contain more than one nucleolus.

c. Chromatin—a material consisting of granules held together in a fine network of fibers, called the *linin network.* Chromatin carries the factors which determine hereditary characteristics. Chromatin derives its name from the fact that it stains deeply with dyes. This staining helps to distinguish the nucleus from the rest of the cell.

2. *The Cytoplasm.* The cytoplasm is all of the protoplasm surrounding the nucleus and bounded by the cell membrane. Under the

influence of the nucleus, cytoplasm performs most of the life functions of the cell. Cytoplasm appears as a clear, somewhat watery liquid in which numerous bodies are suspended.

The three main kinds of bodies present in cytoplasm are:

a. Vacuoles—spaces in the cytoplasm filled with watery fluid called *cell sap*. In animal cells, the vacuoles remain small, but in plant cells the vacuoles gradually enlarge until they occupy most of the cytoplasm.

b. Centrosome—a tiny round body in the cytoplasm, often found in pairs, lying near the nucleus. The centrosome appears only in animal cells and plays an active part in cell division. Surrounding the centrosome is a dense area called the *aster*.

c. Plastids—small living bodies in the cytoplasm found especially in plant cells. Different types of plastids perform different functions. In the green plant, the *chloroplasts* are important plastids. The chloroplasts contain the green coloring matter, *chlorophyll*, which is essential in the plant's food-making process called photosynthesis.

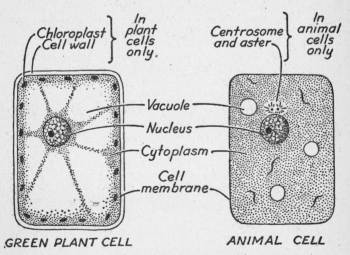

Fig. 5. Typical Cells

3. *The Cell Membrane* (*or Plasma Membrane*). The cell membrane, or the plasma membrane, is a thin layer of denser protoplasm that bounds the cell. The cell absorbs needed materials and gives off wastes through the cell membrane by the process of osmosis. The cell membrane exists in all cells, plant and animal.

4. *The Cell Wall.* The cell wall, found only in plant cells, is an additional external layer surrounding the cell. This wall is composed of *cellulose,* a hard, non-living material secreted by the cytoplasm. The cell wall not only protects the inner protoplasm from injury, but also helps maintain the shape of the cell.

Plant and Animal Cells Compared. Although all cells are fundamentally alike, plant and animal cells have certain basic differences.

Plant Cells	Animal Cells
1. Chlorophyll in chloroplasts.	1. No chlorophyll.
2. Cell wall.	2. No cell wall.
3. Centrosome and aster absent.	3. Centrosome and aster present.
4. Vacuoles large.	4. Vacuoles small.

Cell Division. All living things begin life as a single cell. Growth of an organism is achieved by *cell division.* In this process, a cell divides in half, becoming two cells. The two cells divide and become four cells, and so on. This reproduction of new cells takes place during the entire life of an organism and serves not only for growth, but also to replace injured and worn out cells.

Indirect Cell Division (or Mitosis). A cell is in the *resting stage* while it is growing. When the cell reaches its full growth, it either dies or (as happens more frequently) divides. Cell division is accomplished by a four-step process, called *mitosis,* as follows:

1. *Prophase.* (*Early Stage*) The chromatin granules gather together, forming a long ribbon, called the *spireme.* The spireme breaks up into a definite number of rod-shaped structures, the *chromosomes.* Meanwhile, the centrosome divides into two parts. Raylike fibers appear around each new centrosome, making two *asters.* The asters begin to move to opposite sides of the cell, becoming *poles.* The fibers form a *spindle* connecting the poles. (*Late Stage*) The nuclear membrane around the chromosomes disappears, and the spindle fibers attach themselves to the chromosomes.

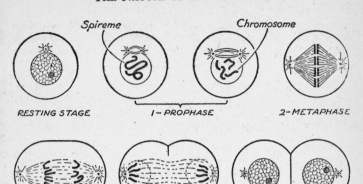

Fig. 6. Stages in Mitosis of an Animal Cell

2. *Metaphase.* The chromosomes move on the spindle fibers to the middle of the cell, or *equator*, halfway between the poles. Once there, each chromosome splits lengthwise, making two sets of identical halves—one set for each of the cells resulting from the division. It is this splitting of the chromosomes which insures each new cell to be formed (in the telophase stage) of having the same amount and type of chromatin. Because the chromatin determines the hereditary traits, the two new cells will be identical to the cell from which they were formed. Therefore, the metaphase is considered the most important stage of mitosis.

3. *Anaphase.* The two sets of chromosomes separate. Both sets are drawn on the spindle fibers to opposite poles.

4. *Telophase.* The chromosomes in each set gather together at opposite poles and break up into chromatin granules. The nuclear membrane reappears around the chromatin, thus forming two new nuclei. The cytoplasm divides in the middle of the cell, resulting in two new cells, called *daughter cells.* Each of the daughter cells, now about one-half the size of the mother cell, grows to maximum size and then divides.

Both plant and animal cells perform the same basic steps in cell division. In plant cells, however, the spindle is formed just as in animal cells, except for the absence of centrosomes.

Specialized Cells. In unicellular plants and animals, the single cell carries on all the life functions by itself. In multicellular forms, however, the cells become *specialists*. The cells perform separate functions, but all cells cooperate for the good of the individual. Since specialization makes for greater efficiency, the higher forms of life show greater specialization.

Examples of specialized cells in man and other higher animals are:

1. *Fat cells* store oil, fat and vitamins.
2. *Bone cells* support the body.
3. *Muscle cells* move the parts of the body.
4. *Nerve cells* carry nervous impulses (messages) to the organs, thus enabling the body to function harmoniously as a whole.
5. *Blood cells* (red) carry oxygen to all body cells.
6. *Epithelial cells* line body cavities and cover internal organs.

In plants, specialized cells include the *epidermal cells* of the leaf for covering and protection, and the *palisade cells* for food making.

TISSUES, ORGANS, ORGAN SYSTEMS

Animal Tissues. A group of similar specialized cells forms a *tissue*. Most of the cells in a particular tissue are the same in size, shape and nature of the work they do, but the cells of different kinds of tissue vary greatly. Between the cells of certain tissues lies matter, called *intercellular material*, which has been secreted by the cells.

Higher organisms have four different types of tissue: *epithelial, connective, muscle* and *nerve*.

1. *Epithelial Tissue.* Epithelial tissue, or epithelium, is composed of closely fitting cells. There is little intercellular material. The two chief functions of epithelial tissue are: (*a*) *For protection.* The skin and the moist mucous membrane which lines the nose and mouth are epithelial tissue. Epithelium also lines the digestive tract and the body cavities. (*b*) *For secretion.* Epithelial tissue found in the glands gives off useful secretions.

2. *Connective Tissue.* Connective tissue is composed of cells surrounded by a large amount of intercellular material. Connective tissue performs several functions: (*a*) *fat tissue* stores oil, (*b*) *fibrous tissue* binds the body together, (*c*) *cartilage tissue* and *bone tissue* support the body.

Blood, which is usually classed as a connective tissue, will be discussed in detail in Chapter XII.

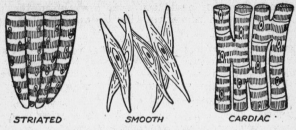

STRIATED   SMOOTH   CARDIAC

Fig. 7. Types of Muscle Tissue

3. *Muscle Tissue.* Muscle tissue is composed of elongated cells which contract and relax, thus producing movement. There are three types of muscle tissue: (*a*) *Striated muscle.* This type derives its name from striations, or stripes, visible on the cells. Striated muscles perform voluntary acts, that is, acts controlled by the will, such as the movements of the arms and hands. Striated muscle is found only on the skeletal system. (*b*) *Smooth muscle.* Cells of smooth muscle tissue show no striations. Smooth muscles perform involuntary acts, that is, acts not controlled by the will, such as the movements of the stomach wall. Smooth muscle is present only in internal organs. (*c*) *Cardiac muscle.* Cells of cardiac muscle are intermediate in appearance between striated and smooth muscle cells. Cardiac muscle is found only in the heart.

4. *Nerve Tissue.* Nerve tissue is composed of nerve cells which have long thread-like projections that carry nervous impulses to all parts of the body. We shall learn more about nerve tissue in Chapter XV.

Plant Tissues. The tissues of plants are very simple, resembling animal epithelium. The various cell layers found in leaves and the protective epidermal layer of roots are examples of plant tissues.

Organs. Tissues combine to form organs. An *organ* is a group of related tissues acting together to perform a specific function. The stomach, for example, is an organ comprised of many tissues which together aid in the digestion of food. Some of these tissues, to name only a few, are *muscle tissue*, which helps churn the food and move it along the alimentary canal; *gland tissue*, which aids the digestive process by secretions of enzymes; and *nerve tissue*, which stimulates the muscular and glandular activities.

Some animal organs, in addition to the stomach, are the lungs, heart, liver, eyes, ears, kidneys, etc. Plant organs are the leaf, flower, stem, root.

Organ Systems. Related organs form organ systems. An *organ system* is a group of related organs which work together in the performance of a certain activity. Some organ systems in man are the skeletal system, digestive system, respiratory system, circulatory system, excretory system, etc.

Organisms. Every living thing is called an *organism.* There are many microscopic organisms, consisting of a single cell or a small group of cells. But most living things are complex, consisting of many different organ systems, all working together for the welfare of the organism.

The Modern Cell Theory. During the past century, the *cell theory* has been greatly developed and expanded, as stated below:

1. All living things are composed of one or more units called cells.
2. The life functions are carried on by single cells or groups of cells.
3. Every cell is derived from a pre-existing cell.
4. During cell division, the determiners for hereditary characteristics are passed on from parent cell to daughter cells.

Completion Questions

1. The material that forms the physical basis of life is called _____.

2. The only substance capable of growth and self-repair is _____.

3. The process of changing food into soluble form to permit its passage into the blood is called _____.

4. The life process by which digested food becomes a part of the protoplasm of a cell is called _____.

5. The life process by which the contents of a cell grows is _____.

6. The life function by which plants take in oxygen and release carbon dioxide is _____.

7. A life function that is essential to the species but not to the life of the animal is _____.

8. The sum total of the processes involved in the breaking down and building up of protoplasm is called _____.

9. The unit of structure and function in plants and animals is the _____.
10. Box-like structures in cork were called cells by _____.
11. The dense structure in the center of the cell is called the _____.
12. The material in the nucleus that takes stain readily is _____.
13. The living part of a cell that surrounds the nucleus is called the _____.
14. The large spaces in plant cells filled with sap are called _____.
15. Animal cells are enclosed by a (an) _____.
16. Cell walls of plants are composed of _____.
17. Most living cells after a certain period of time must die or _____.
18. Cells divide by a process called _____.
19. The nuclear substance from which the spireme is formed is _____.
20. During the process of cell division, hereditary characteristics are thought to be carried by bodies called _____.
21. A group of similar cells specialized to perform a definite function is called a (an) _____.
22. The cells that line the mouth are called _____ cells.
23. _____ is composed of tissue cells specialized for producing motion.
24. The principal function of epidermal cells is _____.
25. The name given to a group of tissues performing a special function is _____.

Multiple-Choice Questions

1. The fact that it is the protoplasm in all living things that performs the life functions was first expressed clearly by (1) Schleiden (2) Leeuwenhoek (3) Pasteur (4) Schultze.
2. The substance present in largest amount in protoplasm is (1) water (2) protein (3) iodine (4) starch.
3. The chemical process by which energy is released in living things is (1) secretion (2) oxidation (3) photosynthesis (4) assimilation.
4. All living organisms are composed of one or more (1) tissues (2) cells (3) organs (4) muscles.

5. Hooke used the word cell when he studied (1) cork (2) leaves (3) insects (4) his own tissue.
6. The fact that the cell is the unit of structure in plants was discovered by (1) Linnaeus (2) Brown (3) Schleiden (4) Darwin.
7. Our knowledge of cell structure was increased greatly by the work of (1) Banting (2) Lamarck (3) Goldberger (4) Wilson.
8. A structure near the nucleus of an animal cell that takes part in cell division is the (1) chromosome (2) centrosome (3) vacuole (4) nucleolus.
9. Chromatin derives its name from the fact that (1) it appears colored in the living cell (2) it is necessary in cell division (3) it determines the color of the hair (4) it takes a deep stain when dyed.
10. A plant cell contains (1) living and lifeless matter (2) only living matter (3) only inorganic matter (4) no matter.
11. Plant and animal cells are alike in possessing (1) cellulose cell walls (2) chloroplasts (3) nuclei (4) small vacuoles.
12. The centrosome functions as (1) the starch-making center of the cell (2) the place of origin of the spindle fibers (3) the equator of the spindle (4) the regulator of osmosis.
13. Nuclear division by mitosis insures an exact division of the (1) vacuoles (2) cytoplasm (3) chloroplasts (4) chromatin.
14. Substances pass into and out of the protoplasm of living cells through the (1) villi (2) mucous membrane (3) plasma membrane (4) capillaries.
15. One of the body's connective tissues is (1) bone (2) epithelium (3) muscle (4) nerve.

Modified True-False Questions

In some of the following statements the term in italics makes the statement incorrect. For each *incorrect* statement, write the term that must be substituted for the italicized term to make the statement correct. For each *correct* statement, write the word *true*.

1. The term "cell" was introduced by *Harvey*.
2. The contributions of Schleiden and Schwann to biology were in the field of *cytology*.
3. The protoplasm of the nucleus is *denser* than the protoplasm of the rest of the cell.
4. Chromatin is ordinarily found in the *chloroplasts* of a cell.

5. The cell membrane is composed of *cellulose*.
6. When a cell reaches a certain limit of growth, it usually *dies*.
7. In mitotic division of the nucleus, the *vacuoles* split lengthwise.
8. During nuclear division, the chromatin takes the form of *nucleoli*.
9. The cells in higher forms of life show a high degree of *specialization*.
10. The cells that line the cavities of the human body are *muscle* cells.

Essay Questions

1. *a.* Make a diagram of either a plant cell or an animal cell, labeling five essential structures.
   b. Give one function of each part labeled.
   c. Name two ways in which plant and animal cells differ.

2. The following structures are found in cells: cellulose wall, centrosomes, nucleus, chloroplast, vacuole, cytoplasm, plasma membrane.
   a. Which of the above structures are common to both plant and animal cells?
   b. Name the structure not found in plant cells.
   c. Name two structures not found in animal cells.
   d. State the function of each of the structures given above.

3. *a.* Give a reason why cells divide when they reach their maximum size.
   b. Make a labeled diagram to show an important stage of cell division by mitosis.
   c. Give one advantage to organisms of specialization of cells.

4. *a.* Give four general functions carried on by both plants and animals.
   b. Make a diagram of a typical cell; label three of its parts.

5. *a.* Modern microscopes make it possible to observe and to study the details of cell structure. State three such details that were unknown to Hooke.
   b. Explain the following statement: "Every cell comes from a pre-existing cell."
   c. Explain how the study of different kinds of tissue furnishes evidence that supports the cell theory.
   d. Explain why the nuclei of cells on permanent slides show much more clearly than do those in fresh tissue cells.

6. *a.* A pupil used a microscope to examine prepared slides. On the first slide was a bit of epithelial tissue; on the second, a bit of onion tissue; and on the third, a green plant cell.
  (1) On which slides could the pupil see that the cells had walls?
  (2) Of what substance are these walls composed?
  (3) What is the fundamental material in all three types of cells?

  b. State two important ideas that make up the cell theory.
  c. Why is it necessary that higher animals have many kinds of cells?

7. *a.* Draw a simple plant cell and label two parts not commonly found in animal cells.
  b. Use specific examples of organisms to explain the meaning of the statement: "Cells are the unit of structure and function of living things."
  c. Make five labeled diagrams each representing a different step in the process of mitosis.

8. All living things are composed of cells.
  a. Name two scientists who helped develop this idea.
  b. Mention two tissues (plant or animal) and give a specialized function of each.
  c. Mention two structures common to all cells and give a function of each structure you have named.

9. *a.* The ameba and man belong to the animal kingdom. Name four vital processes common to both.
  b. State two ways in which the nucleus is of importance to the cell.

10. *a.* State one fundamental requirement for the growth of an animal cell.
  b. Why does growth cause a cell to divide?
  c. Why are cells of any one tissue much alike?
  d. Name two different kinds of tissue in a green leaf and state the special function of each tissue named.

Chapter V

THE CLASSIFICATION OF LIVING THINGS

Why Are Things Classified? Similar things are arranged in related groups in order to make them easy for us to find and use. We daily come upon such evidences of *classification*. Items in a large store are arranged by *department*: clothing, furniture, hardware. Non-fiction books in a library are grouped by *subject*: science, history, religion. Stamps in an album are arranged by *country*. Words in a dictionary are listed *alphabetically*. Each of these divisions can be further classified. In a clothing department, for example, areas are set aside for shoes, suits, dresses, hats, etc.

Classification in Biology. When you visited the zoo, you probably noticed that the animals are divided into different groups, as the bird house, snake house, etc. Moreover, you must have noticed, with bewilderment, the strange names given to animals. For example, a lion bears the name *Felis leo;* a leopard, *Felis pardus.* How was the grouping of animals decided upon? Who chose these odd names, and what do they mean? The answer is not so difficult, as you shall see presently.

Taxonomy, the Science of Classifying Living Things. When we consider that there are over a million different kinds of plants and animals on earth, we see the need for an efficient system of classification in biology. The classifying and naming of living things is a science called *taxonomy*.

The first attempts at classification were based on habitat; plants and animals were considered as waterdwellers or landdwellers. Investigators then turned to classifying plants and animals according to both habitat and similarities in structure. Such a system was first devised by *Aristotle,* the Greek philosopher, in the 4th century B.C.

Aristotle's system was used for many centuries by early biologists. Then improved systems were devised, but they all had these significant shortcomings: (1) Newly discovered plants and animals could not be accurately classified because of the limited number of groupings. (2) The practice of naming organisms by describing their characteristics in long Latin phrases led to confusion. (3) Scientists in different countries gave different Latin names to the same organism.

In the 18th century, *Carolus Linnaeus*, a Swedish botanist, devised a system by which he classified all plants and animals entirely on *similarities in structure*. For the most part, it is the basis of our present-day method of taxonomy.

The Linnaean System of Classification. About the year 1750, Linnaeus published a book describing his new system of classification. He divided all plants and animals into four groups, and gave each organism a scientific Latin name consisting of two words. The Linnaean system, therefore, is known as the *binomial system of nomenclature*. (*Binomial* means "consisting of two terms"; *nomenclature* means "a system of names.") The first word is the name of the *genus* to which the organism belongs; the second word is the name of the *species*. For example, modern man is called *Homo sapiens*, a Latin name meaning "Man, the wise." *Homo* is the genus name; *sapiens*, is the species name. The first letter of the genus name is always capitalized; the species name is written in small letters. Genus and species are subdivisions in the modern system of classification of living things.

Modern Taxonomy. Recognizing the practicability of the Linnaean system, scientists adopted it and gradually improved upon it. As in the Linnaean system, modern taxonomy is based on *similarities in structure* of the body. Every living thing is placed in either the plant kingdom or the animal kingdom. Then:

Each *kingdom* is divided into related *phyla* (phylum, sing.).

Each *phylum* is divided into related *classes*.

Each *class* is divided into related *orders*.

Each *order* is divided into related *families*.

Each *family* is divided into related *genera* (genus, sing.).

Each *genus* is divided into related *species*.

Each *species* is a subdivision of a genus and refers

to a particular kind of plant or animal.

Note: A *species* is sometimes further divided into *varieties*.

In the following chart, man and the red squirrel are classified according to the modern system of taxonomy.

Man	Red Squirrel
Kingdom: Animal	*Kingdom:* Animal
Phylum: Chordata	*Phylum:* Chordata
Class: Mammalia	*Class:* Mammalia
Order: Primates	*Order:* Rodentia
Family: Hominidae	*Family:* Sciuridae
Genus: Homo	*Genus:* Sciurus
Species: sapiens	*Species:* hudsonicus

Sapiens is the only living species of the genus *Homo.* However, there are several species belonging to the genus *Sciurus.* The gray squirrel, for example, is *Sciurus carolinensis.*

Note from the above chart that man and squirrel are distantly related, belonging to the same *kingdom* (because they are animals); to the same *phylum* (because they have backbones); and to the same *class* (because they feed their young on milk). From *order* downward, however, they differ. For example, man is placed in the order *Primates,* because he possesses nails on his fingers and toes. The squirrel is placed in the order *Rodentia,* because it is a gnawing mammal provided with chisel-like front teeth.

The system of taxonomy has been so well established through the years that newly-discovered plants and animals have been readily classified according to kingdom, phylum, and so on, through genus. As new organisms are discovered, new species names are created. The name selected for the species may be in honor of the discoverer, or some other individual. For example, the Japanese barberry was named Berberis *thunbergii* in honor of Carl *Thunberg,* a Swedish botanist. Or the name may describe the color or some other characteristic of the organism. For example, the "big tree" of California was named Sequoia *gigantea* because of its *gigantic* size. Or the name may denote the region where the organism was found. For example, the red squirrel, Sciurus *hudsonicus,* was named after the *Hudson* Bay.

The Value of Modern Taxonomy. Taxonomy has brought many benefits to both scientist and layman, as follows:

1. Taxonomy, as a branch of biology, is now a uniform system used by scientists the world over. Thus, scientists doing research work can immediately identify an organism and its characteristics by referring to taxonomy tables. Needless duplication of established work is therefore avoided.

2. The names of living things have been Latinized because Latin is an old, unchanging, universal language. Since scholars everywhere in the world understand Latin, confusion due to language differences is avoided.

3. Classification aids scientists in recognizing and controlling disease-producing organisms and other pests. These species are first identified. Then, known methods of control are found by reference to appropriate literature.

4. Exhibitors of birds, moths, butterflies, etc., use taxonomy to identify their collection.

Completion Questions

1. _____ is the department of the science that deals with the classifying and naming of living organisms.
2. _____ was a Greek philosopher who devised an early system of classification.
3. Man belongs to the order _____.
4. An animal genus that consists of a single species is _____.
5. The first letter of the name of the (*species, genus*) _____ must always be capitalized.

Multiple-Choice Questions

1. Modern classification of plants and animals is based on a system devised by (1) Aristotle (2) Darwin (3) Linnaeus (4) Morgan.
2. Scientific classification is based primarily on (1) utility (2) similarity of structure (3) function (4) size.
3. In the (1) alphabetic (2) Aristotle (3) binomial (4) monomial system of nomenclature, a name consists of two words.
4. The scientific name of any organism consists of (1) phylum and class (2) class and species (3) phylum and genus (4) genus and species.

Chapter VI

THE PLANT KINGDOM

The Divisions of the Plant Kingdom. Scientists believe that the first living things to inhabit the earth were plants. The plants provided food for the animals that followed.

The plant kingdom consists of nearly 350,000 different species, divided into four phyla: *Thallophyta, Bryophyta, Pteridophyta, Spermatophyta.* Each phylum includes plants having common structural similarities. The phyla are presented in the probable order of appearance on earth. Each phylum shows greater complexity of structure than the preceding phylum.

PHYLUM I—THALLOPHYTA

Simple Plants: Algae and Fungi. All plants in the Phylum Thallophyta are simple in structure, that is, they have no true leaves, stems or roots. They do not produce flowers or seeds. Thallophytes are divided into two subphyla: *algae* and *fungi.*

Algae, Simple Green Plants. Algae, being green plants, contain chlorophyll and therefore manufacture their own food. Chlorophyll-bearing plants, such as algae, are called *independent* plants.

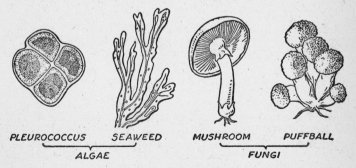

PLEUROCOCCUS   SEAWEED   MUSHROOM   PUFFBALL

ALGAE   FUNGI

Fig. 8. Thallophytes

One species of algae, which grows on the shady side of tree trunks or moist rocks, is called *pleurococcus*, or *protococcus*. This plant exists as a single independent cell, but lives in a *colony* of a few cells, one cell being attached to another. A great number of these colonies form a mass visible to the naked eye.

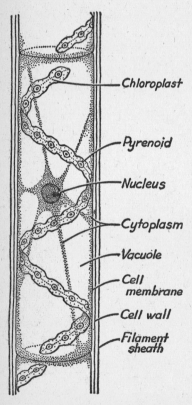

Another species of algae, which floats in a slimy mass on the surface of ponds and lakes, is called *pond scum*, or *spirogyra*. This plant exists as a single independent cell, but lives in a string-like colony. Under the microscope, the string, or *filament*, can be seen as a group of cylindrically-shaped cells, united end to end, for a length of several inches. The filament is encased within a *filament sheath*.

A distinctive feature of the spirogyra cell is the spiral-shaped *chloroplast*, which contains chlorophyll. On the chloroplast, at regular intervals, are small round bodies known as *pyrenoids*. The pyrenoids store starch manufactured by the chloroplast.

As in any other plant cell, the spirogyra cell has a *cell wall* and a *cell membrane*. Cytoplasm lines the inside of the cell membrane and extends in thin strands to the center of the cell. Here, the cytoplasm surrounds the *nucleus*, holding it in place. Occupying the remainder of the cell is a *cell vacuole*, which contains cell sap.

Chloroplast

Pyrenoid

Nucleus

Cytoplasm

Vacuole

Cell membrane

Cell wall

Filament sheath

Fig. 9.   The Spirogyra

Most algae reproduce by *binary fission,* which is reproduction by cell division. Some algae reproduce by *conjugation,* a process whereby two cells fuse together and then develop a new individual by repeated cell division. These methods of reproduction are more fully discussed in later chapters.

Algae are of economic benefit to man: (1) Algae form the diet of many fishes. (2) Some algae are used as soil fertilizers. (3) The kelps and other seaweeds, which are species of algae, are sources of iodine. (4) Certain algae, such as seaweeds, are sources of agar-agar, a gelatin used for growing bacteria for bacteriological research.

Some algae are harmful to man because they render drinking water distasteful or unfit to use.

Fungi, Simple Non-green Plants. Fungi do not contain chlorophyll and therefore cannot make their own food. Fungi are *dependent* plants, living on organic matter. *Organic matter* is a substance that is alive, or was once alive, or was produced by a living thing—either a plant or an animal. In contrast to organic matter is *inorganic matter,* which is a substance that is neither alive nor was produced by a living thing.

Some fungi, such as mushrooms, live on *dead* organic matter. They are classified as *saprophytes.* Other fungi, such as certain types of bacteria, live on or within *living* organisms. They are classified as *parasites.* In parasitism, the parasite derives its food from the living tissue of another living organism, called the *host,* but the parasite gives nothing in return to the host. As a result, the host is injured or even destroyed.

Bacteria. These unicellular fungi are the smallest plants, some being barely visible under the microscope. Bacteria are of three types: *coccus*—round, *bacillus*—rod shaped, *spirillum*—spiral shaped.

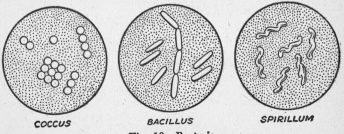

COCCUS　　　　BACILLUS　　　　SPIRILLUM

Fig. 10. Bacteria

Bacteria occur everywhere: in the air, soil, water and in or on living and dead organisms. A few species of bacteria are harmful. Some cause disease in plants and others cause disease in animals. Most bacteria, however, are beneficial—even essential to living things. Some bacteria help in the making of butter, cheese and sauerkraut. Other bacteria assist in fermentation, and in the decay of dead organisms. The process of decay adds valuable nitrates to the soil. Bacteria reproduce by binary fission.

Yeasts. These are microscopic, single-celled fungi. They bring about *fermentation,* a process whereby sugar is changed to carbon dioxide and alcohol. Fermentation takes place in the making of bread and alcoholic beverages. Yeast reproduces by an unequal cell division, called *budding,* by which a small bud is formed on the parent cell (see page 201).

Molds. If a piece of moist bread is kept in a warm dark place, it may soon become covered with a mold. Most molds consist of tiny threads, some of which penetrate into the bread to absorb food materials. Other threads, called *hyphae,* project upward and produce *spore cases* on their tips. These spore cases contain many *spores,* which are tiny cells that may produce a new growth of mold. Molds are of economic importance in the production of drugs, such as penicillin and aureomycin, and in the flavoring of certain cheeses.

Mushrooms. The most complex fungi plants are the mushrooms. They are saprophytic plants because they grow in rich moist soil containing a large amount of decaying organic matter. The mushroom plant consists of a great mass of branching filaments, which penetrate the soil for the purpose of absorbing food materials. The umbrella-shaped portion of the mushroom is merely the reproductive structure, on the underside of which numerous spores are produced. These spores are tiny reproductive bodies which may give rise to new mushrooms. Some mushrooms are edible, but others are deadly poisonous.

Other fungi are: *toadstools, puffballs, bracket fungi, mildews, rusts* and *smuts.* The latter two are economically important as parasites which destroy plant life.

The Lichen. The lichen is a gray-green, crust-like growth found on tree trunks and rocks. The lichen actually consists of two plants, a fungus and an alga living together for mutual assistance. The fungus provides the alga not only with a place to live, but also with water and carbon dioxide. These materials are used in photosynthesis by the alga, which thus provides the fungus with food. Such a relationship, in which two organisms of different species live together to the benefit of each other, is called *symbiosis*. The two organisms living in symbiotic relationship are called *symbionts*.

PHYLUM II—BRYOPHYTA

Characteristics of the Bryophytes. The plants in this phylum possess simple stems and small leaves. Instead of roots, they have delicate root-like structures, called *rhizoids*. The rhizoids penetrate the soil, anchoring the plant and absorbing water. Bryophytes never grow more than two or three inches high. This is because their stems have no woody tissue, which is needed to support a taller plant. Since bryophytes contain chlorophyll, they are independent plants, making their own food by photosynthesis.

Reproduction is by *alternation of generations*. In this method of reproduction, there is first a sexual generation, then an asexual generation. (See pages 212-213 for the life cycle of the moss.)

The two types of plants making up this phylum are *mosses* and *liverworts*.

MOSS   LIVERWORT

Fig. 11. Bryophytes

Mosses. The moss plant has an upright simple stem surrounded by a mass of tiny leaves. Mosses grow in moist earth, on rocks and the bark of trees. A few grow in water.

Mosses are of some economic value to man. The most important kind is *peat moss*, or *sphagnum*. This moss grows only in very wet places, such as swamps. As the moss decays, a substance, called *peat,* is formed. Peat is used in the soil, where it aids in retaining moisture for the soil. In some countries, peat is dried and used as a fuel.

Liverworts. The typical liverwort plant consists of three or four simple branching leaves, lying flat on the ground. Clusters of liverworts are found only in moist places: on soil, rocks and logs. Some grow in water. No economic importance is attached to the liverworts.

PHYLUM III—PTERIDOPHYTA

Ferns, Horsetails and Club Mosses. Because pteridophytes have true roots, stems and leaves, they are more advanced than the plants in the first two phyla. But, like the early plants, pteridophytes never produce flowers or seeds. Pteridophytes contain chlorophyll, and thus make their own food. Reproduction is by alternation of generations.

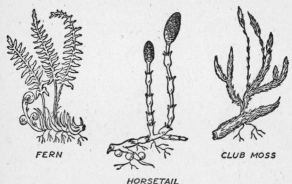

FERN

HORSETAIL

CLUB MOSS

Fig. 12. Pteridophytes

Of the plants in this phylum, you are probably most familiar with the ferns. Their roots and stems grow underground. The stems, called *rhizomes,* send up new leaves each year. The leaves are graceful, and are used by florists for decorative purposes.

Pteridophytes never grow more than two or three feet high, with the exception of some tropical ferns, which may grow to a height of fifty feet. These resemble the ancient ferns that lived many millions of years ago. At that time, the pteridophytes were the predominant form of vegetation on the earth. When these plants died and decayed, they formed the vast coal deposits now so valuable to mankind. The ferns, horsetails and club mosses of today are of little economic importance.

PHYLUM IV—SPERMATOPHYTA

Seed Plants. These are the most highly developed plants, having true leaves, stems and roots. All these plants reproduce by *seeds*. (Seeds are discussed on page 216.) Although they were the last plants to appear on the earth, the seed plants, or spermatophytes, are now the dominant form of plant life. Some spermatophytes live on land and some in water. With few exceptions, they can manufacture their own food by photosynthesis. Seed plants are of the greatest economic importance to man.

Spermatophytes are divided into two groups: *gymnospermae* and *angiospermae*.

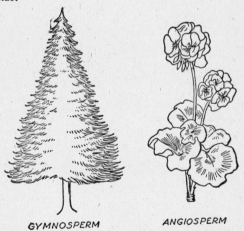

GYMNOSPERM   ANGIOSPERM

Fig. 13. **Spermatophytes**

Gymnosperms. These produce seeds which are *uncovered;* that is, the seeds are not enclosed in a protective covering. The best known plants in this group are the evergreen trees, such as the pine, spruce and cedar. Their seeds may be found lying exposed on the cones. The evergreens provide us with most of our lumber, and with pulp for making paper.

Angiosperms. These have flowers which produce *covered* seeds. The seeds are enclosed in the fruit. Most plants found in the world today are angiosperms. Angiosperms include the true flowering plants: buttercups, tulips and orchids. Other angiosperms are the various trees, such as the oak, maple and walnut, which are used extensively in the manufacture of furniture. The most important of all the angiosperms are the common grasses, such as wheat, corn and oats. These crop plants are the main source of man's food supply.

Angiosperms are divided into the *monocotyledons* (or monocots) and the *dicotyledons* (or dicots). These terms are derived from the fact that the seeds of monocots have one cotyledon, while the seeds of dicots have two cotyledons. (The nature of a cotyledon is explained under seed structures on page 216.) Monocots can be distinguished from dicots by the fact that monocot leaves are long and narrow and show *parallel veining*, as in corn. Dicot leaves are broad and have *netlike veining*, as in the maple. Also, in monocots, the vascular bundles are often scattered, while in dicots the conducting tissues are arranged in a definite ring (see pages 65-66.)

Completion Questions

1. Most algae reproduce by the process of _____.
2. The spirogyra belongs to a group of plants known as the _____.
3. The characteristic spiral structure in spirogyra contains a green substance called _____.
4. A general name for non-green plants that have no roots, leaves or stems is _____.
5. A rod-shaped bacterium is called a (an) _____.
6. An organism that lives on another living organism to the injury of the latter is called a (an) _____.
7. The plant or animal on which a parasite lives is called the _____.
8. The type of nutrition in a plant that feeds on dead organic matter is _____.
9. Mosses and liverworts are placed in the Phylum _____.
10. The simplest plants which have true roots, stems and leaves are the _____.

Multiple-Choice Questions

1. The largest groups of the plant kingdom are known as **(1)** classes (2) phyla (3) orders (4) genera.

2. One-celled plants containing chlorophyll are called (1) fungi
   (2) algae (3) bacteria (4) protozoa.
3. Plants containing chlorophyll illustrate the type of nutrition
   called (1) independent (2) dependent (3) parasitism (4)
   saprophytism.
4. Bacteria are usually classified as (1) animals (2) minerals
   (3) plants (4) viruses.
5. Fermentation of sugar is caused by (1) algae (2) mildew
   (3) molds (4) yeast.
6. Molds cannot carry on the process of (1) assimilation (2) diffusion (3) excretion (4) photosynthesis.
7. The mushroom is an example of (1) an independent plant
   (2) a parasite (3) a saprophyte (4) a symbiont.
8. A lichen is made up of a fungus and (1) an alga (2) a non-
   green plant (3) yeast (4) mold.
9. An organism that lives in a mutually helpful relationship with
   another organism is called a (1) symbiont (2) parasite (3)
   saprophyte (4) free-living organism.
10. The group of plants that appeared most recently on earth is the
    (1) bacteria (2) fungi (3) mosses (4) seed plants.

Essay Questions

1. *a.* Make a labeled diagram of a cell of a spirogyra plant.
   b. Give the special function of each structure labeled.
2. *a.* Describe how a mold plant obtains its nourishment.
   b. State a beneficial value of each of the following: mold, yeast,
   saprophytic bacteria.
3. Give a biologic significance of each of the following statements:
   a. Many saprophytic organisms are harmful to man.
   b. The lichen illustrates a valuable relationship between organisms.
4. *a.* Some plants cannot manufacture food. Name two types of
   nutrition represented by such plants and describe both types,
   giving an example of each.
   b. State one fact to support the statement: "All plants do not
   have flowers."
5. On your answer paper list the following plants: toadstool, club
   moss, oak, fern, spruce, bacterium, moss, apple, dandelion, protococcus. After each plant listed, write the name of the phylum
   to which it belongs. Tell why each plant listed belongs in the
   phylum named.

Chapter VII

THE GREEN PLANT—THE WORLD'S FOOD FACTORY

ACTIVITIES OF GREEN PLANTS

What Are Green Plants? The term "green" plants, strangely enough, is not used in biology merely to denote plants which are green in color, but specifically to indicate plants having the particular type of green pigment called *chlorophyll*. A red plant, such as the red maple, actually is a "green" plant because it possesses chlorophyll. The green color of the chlorophyll is hidden by the leaf's red pigment. On the other hand, the mold, penicillium, although green in color, is a fungus. It is not a "green" plant, in a biologic sense, because it does not contain chlorophyll.

Importance of Green Plants. Green plants are the only living things able to manufacture their own food. They convert the elements carbon, hydrogen, oxygen and nitrogen into sugars, starch, proteins, fats, oils and vitamins. The plant uses some of these food substances for its own life activities, and stores the surplus. If the plant is eaten by an animal which lives on plants (a *herbivorous* animal), the nutrients in the plant are passed along to the animal for its life activities. If this animal is eaten by another animal that lives on meat (a *carnivorous* animal), the nutrients from the plant-eating animal are then passed along to the meat-eating animal. Since green plants furnish food to all animals, directly or indirectly, green plants are called "the world's food factories."

Photosynthesis: Green Plants Manufacture Carbohydrates. Sugars and starch are called carbohydrates. They are manufactured in the green plant by the process of *photosynthesis*. The raw materials for photosynthesis are *carbon dioxide* and *water*. Carbon dioxide is obtained from the air through the leaves of the plant. Water is secured from the soil by the plant's roots. *Light*, especially sunlight, provides the energy needed for the process. *Chlorophyll*, the green matter present in the chloroplasts (see page 25), is essential to the reaction. Without chlorophyll, photosynthesis cannot take place. In photosynthesis, carbon dioxide and water react chemically to form simple sugar. Oxygen is given off as a by-product.

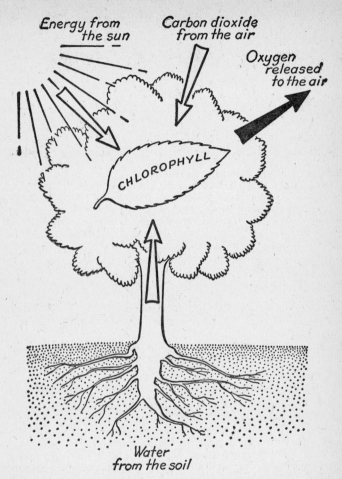

Fig. 14. The Manufacture of Carbohydrates by Photosynthesis

The chemical equation for photosynthesis is as follows:

$$6CO_2 \; + \; 6H_2O \xrightarrow[\text{(catalyst)}]{\text{chlorophyll}} C_6H_{12}O_6 \; + \; 6O_2$$

six molecules of carbon dioxide	six molecules of water	one molecule of sugar	six molecules of oxygen

Note that six molecules of carbon dioxide and six molecules of water are necessary to produce one molecule of sugar. Observe also that the chlorophyll appears in the equation as a *catalyst*, or *catalytic agent*. A catalyst is a substance which promotes the chemical reaction but does not itself become changed. Therefore, the chlorophyll does not become part of the sugar molecule.

A sugar molecule, broken down chemically, is found to consist of carbon, hydrogen and oxygen. But a recombination of these three elements—as tried by chemists for many years—does not readily produce sugar. This food can be made only by a living green plant, and only because of the *energy* it obtains from the sun. The energy is stored in the sugar, and is released when the sugar is oxidized in the cells of an organism.

By a complicated chemical process in the plant, the sugar produced in photosynthesis is converted into starch and stored for later use as food.

Photosynthesis Experiments:

1. *To prove that light is necessary for photosynthesis.* Cover a part of a geranium leaf on both the top and bottom surfaces with carbon paper held in place by paper clips. Place the plant in strong sunlight for two hours. Remove the leaf, boil it in water for a few minutes, and then boil in alcohol until all chlorophyll is removed. [*Caution: Care must be taken not to ignite the highly inflammable alcohol.* It is therefore advisable to boil the alcohol over a steam bath or in a double boiler.] The leaf will then appear white. Stain the leaf with iodine solution. The part of the leaf that was exposed to the light appears blue-black in color, thus indicating that starch has been made. The part of the leaf that was covered with carbon paper does not turn blue-black but remains iodine-colored, thus indicating the absence of starch.

Fig. 15. Light Is Necessary for Photosynthesis

2. *To prove that chlorophyll is necessary for photosynthesis.* Expose a plant having variegated leaves (partly green and partly white) to bright sunlight for two hours. Remove a leaf and treat it as in Experiment 1 above. Starch is found to have been formed only in the green parts of the leaf.

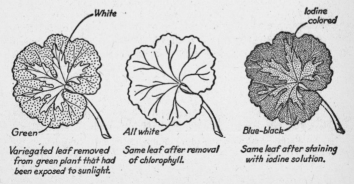

Fig. 16. Chlorophyll Is Necessary for Photosynthesis

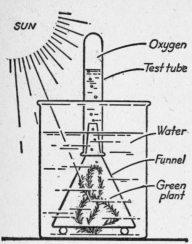

Fig. 17. Oxygen Is Given off
During Photosynthesis

3. *To prove that oxygen is given off during photosynthesis.* Place a few sprigs of elodea in a large beaker of water. Over the elodea, invert a glass funnel with a test tube of water on its stem. Place the apparatus in bright sunlight. Gas bubbles will issue from the elodea and finally fill the inverted test tube. Test the gas by inserting a glowing splint into the tube. The splint will burst into flame, thus showing the presence of oxygen. For a control, place a similar apparatus in a dark closet. A test of the gas that accumulates in the test tube will show that the gas is not oxygen.

Protein Synthesis: Green Plants Manufacture Proteins. As stated on page 48, soil water is absorbed by the roots of the plant and carried up the stem to the leaves. There, the water is used in photosynthesis as a raw material for the manufacture of carbohydrates. But the soil water carries with it other raw materials which the green plant converts to food. These materials are dissolved mineral salts, particularly nitrates, sulfates and phosphates. The plant first removes the elements nitrogen, sulfur and phosphorus from the mineral salts. Then the plant unites these elements with the elements carbon, hydrogen and oxygen present in the sugar molecule. The resulting products are *amino acids,* which combine to form various *proteins.* This process of combining elements to produce proteins is called *protein synthesis.* Sunlight and chlorophyll are *not* necessary for protein manufacture.

Green Plants Also Manufacture Fats, Oils and Vitamins. The chemical processes by which fats, oils and vitamins are made in green plants are very complicated. Nevertheless, the basic ingredients are the elements carbon, hydrogen and oxygen—which are also present in carbohydrates and proteins, but in different chemical arrangement.

The Nitrogen Cycle. Plants must have the element nitrogen as an ingredient for the manufacture of plant protein. Although nitrogen gas comprises four-fifths of the air, plants are not able to use this free nitrogen. The nitrogen in the air must first be combined with other elements to form *nitrates*, which can be used by the plant.

In the *nitrogen cycle*, nitrogen is taken in from the atmosphere by *nitrogen-fixing bacteria* (see 1 on Fig. 18). These bacteria live in *nodules*, or tiny lumps, on the roots of leguminous plants (clover, beans, alfalfa). The nitrogen-fixing bacteria combine the atmospheric nitrogen with other elements to form *nitrates*. Being soluble, the nitrates are added to the soil. The roots of the green plant (2) absorb the nitrates, and then convert the nitrates into plant protein. The

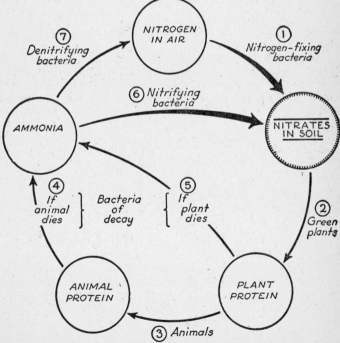

Fig. 18. The Nitrogen Cycle

plant protein is transformed into animal protein when the plant is
eaten by an animal (3). If the animal dies (4), its body decays. If
the plant is not eaten, it will eventually die (5), and its body will
decay.

The process of decay is due to bacterial action. Many types of bacteria which feed on dead matter live in the soil. In decomposing the
tissues of the dead plants and animals, the bacteria of decay change
the tied-up nitrogen compounds into simpler substances such as
ammonia. The *nitrifying bacteria* (6) then continue the process. The
nitrite bacteria convert ammonia into nitrites, which however cannot
be used by the green plants. The *nitrate bacteria*, by adding more
oxygen to the nitrites, change them into the nitrates which can be
used by the green plant. Still other bacteria, the *denitrifying bacteria*
(7), convert the ammonia into free nitrogen, which escapes into the
air. The free nitrogen is converted into nitrates and restored to the
soil by the nitrogen-fixing bacteria. Thus, the nitrogen cycle is complete.

The nitrogen-fixing bacteria provide nitrates for the green plant.
The green plant provides the bacteria with food, moisture and a place
to live. This is another example of symbiosis (see page 43).

Man aids nature in maintaining the amount of nitrogen needed
by plants. He plants clover and adds chemical fertilizers to restore
nitrates to the soil. (We shall discuss this at greater length later in
Chapter XXV on Conservation.)

Respiration in Green Plants.   In respiration, the plant takes in
oxygen and combines it with foods in the process of oxidation.
Energy is released and carbon dioxide and water are given off as
waste products. Chemically, respiration is the *opposite* of photosynthesis, as follows:

Photosynthesis: carbon dioxide + water ⟶ sugar + oxygen
Respiration: oxygen + sugar ⟶ carbon dioxide + water

Chlorophyll and sunlight are *not* required for respiration. Consequently, respiration takes place in all cells of the plant, and at all
hours—hours of light and darkness. During the hours of sunlight,
the green plant obtains oxygen from its tissues, where oxygen is produced by photosynthesis. During the hours of darkness, when the
plant is not undergoing photosynthesis, the plant obtains oxygen
from the atmosphere. Photosynthesis is a *constructive* (building-up)
process, since it results in the making of food; but respiration is a
destructive (tearing-down) process, since it results in the breaking
down of food.

Respiration Experiments:

1. *To prove that oxygen is necessary for respiration.* Soak some seeds overnight, and then plant half of them on wet cotton in each of two fruit jars. Place the cover on one jar to keep out the air. Leave the other jar uncovered. The seeds in the uncovered jar will sprout, while those in the covered jar will die for want of air (oxygen).

2. *To prove that heat is produced in respiration.* Label two vacuum bottles A and B. Place live sprouting beans in bottle A, and dead sprouting beans (killed by boiling) in bottle B. Into each bottle, fit a stopper bearing a thermometer. Later, it will be found that the temperature of bottle A is higher than that of bottle B, due to the heat produced by the respiration of the beans.

3. *To prove that carbon dioxide is given off in respiration.* Place a dish of limewater in a loosely covered jar, A, containing sprouting seeds. For a control, set up a similar jar, B, containing sprouting seeds that have been killed by boiling. The limewater in jar A soon turns milky, proving that carbon dioxide has been given off by the seeds. In jar B, the limewater remains clear.

Contrasts Between Photosynthesis and Respiration. These two life functions of green plants are frequently confused, although they are markedly different, as shown in the chart below.

Photosynthesis	Respiration
Takes place only in plant cells having chloroplasts.	Takes place in all living cells, both in plants and animals.
Occurs only during hours of daylight.	Occurs at all times, day and night.
Carbon dioxide and water are the raw materials.	Foods and oxygen are the raw materials.
Sugars and starch are produced.	Energy is produced by oxidation of foods.
Oxygen is a by-product.	Carbon dioxide and water are by-products.
A constructive process.	A destructive process.
Energy is stored.	Energy is released.

The Carbon Dioxide-Oxygen Cycle. In the *carbon dioxide-oxygen cycle,* plants and animals help each other obtain the gas they need for life. As a result of respiration, animals give off carbon dioxide. The carbon dioxide is taken in by the green plants and used in photosynthesis. The oxygen set free by the plants in photosynthesis is then taken in by the animals for respiration. Thus, green plants not only make food, but also help maintain a balanced composition of the air —taking in carbon dioxide and releasing oxygen.

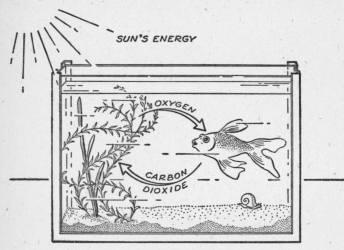

Fig. 19. The Balanced Aquarium

The *balanced aquarium* illustrates the carbon dioxide-oxygen cycle. A tank of water contains just enough animal life (fish) and plant life needed to maintain each other. Snails are usually added to act as scavengers, keeping the tank free of animal wastes.

STRUCTURES OF GREEN PLANTS

Vegetative Structures of Green Plants. A green plant is composed of three principal parts: the *root, leaf, stem*. These organs are known as *vegetative* structures, since their activities are concerned with the nutrition of the plant.

THE ROOT

Functions of the Root. The chief functions of the root of a plant are:

1. *Anchorage.* Underground roots hold the plant securely in the soil.

2. *Absorption.* The root absorbs soil water containing dissolved minerals.

3. *Storage.* The root of some plants, such as the beet, is the storage organ of the plant's reserve food supply.

The Root System. The first root to develop from a seed is called the *primary* root. Branches arising from the primary root are *secondary* roots. Branches which emerge from the secondary roots are *rootlets.* All the roots of the plant make up the *root system.*

In some plants, such as the carrot, the single primary root is long, and much larger than the secondary roots. This is called a *taproot system.* In other plants, as grass, the root system consists of numerous fine roots branching in all directions. This is a *fibrous root system.* Some taproots, such as the carrot and beet, and certain fibrous roots, such as the sweet potato, are the storage areas of food. They are called *fleshy roots.*

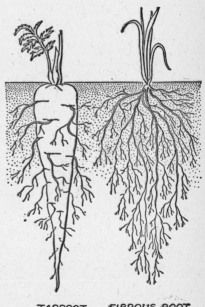

TAPROOT OF CARROT   FIBROUS ROOT OF GRASS

Fig. 20. Root Systems

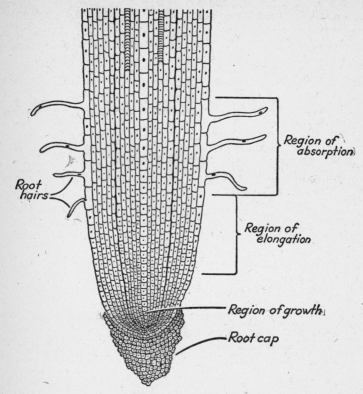

Fig. 21. The Root Tip

Structures of the Root. A root tip cut lengthwise and examined under the microscope is found to consist of the following parts:

1. *Root Cap.* Covering the end of the root tip is a protective thimble-like mass of cells called the root cap. The root cap prevents injury to the end of the root tip as the root works its way through the soil.

2. *Region of Growth.* This is at the end of the root tip, protected

by the root cap. In the region of growth, the cells are dividing and the various stages of mitosis are present.

3. *Region of Elongation.*   Next to the region of growth is found the region of elongation. Here, the cells produced in the region of growth enlarge and become much longer.

4. *Region of Absorption.*   Next to the region of elongation is the region of absorption. Here, ground water is absorbed. This region is identified by the presence of numerous root hairs.

Root Hairs.   A root hair is a projection from an epidermal cell of the root. The root hair is characterized by a large vacuole, containing many substances dissolved in water. Root hairs increase the surface area of the root through which the plant absorbs soil water with its minerals. The soil water with its minerals passes through the cell membrane of the root hair into the vacuole. From here the soil water and minerals are taken by other cells and circulated through the plant.

Root hairs can be observed by germinating radish seedlings on wet blotting paper in a Petri dish. Under the microscope, the root hair appears as follows:

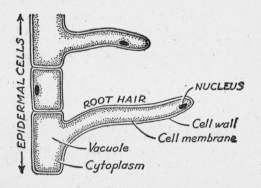

Fig. 22. The Root Hair

Diffusion. The root absorbs soil water through its root hairs by osmosis, which is a special type of diffusion. *Diffusion* is the process by which molecules of a gas or a liquid of different density equalize each other. The molecules from an area of greater concentration pass to an area of lesser concentration.

Diffusion can be observed by placing a few drops of ink in a glass of water. The ink will circulate through the water until the water becomes uniformly colored.

Osmosis. As said before, osmosis is a special type of diffusion In the process of osmosis, molecules of a gas or a liquid diffuse through a moist *semi-permeable* membrane. This type of membrane is believed to have pores, or tiny openings, through which certain molecules can pass.

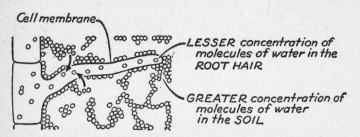

Fig. 23. Osmosis in the Root Hair

Osmosis can be demonstrated as follows: Holding the thumb over the narrow end of a thistle tube, fill the enlarged end with molasses solution. Tie an animal membrane over the enlarged opening of the thistle tube. Still holding the thumb over the narrow opening, invert the tube into a beaker of water, without touching the bottom of the beaker. Clamp the thistle tube in a ring stand and allow the apparatus to stand. After a few hours, the molasses solution will be seen to have risen in the thistle tube. The water molecules surrounding the thistle tube, which were of greater concentration, passed through the membrane and into the tube, where the water molecules were of lesser concentration. Some molasses will pass from the tube into the beaker of water, but only very little. Osmotic pressure from the water molecules will be great enough to cause the water to rise up the thistle tube.

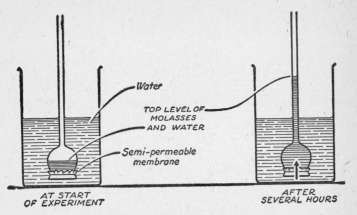

Fig. 24. Osmosis Experiment

THE LEAF

Functions of the Leaf. The principal activities of the leaf are:

1. *Photosynthesis.* This is the chief function of the chlorophyll-bearing leaf. In the presence of light, carbon dioxide is taken in from the air and combined with water taken in from the soil to form sugar. Oxygen is given off to the air.

2. *Respiration.* The leaf takes in oxygen for oxidation, which takes place in all cells of the plant. Energy is released, and carbon dioxide and water vapor are given off to the air.

3. *Transpiration.* Through tiny openings in the leaf, the plant gives off an enormous quantity of water vapor. This loss of water is known as transpiration.

Transpiration can be demonstrated as follows: Obtain a potted plant, and surround the pot with a piece of rubber sheeting. Tie the sheeting securely around the stem to prevent evaporation from the pot and from the soil. Then invert a bell jar over the plant. Droplets of water given off from the *leaves* collect on the inside of the jar.

If a plant does not take from the soil as much water as it loses by transpiration, the plant wilts.

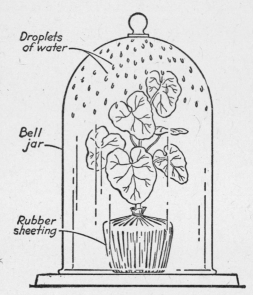

Droplets of water

Bell jar

Rubber sheeting

Fig. 25. Transpiration

Structures of the Leaf. A microscopic examination of a leaf, **cut** cross-sectionally, shows *veins*, which are the leaf's conducting tubes; and four distinct *cellular layers*, as follows:

1-2. *Two Epidermal Layers: The Upper and Lower Epidermis.* The leaf's top surface layer of cells is called the *upper epidermis*. The bottom surface layer of cells is the *lower epidermis*. Each of these tissues is usually a single layer of cells, serving as a protective covering.

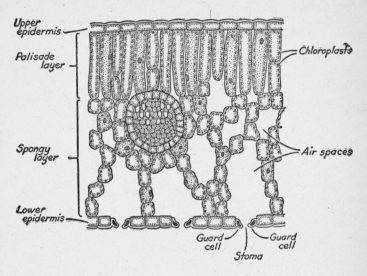

Fig. 26. Cross Section of a Leaf

The upper epidermis has a waxy coating, which prevents the escape of water by evaporation. The lower epidermis contains tiny openings, called *stomata*. Each stoma lies between a pair of specialized cells, called *guard cells*, which regulate the size of the opening of the stoma. Through the stomata, the plant exchanges gases with the air as follows:

Process	Taken In	Given Off
photosynthesis	carbon dioxide	oxygen
respiration	oxygen	carbon dioxide and water vapor
transpiration		water vapor

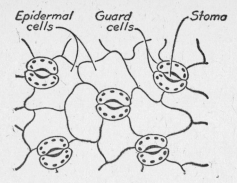

Fig. 27. The Lower Epidermis of a Leaf

3. *The Palisade Layer.* This tissue may consist of one or several layers of elongated cells lying directly below the upper epidermis. The palisade layer of cells is richly supplied with chloroplasts, the bodies containing chlorophyll. Because the cells of the upper epidermis are transparent, light penetrates the upper epidermis to the chloroplasts for photosynthesis. The palisade layer is the principal food-manufacturing part of the plant.

4. *The Spongy Layer.* Between the palisade layer and the lower epidermis is the spongy layer. The cells in this layer are round and loosely arranged. In between the cells are large air spaces that lead to the stomata. Through the stomata, outside air, with its carbon dioxide, reaches the various leaf cells for photosynthesis. Photosynthesis takes place in the spongy layer, but to a lesser degree than in the palisade layer.

THE STEM

Functions of the Stem. Typical stems perform the following functions:

1. *Support.* The stem holds the leaves up to the light to help them carry on photosynthesis.

2. *Conduction.* In the stem are the two systems of conducting tubes, the xylem and phloem, which transport soil water containing dissolved minerals upward, and food materials downward to all living cells in the plant.

3. *Storage.* The stem of some plants serves as a storage organ for food and water.

4. *Food making.* Some stems contain chlorophyll, and therefore carry on photosynthesis.

Structures of the Stem. The stems of higher, or seed-forming plants, are of two kinds according to structure: *monocot* and *dicot*.

1. *The Monocot Stem.* This type of stem consists almost entirely of a loose, spongy, supporting tissue, called *pith*. Scattered at random through the pith are the *fibrovascular bundles.* These are bundles of tubes, actually strings of elongated xylem and phloem cells, which conduct liquids. Soil water with its dissolved mineral salts is taken in by the root hairs and conducted by the *xylem* cells through the roots, *up* the stem, and to the leaves for photosynthesis and protein synthesis. The dissolved foods manufactured by these processes are then conducted by the *phloem* cells *down* the stem to the roots.

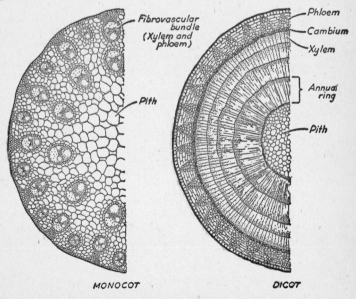

Fig. 28. Types of Stems

2. *The Dicot Stem.* This type of stem, found on common woody trees, contains a soft *pith*, especially present in young stems. The bulk of the stem is made up of rings of woody tissue, the *xylem.* Surrounding the xylem is a layer of growing tissue, the *cambium,* which is not present in the monocot stem. By repeated cell division, the cambium each growing season gives rise to xylem cells on its inner surface and *phloem* cells on its outer surface. Thus are formed concentric circles, or *annual rings.* The number of annual rings is a clue to the age of the tree. Also, the varying widths of the annual rings are an indication of the amount of rainfall in successive years. A wide ring is made in a year of abundant rain; a narrow ring is produced in a season of scanty rain. *Bark* covers the outside of the stem. Breathing pores, called *lenticels,* are present on the thin, young bark of twigs.

INSECTIVOROUS PLANTS

What Are Insectivorous Plants? Some chlorophyll-bearing plants, in addition to manufacturing their own food by photosynthesis, eat insects. These are called *insectivorous plants.* Examples are the V*enus's flytrap, sundew* and *pitcher plant.* All are found in the swampy regions of some of our Southeastern states.

The leaves of insectivorous plants are structures specialized for the trapping of insects.

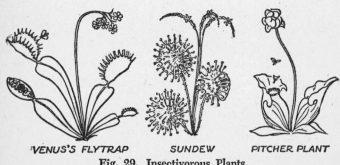

VENUS'S FLYTRAP   SUNDEW   PITCHER PLANT

Fig. 29. Insectivorous Plants

1. *Venus's Flytrap.* At the end of each leaf of the Venus's flytrap, there are two hinged pads edged with hairs. When an insect touches the hairs, the pads shut rapidly, trapping the insect.

2. *Sundew.* The sundew has a ball of sticky spines, which, when touched by an insect, bend over and imprison the insect.

3. *Pitcher Plant.* The leaves of the pitcher plant, which are shaped like a pitcher, hold a quantity of fluid. An insect can enter the leaf, but cannot escape. Numerous hairs on the leaf serve as a barrier. Eventually the insect drowns in the fluid.

Insectivorous plants produce enzymes with which to digest insects, thus converting the digested material into protoplasm.

Completion Questions

1. The green coloring matter of the plant cell is _____.
2. Chloroplasts enable plants to perform the function of _____.
3. Three elements used by green plants in the making of foods are _____, _____ and _____.
4. A substance taken in by a green plant cell but not by an animal cell is _____.
5. Photosynthesis involves water, carbon dioxide, chlorophyll and energy in the form of _____.
6. The gas given off in excess by a green plant cell in sunlight is _____.
7. Substances that produce a chemical change in other substances without being changed themselves are called _____.
8. Mushrooms cannot make starch because they lack _____.
9. A green plant usually stores its carbohydrate food in the form of _____.
10. Green plant cells take in oxygen in the process of _____.
11. The waste product (gas) given off by green plants during the process of respiration is _____.
12. The plants in a balanced aquarium furnish food and _____ for the fish.
13. Green plants help to maintain a balanced composition of the air by taking in _____.
14. A plant wilts when it loses by transpiration more _____ than it takes from the soil.
15. The movement of molecules from an area of greater concentration to an area of lesser concentration is called _____.
16. Gases pass in and out of the leaves of a plant through openings called _____.
17. Photosynthesis takes place mainly in the part of the leaf called the _____.

18. The layer of growing cells in the stem of a tree is called the _____.

19. The cells that conduct dissolved foods from the leaves to the roots are the _____.

20. Venus's flytrap not only makes some of its own food, but also eats _____.

Multiple-Choice Questions

1. The food supply of the world can be traced to the activity of (1) cytoplasm (2) chromatin (3) cellulose (4) chlorophyll.

2. Photosynthesis is a process that occurs in (1) bacteria (2) animals (3) geraniums (4) saprophytes.

3. Sugar and starch are (1) minerals (2) liquids (3) carbohydrates (4) enzymes.

4. Carbohydrate manufacture in green plants may be described as (1) saprophytic (2) constructive (3) destructive (4) parasitic.

5. Green plants absorb (1) nitrates (2) carbohydrates (3) oxygen (4) carbon dioxide from the soil.

6. The process in which green plants use nitrates is (1) photosynthesis (2) protein-synthesis (3) respiration (4) digestion.

7. An element present in proteins but not in sugars is (1) carbon (2) hydrogen (3) nitrogen (4) oxygen.

8. The amount of nitrogen compounds in soil is often increased by growing (1) clover (2) corn (3) potatoes (4) sunflowers.

9. Decay of fallen leaves depends primarily upon (1) dehydration (2) bacterial action (3) erosion (4) frost action.

10. Bacteria that live in the nodules of leguminous plants are (1) bacteria of decay (2) nitrifying bacteria (3) nitrogen-fixing bacteria (4) nitrite bacteria.

11. Respiration in plants and animals (1) is identical (2) is opposite (3) releases oxygen (4) is a building-up process.

12. In the dark, a green plant cell excretes (1) hydrogen (2) carbon dioxide (3) oxygen (4) nitrogen.

13. Water and dissolved mineral salts enter plants through the (1) cortex (2) root cap (3) guard cells (4) root hairs.

14. The passage of dissolved materials through a membrane is called (1) mitosis (2) osmosis (3) binary fission (4) transpiration.

15. The process of cell division in a plant can best be seen in the (1) root cap (2) region of growth (3) root hair (4) region of elongation.

Essay Questions

1. Vaseline was applied to a small area on the lower surface of a leaf. The plant on which this leaf was growing was watered and placed in the sunlight. Later, the leaf was removed from the plant, boiled in alcohol and treated with iodine solution. The leaf turned brown where the vaseline had been, and blue-black elsewhere.

   a. What substance was absent in the brown area?
   b. As shown by the iodine test, with what process did the vaseline interfere?
   c. What compound was not available for the green cells in the area covered by the vaseline?
   d. What structures were filled by the vaseline?
   e. With what process, other than the one indicated in b, did the vaseline interfere? Explain.
   f. State the problem (object) and give the observations of another experiment in which the iodine test is used on a plant leaf.

2. With reference to the green plant, answer the following questions concerning the manufacture of carbohydrates:

   a. By what process are carbohydrates manufactured?
   b. What are the raw materials that enter the plant?
   c. What is the source of energy for this process?
   d. What structure in the cells carries on this process?
   e. What waste product is given off as a result of this process?

3. a. Each of the following substances is involved in some cell process: carbon dioxide, water, oxygen, nitrates, phosphates, amino acids, sugars. Selecting terms from this list,

      (1) Name two substances used by plant cells to make carbohydrates.
      (2) Name two substances used by the green plant for the release of energy.
      (3) Name one substance produced by oxidation in both plant and animal cells.

   b. What basic process would be interrupted if the chloroplast of a green plant cell is removed?

4. Describe a properly controlled experiment to prove each of the following:

   a. A geranium plant makes starch.
   b. Green plants give off carbon dioxide in the process of respiration.

5. *a.* Tell why the world's food supply depends on green plants.
   b. In what way do non-green plants resemble animals in their food requirements?
   c. Name one type of bacterium that helps keep the soil fertile and tell in some detail how it does this.
6. Give the biologic significance of each of the following statements:
   a. Green plants are important agents in storing energy.
   b. Animals release stored energy.
   c. The protein food found in plants contains elements other than carbon, oxygen and hydrogen.
   d. The yield of the potato crop may be estimated from the vigor and size of the plants.
   e. Clover is being used to supply nitrates for corn land.
   f. The annual rings of wood found in the redwoods of California vary in width.
   g. The sun is the source of the energy that the heart uses in beating.
7. *a.* State two functions of each of the following: (1) roots of a tree, (2) leaves of a plant.
   b. State an important function of each of the following cells: (1) guard cell, (2) xylem cell, (3) palisade cell, (4) cambium cell.
8. *a.* Name two substances that enter a green plant cell and state the uses they serve.
   b. Name two substances that leave a green plant cell and tell how they originate.
9. *a.* A leaf, partly green and partly white, taken from a plant that had been standing in the sun, was tested for starch. State the object or problem of this experiment.
   b. Part of a green leaf is covered on both sides so as to exclude light. After several hours, the chlorophyll is removed and the leaf is tested with iodine. State one observation that could be made.

Chapter VIII

The Animal Kingdom

The Divisions of the Animal Kingdom. In this, the second great kingdom of living things, over 800,000 different species of animals have been classified. As in the plant kingdom, classification is based on structural similarities.

Scientists do not agree on the exact number of animal phyla, but there are ten important ones which we shall study in this chapter. Phylum I includes all one-celled animals. These are called *protozoa,* or *protozoans.* Phyla II through X consist of all multicellular animals. These are called *metazoa,* or *metazoans.* Each phylum shows increasing specialization of cells, as the animals become more complex in structure.

PHYLUM I—PROTOZOA

One-celled Animals. It is believed that the first animals to appear on earth were the protozoans. This phylum embraces the simplest animals known, all unicellular. Being microscopic in size, they are termed *microorganisms.* Special structures within the cell enable the

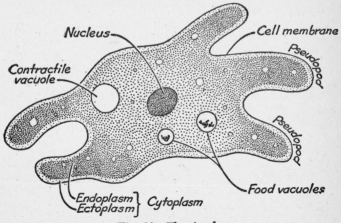

Fig. 30. The Ameba

71

protozoan to carry on all its life functions independently. Some protozoa form colonies of independent cells.

Protozoans live in water and in moist places. Many exist as parasites in the bodies of higher animals, including man, where they may cause serious disease. Some examples of protozoa are the *ameba, paramecium, stentor* and *vorticella*.

Ameba, the Simplest Protozoan. We study the ameba, a common inhabitant of ponds and streams, because it is the simplest animal. It is a tiny mass of transparent protoplasm which constantly changes its shape. It is distinguished by one or more *pseudopods*, or false feet. Pseudopods are temporary projections of protoplasm extending from the body in various directions. The ameba has a *nucleus, cell membrane* and *cytoplasm*. The cytoplasm consists of a layer of clear protoplasm (*ectoplasm*) just inside the cell membrane, and a denser granular type of protoplasm (*endoplasm*) composing the remainder, or greater part, of the cytoplasm.

The ameba performs all the life functions independently, as follows: For locomotion, the ameba forms pseudopods in the direction of movement, at the same time withdrawing all the other pseudopods. The movement of the ameba is slow, its shape changing as the protoplasm flows in different directions.

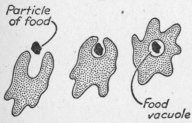

Fig. 31. **Ameba Engulfing Food**

The ameba feeds upon smaller microscopic plants and animals, and on dead organic matter. It engulfs the food by surrounding it with its pseudopods, and takes the food into the cell along with a drop of water. The food and water form a globule, called a *food vacuole*, where digestion takes place with the aid of chemical substances, *enzymes*, secreted by the cytoplasm. The digested part of the food is absorbed and used by the cytoplasm for the ameba's life activities. The indigestible solid parts of the food pass out of the cell through a temporary opening in the cell membrane.

Water and other liquid wastes collect in the *contractile vacuole*. When full, this vacuole contracts and expels its contents through the cell membrane. The vacuole thus serves as an excretory organ.

In carrying on respiration, ameba absorbs oxygen from the surrounding water, oxidizes food inside the cell, and gives off carbon dioxide. The exchange of gases—taking in oxygen and giving off carbon dioxide—takes place through the cell membrane by osmosis.

Ameba responds to changes (*stimuli*) in its environment. For example, the ameba moves away from intense heat or light, sharp objects and irritating substances, such as acetic acid (vinegar). It moves toward food, moisture, smooth surfaces and moderate light. These responses to stimuli are known as *tropisms* (see page 172).

If conditions are unfavorable for carrying on the life functions, the ameba secretes a thick covering, or *cyst*, around itself, and suspends all life activities. When favorable conditions are restored, the cyst breaks open and the ameba resumes its normal life.

Reproduction in ameba is by binary fission, that is, when the ameba reaches full size, it divides equally, forming two small amebas. (See Fig. 75 on page 200.)

Paramecium, a More Complex Protozoan. The paramecium is a one-celled animal, like the ameba, but more complex in structure. The paramecium is easily recognized by its unchanging, slipper-like shape. It is rounded at the front end and pointed at the hind end.

The typical paramecium contains two *nuclei*—the larger *macronucleus*, which regulates the animal's life functions, and the smaller *micronucleus*, which is concerned with the animal's reproduction. A stiff outer membrane, the *pellicle*, surrounds the animal, giving it a definite shape. Hair-like projections of protoplasm, called *cilia*, extend through tiny openings in the pellicle. On one side of the paramecium is a depression, the *oral groove*, which leads particles of food into the *gullet*. One or more *food vacuoles* circulate through the *cytoplasm*. There are two *contractile vacuoles*, one at either end of the cell. Toward the hind end is an opening in the pellicle, called the *anal spot*.

Paramecium moves swiftly by the rhythmic beating of its cilia, which drive the animal through water somewhat in the same manner as oars propel a boat. In food-getting, cilia, lining the oral groove, sweep the food particles and a drop of water into the oral groove, to the gullet, where a food vacuole is formed. When the vacuole reaches a certain size, it is detached from the gullet and carried throughout the cell. As in the ameba, the cytoplasm secretes enzymes into the vacuole for digestion, and then absorbs the digested food. Any indigestible materials are carried to the anal spot, which opens and discharges these solid wastes from the cell.

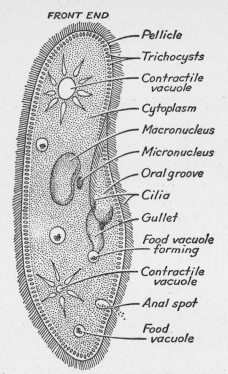

Fig. 32. The Paramecium

Through the pellicle, the paramecium takes in oxygen and gives off carbon dioxide. By means of the two contractile vacuoles, the animal excretes water and other liquid wastes. In the cytoplasm, just within the pellicle, are tiny oval-shaped sacs, called *trichocysts*, which, when stimulated, discharge long poisonous threads into the surrounding water. Paramecium is thus provided with a means of defense.

Paramecium, as the ameba, responds by tropisms; it avoids irritating chemicals and extreme temperatures. Reproduction is mainly by

binary fission, sometimes by conjugation. In conjugation, two paramecia come together and exchange nuclear material. They then
separate and reproduce by binary fission with renewed vigor. (See
page 210.)

The Plant-Animals. There are some living things which biologists
cannot definitely classify as either plant or animal, because these
forms of life possess both plant and animal characteristics. Two examples of the so-called plant-animals are *euglena* and *volvox*. Some
biologists consider them to be plants, but most biologists regard them
as animals.

**Euglena, a One-Celled
Plant-Animal.** This plant-
animal inhabits lakes and
streams. It consists of a
single cell, somewhat ob-
long in shape. At the front
end of the cell, a long whip-
like structure, the *flagellum,*
extends from an opening
called the *mouth.* The flagellum lashes the water and
thus propels the euglena.
Hence, in carrying on ac-
tive swimming, the euglena
resembles an animal.

A canal, resembling a
gullet, leads from the mouth
into the *reservoir.* Wastes
are emptied into the reservoir by a number of sur-
rounding *contractile vacuoles.*
All these structures are typical of animals.

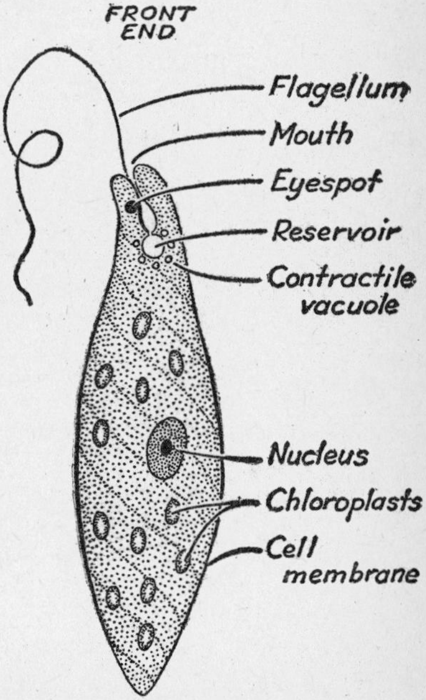

Scattered around a well-
defined *nucleus* are many
chloroplasts. These enable
the euglena to make its own
food by photosynthesis—a
plant characteristic. A red
eyespot, located near the

Fig. 33. The Euglena

mouth, is sensitive to light and thus guides the euglena toward light for
photosynthesis. When the euglena is unable to make its own food, it

absorbs food matter through the *cell membrane*—another animal characteristic.

Like the ameba, the euglena can form a cyst about itself when conditions are unfavorable. Euglena reproduces by binary fission.

Volvox, a Colonial Plant-Animal.   This is another plant-animal inhabitant of lakes and streams. It is a colony of thousands of independent cells held together by protoplasmic strands in the shape of a hollow sphere.

Each cell possesses two *flagella*, which propel the volvox through water. This power of locomotion we know to be an animal characteristic. However, volvox, like euglena, manufactures its own food by photosynthesis, thus resembling a plant.

Volvox shows the beginning of specialization. Although each cell carries on all the life functions, some cells are specialized to carry on reproduction. These reproductive cells pass to the central cavity where, by repeated divisions, they give rise to daughter colonies. The parent colony then breaks open and the daughter colonies escape.

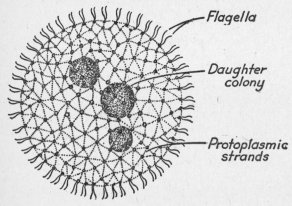

Fig. 34. Volvox, a Colonial Plant-Animal

PHYLUM II—PORIFERA

Sponges, the Pore-Bearing Animals.   Phylum Porifera is made up of the sponges. Some are fresh-water inhabitants, but most are salt-water (marine). All are *radially symmetrical*. This means that the body parts are regularly arranged about a central point from which the parts radiate, just as the spokes of a wheel radiate from the hub.

Sponges generally grow on rocks, somewhat in the manner of plants. Commercial sponges are really the mineral skeletons of marine sponges—gathered, dried out, and made ready for use in the home and elsewhere as cleaning aids.

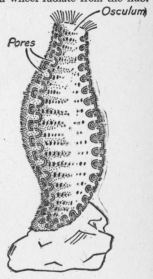

The sponge is hollow, usually vase-shaped, and characterized by *pores* spread over the body. One end of the sponge is permanently attached to a rock, or some other firm base. The open end is called the *osculum.* Water enters the sponge through the pores, and leaves by way of the osculum. A skeleton supports the sponge and maintains its shape.

Although the simplest of the multicellular animals, the sponge shows true specialization. Different cells perform special functions for the good of the animal as a whole.

Fig. 35. The Sponge

Two layers of cells, with a jelly-like substance in between, make up the body of the simple sponge. The outer layer serves as a protective covering. The inner layer contains cells possessing flagella, which, by their beating action, cause the constant flow of water into the pores and through the body. The water carries dissolved oxygen to all the cells, and food particles to digestive cells on the inner layer. The water also removes carbon dioxide and indigestible substances from the animal.

Reproduction may be (1) *asexual,* by budding, a process in which a small new individual forms as a bud on the side of the parent, or (2) *sexual,* by fertilization, in which a reproductive cell is produced by each of the two parents. The male reproductive cell is the sperm; the female reproductive cell is the egg. These reproductive cells fuse together, forming a single cell which develops into a new individual.

PHYLUM III—COELENTERATA

Coelenterates, the Hollow-bellied Animals. Almost all coelenterates live in salt water. One of the most familiar kind is the transparent, cup-like *jellyfish,* whose body is 99% water. The jellyfish is very different in outward appearance from the *sea anemone,* which is flower-like. A third member of this phylum is the *coral.* Corals live in colonies, forming large reefs, even islands. The mineral skeleton of the precious coral is used in making jewelry.

Hydra, a Typical Coelenterate. The hydra is one of the few coelenterates found in fresh water ponds and streams. About a half inch in length, it appears to the naked eye as a piece of string frayed at one end. The hydra's body is a hollow tube with one end closed.

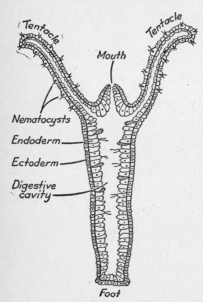

Fig. 36. The Hydra

This end is usually attached to an underwater plant or rock. The other end has a *mouth,* surrounded by *tentacles.* The mouth leads into the *digestive cavity.*

The two layers of cells composing the body wall are the *ectoderm,* or outer layer, and the *endoderm,* or inner layer. Between them lies a non-cellular, jelly-like material. Hydra has many specialized cells. Stinging cells (*nematocysts*) aid in food-getting. Although these nematocysts are all over the body, they are particularly numerous on the tentacles. When stimulated, the stinging cells shoot out harpoon-like threads that paralyze smaller animals, which the hydra then takes in for food. The tentacles surround the food and push it through the mouth into the digestive cavity. Here, gland cells on the endoderm secrete enzymes which aid the digestive process. Particles that cannot be digested are later ejected through the mouth.

In reacting to stimuli, the hydra has nerve cells, which send messages throughout the body and aid muscle cells in working together for movement (see page 176). The hydra moves by sliding along on its base, or *sticky foot*, which is attached to some object. At times, the hydra may walk on its tentacles, or move by a succession of somersaults.

Reproduction is usually asexual, by budding. With the coming of cold weather, sexual reproductive organs appear and eggs and sperm cells are produced. Hydra is the first animal, in our discussion, that has both male and female sex organs (a *hermaphrodite*).

PHYLUM IV—PLATYHELMINTHES

Flatworms, the Lowest Form of Worms. Worms are divided into three phyla, according to increasing complexity in structure: *flatworms, roundworms, segmented worms.* The first phylum contains only the lowest form of worms, the flatworms. Some are fresh-water inhabitants, but the majority live as parasites in the bodies of higher

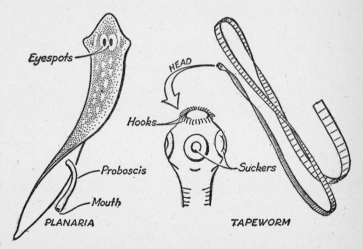

Fig. 37. Flatworms

animals, including man. A flatworm's body is soft, flat, ribbon-like, and three-layered. The body is *bilaterally symmetrical*. This means that if it were divided lengthwise, the left half and right half would be similar. Since the flatworm consists of definite tissues, organs and organ systems, it is more advanced than the animals previously studied. Reproduction is both by longitudinal splitting and by fertilization.

Flatworms are of three distinctly different types: *planaria, tapeworm, liver fluke*. Planaria is of no economic importance, but the tapeworm and liver fluke cause disease in higher animals, including man.

Planaria, a Fresh-Water Flatworm. The planaria is a free-living flatworm, spending its life under stones in streams. Though planaria is less than an inch in length, it has a distinct head with two eye-spots, and a tail. The planaria's mouth is at the end of a long tube, called a *proboscis*, which protrudes from the under surface near the middle of the body. Planaria has some simple but definite organ systems: digestive, excretory, muscular, nervous, reproductive.

Tapeworm, a Parasitic Flatworm. The tapeworm is a parasite. It lives in the intestines of higher animals, including man, the cow and the pig. The animal on which a parasite lives is called the *host*. The tapeworm has no locomotor organs. The tapeworm clings to the intestinal wall of its host by means of *hooks* and *suckers* on its head. The tapeworm has no digestive system of its own. Instead, the food which has already been digested by the host is absorbed through the tapeworm's body wall. Thus nourished, the worm grows rapidly, sometimes reaching a length of ten feet.

The tapeworm's body is made up of a series of flat, rectangular-shaped sections. Each section is capable of reproduction, and produces thousands of eggs, each able to develop into another tapeworm. The sections ripen, break off the body of the worm, and eventually pass out of the body of the host with wastes. If the eggs carried by the ripened sections are eaten by another animal—for example, a pig— the eggs grow into young worms, or *larvae*, which travel from the pig's intestines to the pig's muscles, where each larva is protected by a cyst wall. Then, if the meat of the pig is eaten by man, the cysts break open and the young tapeworms attach themselves to man's intestinal wall. In this way, the life cycle of the tapeworm goes on. To prevent tapeworm disease, thoroughly cook the meat of the pig and cow.

PHYLUM V—NEMATHELMINTHES

Roundworms, the Second Phylum of Worms. Roundworms have soft, round, slender bodies, usually pointed at both ends. Some are free-living, and are found in the soil. Others live in both fresh and salt water. Most roundworms, however, are parasitic, such as *ascaris, hookworm* and *trichina (trichinella)*. These parasites, especially the hookworm, cause widespread disease.

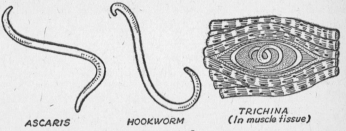

ASCARIS   HOOKWORM   TRICHINA
                                  (In muscle tissue)

Fig. 38. Roundworms

Ascaris. This parasitic worm is one of the largest of the round-worms. It lives in human intestines, especially those of children. The worms enter the host in the form of eggs, which are contained in contaminated food and water. The eggs find their way to the intestines, where they hatch into larvae. The larvae travel through the body and finally return to the intestines, where they mature into adult worms. The eggs produced by the worms then leave the body in the excrement and may be introduced into another host in food or water.

Cleanliness in handling food, and water purification, are the best protections against this parasite.

Hookworm. This parasite of man thrives in a warm climate, such as in the southern part of the United States. The hookworm attacks people who walk barefooted. The larvae, lying in moist soil, enter the body by boring through the skin on the sole of the foot. The worms enter the bloodstream and find their way to the lungs and other organs. Eventually the parasites reach the intestines, where they attach themselves to the intestinal wall and feed on the host's blood. The hookworms' eggs pass out of the body with wastes, enter the soil, and are ready to start the cycle again.

Two means of preventing the hookworm disease are: properly disposing of human wastes, and wearing shoes.

Trichina. This roundworm causes the serious disease, *trichinosis,* which may result in death. Trichinosis, however, is not so widespread as hookworm disease. The trichina lives in the intestines and muscles of man, pig and rat. A pig may be infected with trichina by eating an infected rat. The young worms burrow into the pig's muscles, forming cysts. If a man eats the infected pork without cooking it thoroughly, the cysts break open in his intestines and the worms emerge. These worms lay eggs which develop into young worms that enter the muscles. Intense muscular pains result. To prevent this disease, we should thoroughly cook all meats, particularly pork.

PHYLUM VI—ANNELIDA

Segmented Worms, the Most Complex Worms. Segmented worms are found in salt and fresh water, and in the soil. Their long, round bodies consist of a great many ring-like sections, known as *segments* —structures not found in flatworms and roundworms. Reproduction is sexual.

The best known annelid is the common *earthworm,* which lives in moist soil. No doubt you have seen these segmented worms crawling about on the ground after a rain or thunderstorm. Another annelid, the *leech,* which lives mostly in fresh water, is a temporary parasite. By means of a *sucker* at each end of its body, the leech attaches itself on the outside of another animal and sucks its blood for food. When satisfied, the leech drops off the animal.

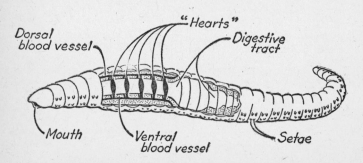

Fig. 39. The Earthworm

The Earthworm, a Common Segmented Worm. The earthworm is probably the only worm whose habits are of economic benefit to man. The burrowing of earthworms brings an enormous amount of sub-soil to the surface. The burrows also enable air and water to penetrate the soil. Body wastes excreted by the earthworm help to enrich the soil.

The earthworm has a long, round body, somewhat flat on the under side. It consists of over one hundred segments. A *body cavity* separates the outer tube, or *body wall,* from an inside tube, the *digestive tract.* Thus, the earthworm is like a tube within a tube.

An earthworm lives in the soil to protect its body. A thin, moist skin is the only covering on the body wall, which is composed largely of muscle tissue. The muscles and the bristles, or *setae,* on the under surface of the body, aid the worm in locomotion. Four pairs of *setae* are found on almost all the segments. The earthworm's digestive tract runs the full length of the animal. At the front end is the *mouth;* at the back end is the *anus.* The earthworm burrows through the earth by taking soil into its mouth. Food particles, such as plant and animal matter contained in the soil, pass into the digestive tract. Here, the food matter is digested and absorbed, but the soil particles pass out of the body through the anus.

The earthworm also has a well-defined nervous system. It consists of two main parts: a *simple brain,* lying dorsally to (above) the digestive tract at the front end of the body; and a *ventral nerve cord,* lying ventrally to (below) the digestive tract and extending the length of the body. A *nerve collar* around the digestive tract connects the brain and nerve cord. Nerves branch out from the brain and nerve cord to all parts of the body. Special nerve cells on the skin respond to stimuli, such as light, touch and food.

The circulatory system of the earthworm consists of two large blood vessels: the *dorsal blood vessel* and the *ventral blood vessel,* both extending the full length of the body. Near the front end of the earthworm, the two blood vessels are connected by five pairs of enlarged, pulsating blood vessels, the "hearts." Blood flows forward through the dorsal blood vessel, and backward through the ventral blood vessel.

The earthworm reproduces sexually.

PHYLUM VII—ECHINODERMATA

Characteristics of the Echinoderms. The animals in this phylum live only in the ocean, mainly in the shallow waters near the shore. The echinoderms include many odd-looking animals, such as the *starfish*, the *sea urchin* and the *brittle star*. Echinoderms have a body covered with a spiny skin. Reproduction is sexual.

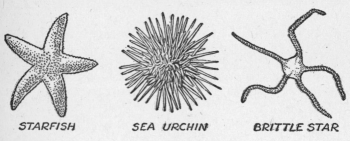

STARFISH   SEA URCHIN   BRITTLE STAR

Fig. 40. Echinoderms

The Starfish, a Well-Known Echinoderm. The best-known animal in this phylum is the starfish. Its body consists of five *arms*, radiating from a *central disc*. The upper (dorsal) surface of the body is covered with many short *spines*. Lining the under (ventral) surface of the arms are hundreds of tiny, finger-like structures, called *tube feet*. The tube feet are used primarily for locomotion. Water from the central part of the body is forced into the tube feet, thus extending them. As the starfish moves along, it attaches its tube feet to some solid object by means of *suckers* at the ends of the feet.

The tube feet also aid the starfish in getting its food, which usually consists of oysters and clams. When the starfish comes upon an oyster, for example, the starfish wraps its body around the oyster and attaches its suckers to the two shells. The starfish exerts a pull upon the shells until the oyster's muscles tire and relax, thus permitting the opening of the shells. The starfish then pushes its stomach, inside out, into the oyster. The starfish eats only the soft part of the oyster, leaving the shell. When the food has been digested, the starfish returns its stomach to the inside of its body.

Because it raids oyster beds, the starfish is an enemy of oyster fishermen. (See page 206.)

PHYLUM VIII—MOLLUSCA

Characteristics of the Mollusks. The two most important mollusks, because of their food value, are the *clam* and the *oyster*. These animals inhabit the ocean. Other salt-water mollusks are the *octopus*, *squid* and *cuttlefish*. Some species of *mussels* and *snails* inhabit fresh water. Other snails live on land, as does the common garden *slug*.

CLAM   SNAIL   OCTOPUS

Fig. 41. Mollusks

Mollusks have soft, fleshy bodies, usually covered by a protective *shell*. Some mollusks, such as the snail, have a single coiled shell, and are known as *univalves*. Others, such as the clam, have two shells connected by a hinge, and are known as *bivalves*. Still others, for example, the slug and the octopus, have no shell. Reproduction is sexual.

All mollusks move by means of a *muscular foot*. In those mollusks having shells, the foot is inside the shell. It is extended outside to serve as an organ of locomotion. In shell-less forms, like the octopus and the squid, the body has many *feet* or *arms*, called *tentacles*, which are covered with suckers. The tentacles are used not only for locomotion, but also for food getting. The octopus has eight tentacles; the squid, ten.

Economic Importance of the Mollusks. Not only clams and oysters, but also scallops and mussels, are commonly used for food. Certain kinds of oysters and clams produce pearls. Buttons and jewelry are made from the shells of clams and mussels. Many people make a hobby of shell collecting.

Some mollusks are harmful or dangerous. The octopus sometimes attacks and kills man. The shipworm, which bores through wood, causes considerable damage to ships and wharves. Slugs feed **on** vegetables and flowers, leaving the plants to die.

PHYLUM IX—ARTHROPODA

Characteristics of the Arthropods. This phylum constitutes the largest group of animals known to man. Arthropods number 675,000 species and are found in all regions of the world. They live on land and in the water. Many familiar animals, such as the *ant, bee, spider, crab, lobster* and *grasshopper,* belong to this group.

Although arthropods differ in outward appearance, they all have three main structural similarities: (1) a segmented body; (2) a jointed external skeleton, called an *exoskeleton,* composed of *chitin,* a horny substance secreted by the animal; and (3) jointed appendages, such as the legs and *antennae* (feelers). The internal structure of the arthropods is complex, several well-developed organ systems, such as the digestive and nervous systems, being present. Reproduction is sexual.

Phylum Arthropoda contains the following four classes: *Crustacea, Myriapoda, Arachnida, Insecta.*

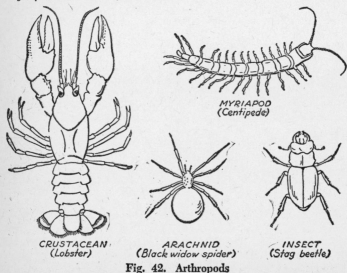

MYRIAPOD
(Centipede)

CRUSTACEAN
(Lobster)

ARACHNID
(Black widow spider)

INSECT
(Stag beetle)

Fig. 42. Arthropods

Crustaceans. Most crustaceans are water dwellers, such as the *lobster, crayfish, shrimp* and *crab.* They have a hard outer crust, or *shell,* covering a segmented body. Crustaceans have many jointed legs for locomotion, and *gills* for respiration. Some of the crustaceans, such as the lobster, shrimp and crab, are very valuable as food.

Myriapods. The chief members of this class, the many-legged *centipedes* and *millipedes,* live on land. Their long, round bodies are made up of numerous segments. In the centipede, nearly all the segments have one pair of jointed legs; in the millipede, the segments have two pairs of legs. Myriapods do not benefit man to any great extent. Some centipedes are valuable because they eat harmful insects. A few species can inflict a painful sting.

Arachnids. The animals in this class are mainly eight-legged land dwellers. Their body is made up of two regions. The most important arachnids are the *spiders,* such as the *garden spider, tarantula* and *trap door spider.* These are not harmful, except for their painful bites. The bite of the *black widow spider,* however, sometimes results in death. Spiders benefit man by eating destructive insects.

The *scorpion,* another arachnid, has a poisonous sting, but is rarely fatal. *Mites* and *ticks* are harmful, for they not only carry disease, but also live as parasites on the skin of animals.

Insects. Insects are the most numerous animals in the world, numbering about 625,000 species. Well known to us are the following common insects: the *grasshopper, moth, butterfly, bee, ant, beetle, bug, louse, fly, mosquito,* to mention only a few. All adult insects are alike in that they have: (1) a body divided into three parts (head, thorax, abdomen); (2) an exoskeleton; (3) three pairs of legs; (4) one pair of antennae; and (5) in most cases, two pairs of wings.

Most insects are destructive, dangerous pests. Some harmful species, such as the *grasshopper, chinch bug* and *European corn borer,* destroy food crops. The *peach tree borer, mealybug* and *tent caterpillar* feed on fruit trees and shade trees. The *moth* eats holes in clothing. The *termite* destroys the wooden framework of homes. Perhaps the worst insect pests are those which spread disease, among them the *fly* and the *mosquito.*

Not all insects are harmful, however. The *honey bee* produces honey and helps in the reproduction of plants by carrying pollen. The *silkworm* makes silk. The *lady bird beetle* (lady bug) and the *praying mantis* eat harmful insects.

The Grasshopper, a Representative Insect. Grasshoppers thrive in warm regions. The ordinary grasshopper we see leaping about in the fields is only one of many species. These animals feed on plant life. When great hordes of a certain species of grasshopper, known as *locusts,* invade a farming area, they completely destroy the vegetation.

The grasshopper's body is covered with an exoskeleton composed of chitin. The body, which is segmented, consists of three distinct parts: the head, thorax and abdomen.

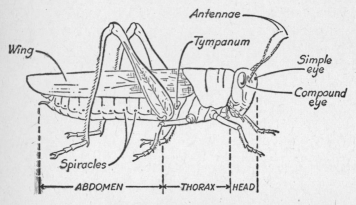

Fig. 43. The Grasshopper

1. *The Head.* Two large *compound eyes,* one on each side of the head, aid the grasshopper in detecting motion. Three *simple eyes,* two in front and one between the compound eyes, distinguish light from dark. The two jointed *antennae* possess the sense of smell and touch. The mouth parts consist of: the *labrum* or upper lip; the *labium* or lower lip; the *mandibles* or toothed jaws; and the *maxillae* or accessory jaws behind the mandibles. The mandibles and maxillae cut, grind and push the food into the mouth.

2. *The Thorax.* This central part of the body is made up of three segments. Each segment contains a pair of jointed legs, a total of six legs for the animal. The grasshopper uses the first and second pairs of legs for walking and climbing. The third pair of legs, with their enlarged muscles, are specialized for jumping. A pair of wings

is located on both the second and third segments of the thorax. The front pair of wings is straight and hard. These wings serve as protective covers for the delicate hind wings, which are used for flight.

3. *The Abdomen.*   There are ten segments in the abdomen. The first segment bears a pair of *tympana*, which are membranes for hearing. Eight of the segments contain a pair of openings, called *spiracles,* on each side of the body. Two pairs of spiracles are also present on the thorax. The spiracles are breathing pores which open into a system of branching air tubes, the *tracheae.* The many branches of the tracheae carry oxygen directly to the cells and remove the carbon dioxide given off in respiration. The grasshopper's digestive, nervous and excretory systems are similar to those of the earthworm.

PHYLUM X—CHORDATA

Characteristics of the Vertebrates.   Phylum Chordata is divided into four subphyla, the only important one being the vertebrates. The vertebrates include *man* and the animals which surround man in his daily life: the *fish, frog, snake, bird, dog,* etc.

A vertebrate is an animal with a backbone (spinal column), consisting of bony segments, called *vertebrae.* The backbone is part of an internal skeleton, called an *endoskeleton.* In contrast, the animals studied in all the previous phyla do *not* have a backbone, and are therefore called *invertebrates.* As we have seen, some of the invertebrates possess an external skeleton, called an *exoskeleton,* which reaches its most advanced form in the insects.

The vertebrates have attained the greatest degree of structural perfection, possessing many highly-developed organ systems. Outstanding is the complex nervous system in man, including a well-developed brain, which accounts for man's high degree of intelligence. All the vertebrates have two pairs of limbs (excepting snakes). In man, the limbs are the arms and legs; in the fish, fins; in the bird, wings and legs. Reproduction is sexual.

All vertebrates have, at some stage of their existence, the following: (1) a central nerve cord dorsal to the alimentary canal, (2) paired gill slits which connect the pharynx with the exterior, and (3) a notochord (skeletal axis) about which the spinal column develops.

Five common classes of vertebrates are: *Pisces* (fishes), *Amphibia,* *Reptilia, Aves* (birds) and *Mammalia.*

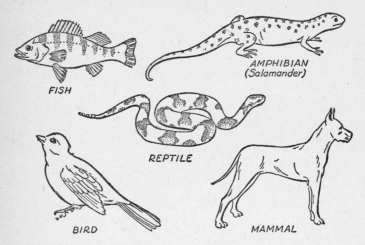

FISH

AMPHIBIAN
(Salamander)

REPTILE

BIRD

MAMMAL

Fig. 44. Vertebrates

Fishes. Although we have studied other animals called "fish," for example, the starfish and crayfish, only the animals in the class Pisces are true bony fishes. This class includes such familiar fishes as the *salmon, trout, cod, mackerel, perch.* These animals inhabit ponds, lakes, rivers and oceans. They vary in size, from small *minnows,* only a few inches in length, to the giant *whale shark,* which may reach a length of 50 feet and weigh several tons. Many fishes are strikingly marked or brightly colored, as their names suggest; for example, the *striped bass* and the *rainbow trout.* Sometimes their names describe peculiar body structures, as the *swordfish,* with its long, sword-like upper jaw.

Fishes show many adaptations for life in the water, which offers greater resistance to movement than does air. A flat, streamlined shape enables the fish to move through the water with great ease. *Fins* are the chief means of locomotion, in particular, the powerful tail fin. An internal organ, the *air bladder,* allows the fish to rise or sink to any desired level in the water.

A fish breathes by means of eight *gills,* four on each side. The gills are located internally, with openings on either side of the neck. The gills are made up of very fine filaments which have many microscopic blood vessels exposing the blood to the water. As water containing dissolved oxygen enters the mouth, the water passes over the gills and there the oxygen is absorbed by the blood. At the same time, the water carries away carbon dioxide released by the blood.

Fishes are *cold-blooded* vertebrates. Their body temperature varies with the temperature of their surroundings. They have a two-chambered heart. Most of the body is covered with *scales,* which serve as protection. Eyelids are absent.

Fishes are important to man for food. Several thousand kinds of fish are edible, among them the *cod, salmon, flounder, halibut, herring, sardine* and *tuna.* Man considers fishing a great sport, and enjoys "fighting-it-out" with such game fish as the *bass* and *trout.* Fish are also used as fertilizer, and as a source of glue and oils, especially cod-liver oil. Some fish feed on mosquito larvae and other insects.

Amphibians. Most amphibians start life in the water. Later they can live both in the water and on the land. Amphibians are the *frog, toad, newt* and *mud puppy.*

Like the fish, the amphibian is a cold-blooded animal. It has a three-chambered heart. The body is covered with a smooth, slimy skin, except in the case of the toad, which has a dry, warty skin. The chief economic value of the amphibians lies in their feeding on insects. The toad, in particular, is valuable to man as an insect-eater.

The frog begins life in the water as a *tadpole,* having a long tail for swiming and gills for underwater breathing. The tadpole then prepares for life on land: Its tail disappears, giving way to legs for locomotion; its gills disappear, being replaced by lungs for air breathing. The toad spends its adult life in fields and gardens, going back to the water only to lay its eggs. The newt and mud puppy are types of *salamanders.* The newt has both water and land stages in its life history. But the mud puppy spends its entire life in the water and therefore never loses its gills.

The Frog, a Typical Amphibian. The frog is frequently used by biologists as a specimen in laboratory work. This is because the body structures and functions of the frog are typical of all the vertebrates.

The frog's body is covered with a smooth, slimy skin. The upper surface may range from yellowish-green to greenish-brown in color. The under surface is grayish-white. The frog's coloring, resembling the animal's surroundings, helps to protect it from its enemies.

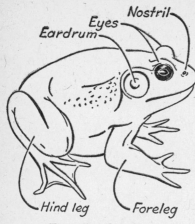

Fig. 45. The Frog

A frog has two pairs of legs: the short *forelegs,* which support the body when the animal is sitting on the ground; and the long *hindlegs,* which the frog uses in leaping and swimming. Powerful muscles in the thighs of the hindlegs enable the frog to leap great distances, considering its size. Webbed toes, also on the hindlegs, aid the frog in swimming.

The frog has a broad, flat head. Two large *eyes* protrude from either side of the head. Behind each eye is an *eardrum,* or *tympanic membrane.* Two nostrils are located above the *mouth.* The mouth is extremely wide, extending from one side of the head to the other.

An internal, bony framework, the *skeleton,* supports the frog's body and protects its delicate internal organs. The skeleton consists of (1) the *skull,* (2) the *backbone,* and (3) the *limb bones.* An elaborate system of muscles moves the body.

A well-developed nervous system consists of a *brain,* located inside the skull, connected to a *nerve cord* (spinal cord) running down the back of the body. Special arches on the vertebrae protect the nerve cord. Many small *nerves* branch off from the nerve cord to all parts of the body.

The frog eats only living things, especially insects. When the frog sees an insect, it flips out its long, sticky, forked tongue which is attached to the front end of the lower jaw. The insect is drawn into the mouth and swallowed whole. The insect passes through the *gullet,* into the *stomach* and then into the *small intestine,* where the food is digested with the aid of enzymes secreted by the *liver* and the *pancreas.* Undigested food passes from the small intestine into the *large intestine,* and then empties into the *cloaca,* where it is excreted through the *anus.*

In respiration, air is drawn through the nostrils and pumped into the lungs by powerful throat muscles situated on the floor of the mouth. Respiration also takes place through the frog's moist skin, both when in water and on land.

The frog has a three-chambered heart. Blood is circulated to all parts of the body through *arteries*, which subdivide many times, becoming microscopic *capillaries*. These blood vessels then recombine, becoming *veins*, which return the blood to the heart.

Wastes in the blood are removed by the *kidneys*.

Reptiles. Many millions of years ago, giant reptiles, called *dinosaurs* (pages 277-278), roamed the earth. The dinosaurs, now extinct, were the ancestors of the present-day reptiles—the *snake, lizard, turtle, alligator* and *crocodile*. These animals may be found in almost all regions, but are most abundant in warm climates. Enormous sea turtles, like the *green turtle*, which may weigh a thousand pounds, live in the seas. The *python*, a snake which may reach a length of thirty feet, lives in the hot jungles of Malaya and Africa. A comparatively small but poisonous reptile, a lizard called the *Gila monster*, inhabits the southwestern part of the United States.

Like fishes and amphibians, the reptiles are cold-blooded animals. However, reptiles have a three-chambered heart and show many advances in structural development. Reptiles are covered with dry scales, never moist or slimy. The turtle is the only reptile with a shell. With the exception of snakes, all reptiles have two pairs of legs for locomotion. Notwithstanding the fact that many reptiles live in water, they have lungs for respiration and come to the surface of the water for air. Most reptiles lay eggs covered with a protective shell. An egg hatches into a young reptile similar in form to the adult. Some reptiles give birth to their young.

Although reptiles, snakes in particular, are generally regarded as harmful, very few species are poisonous or dangerous. Among the deadly poisonous ones are the *rattlesnake, coral snake, copperhead* and *water moccasin*, all found in the United States, and the *cobra*, which kills thousands of people in India every year. The Gila monster is the only poisonous lizard in the United States. Alligators and crocodiles can be dangerous when disturbed, but seldom attack man.

Otherwise, reptiles are useful to man in many ways. The common *garden snake* eats insects, mice and other small animals. Farmers keep the *black snake* in barns because it kills rats and mice. Some people enjoy eating the meat of the *snapping turtle* and the *diamondback terrapin*. The skin of the alligator, crocodile, lizard and snake is used in the making of beautiful leather goods, such as handbags, shoes, belts, etc.

Birds. Birds give man great pleasure. We marvel at the grace of birds in flight. We await the return of the robin in the spring. Opportunities to study birds are unlimited, for they are about us everywhere—in city, town and country. The majority of birds thrive in temperate and hot climates, although some species, such as the *penguin* and the *arctic tern*, live in the cold arctic regions.

In contrast to the fishes, amphibians and reptiles, all birds are *warm-blooded*. That is, their bodies maintain a constant temperature regardless of the temperature of their surroundings. Birds have a four-chambered heart.

Almost all birds are well adapted for flight. The two most important structures for flying are *wings* and *feathers*. The front appendages have been modified to form well-developed wings. Strong bones support the wings, and extremely powerful muscles move them. If the wings are weak and poorly developed, as in the *ostrich*, the bird cannot fly. Feathers not only aid flight, but also insulate the body, preventing loss of heat. This helps the bird to maintain its high body temperature.

In addition to these important structures, birds have a streamlined shape, which reduces air resistance. Hollow bones and air sacs, distributed throughout the body, lighten the bird's body weight.

The legs and feet of birds are modified for special activities. A *robin's* feet are adapted for perching, a *chicken's* for scratching. Those of the *duck* are webbed to aid in swimming, while the heavy curved claws of the *eagle* are used for grasping prey.

The light strong bills (or beaks) of birds also show remarkable adaptations. The short bill of the *sparrow* cracks seeds; the hooked beak of the *hawk* tears at prey; and the long pointed bill of the *woodpecker* drills wood.

Like the reptiles, birds lay eggs covered by protective shells. However, birds also build nests for the protection of their young, or *fledglings*.

Besides giving pleasure to man and providing a hobby for bird lovers, birds are of great economic importance. Their chief value lies in their destruction of insects. Birds also aid the farmer by feeding on weed seeds. Others, like the *owl* and the *hawk*, eat rats and mice. Man has domesticated a number of birds, as the *turkey, goose* and *chicken,* which he uses mainly for food. Sportsmen hunt wild birds like the *pheasant, quail* and *partridge,* which are also used for food. Some birds are destructive. For example, the *crow* and *blackbird* devour crops, such as corn, peas and grain. The *blue jay* destroys the eggs of other birds.

Mammals. This group of animals constitutes the highest class of vertebrates. It includes *man* and those animals most useful to him, such as the *horse, cow, pig, sheep* and *dog*. Because they possess a highly developed brain, the mammals are the dominant form of life on earth today. Man stands far above the other mammals in brain capacity. His ability to think and reason has given him supremacy over the rest of the animal kingdom.

Mammals inhabit almost all regions of the world. The majority live on land but some, such as the *dolphin* and *whale*, live in water. The *bat* is the only mammal capable of true flight.

Birds and mammals are the only two classes of warm-blooded vertebrates, and have a four-chambered heart. Like most other vertebrates, the mammals breathe by means of lungs. Even those mammals living in water have lungs.

Mammals have several distinguishing characteristics. The body is usually covered with hair. An internal muscular wall, the *diaphragm*, divides the body cavity into two parts, the *thorax* and the *abdomen*. The thorax contains the heart and lungs; the abdomen contains the stomach, intestines, liver, kidneys and reproductive organs.

Most mammals are developed in the body of the mother in an organ called the *uterus*. During this development, the unborn mammal derives nourishment from the mother's bloodstream through the *placenta*. The newly-born mammal feeds on milk produced by the mother's *mammary glands*. Some primitive species of mammals, such as the *duckbill* (*platypus*) of Australia, lay eggs. Others, like the *kangaroo*, give birth to immature young, which must be carried in a pouch on the mother's body until more fully developed. The *opossum* is the only pouched mammal found in the United States.

Orders of Mammals. Because of numerous variations in body structure, mammals have been subdivided into smaller groups, called *orders*. Among the most important orders of mammals are the following:

1. *Hoofed Mammals.* The toes of these animals end in *hoofs*. Both domesticated and wild animals belong to this order. The domesticated animals, such as the *pig, cow, sheep* and *goat*, provide man with food and clothing. To a lesser extent, so do the wild *deer, moose* and *antelope*. For many centuries, man has used the *horse, mule* and *camel* as beasts of burden.

2. *Gnawing Mammals.* These animals, called rodents, have chisel-shaped teeth for gnawing. The fur of the *beaver* and *muskrat* make beautiful coats. Although the *rabbit* and *squirrel* are of some benefit

as a source of fur and food, they are at times injurious. Rabbits often feed on shrubs and fruit trees, while squirrels destroy food crops. Man's worst mammalian enemy, the *rat*, is included in this order. The rat not only destroys cereals and grain supplies, but also carries diseases, such as the dreaded bubonic plague.

3. *Flesh-eating Mammals.* The animals in this order have sharp claws on their toes and long pointed teeth to assist them in killing and eating their prey. Most of these mammals supply man with valuable furs, for example, the *fox, raccoon, skunk* and *bear.* Others, such as the *lion, tiger, panther* and *wolf,* can be dangerous and destructive enemies. Two of man's domesticated animals, the *dog* and *cat*, are members of this order.

4. *Erect Mammals.* In this order of mammals are the *monkey, ape* and *man.* They are called *Primates,* a Latin word meaning "first," because they rank first in the animal kingdom. There are two reasons for their superiority: (1) They can stand erect on two limbs. Thus, their other pair of limbs—with their four fingers and opposing thumbs —are able to grasp and hold objects. (2) They possess the most highly developed brain.

Completion Questions

1. If an animal is not a protozoan, is must be a (an) _____.
2. A one-celled organism that engulfs its food is _____.
3. The function of the contractile vacuole found in protozoa is _____.
4. Microorganisms usually reproduce by _____.
5. The _____ is a spherical plant-animal that lives in a colony of cells held together by strands of protoplasm.
6. A hollow water-dwelling animal characterized by pores is the _____.
7. The hydra catches its food and pushes it into its digestive cavity by means of _____.
8. If improperly cooked pork is eaten, there is danger of contracting the disease called _____.
9. The _____, the most familiar segmented worm, lives in moist soil.
10. The _____ is a spiny-skinned sea animal destructive in oyster beds.
11. An eight-armed mollusk is the _____.

12. A class of animals having a body of two segments and eight legs is _____.
13. The grasshopper obtains air through openings called _____.
14. Animals with endoskeletons are known as _____.
15. The invertebrates include all animals that have no _____.
16. The fish is a cold-blooded vertebrate that breathes through _____.
17. An animal that spends part of its early life in water and part of its adult life on land is a (an) _____.
18. An animal that has scales, teeth and a backbone and that breathes air throughout its life belongs to the class named _____.
19. Two warm-blooded vertebrate groups are the mammals and the _____.
20. The _____ are the most advanced order of mammals.

Multiple-Choice Questions

1. An ameba moves by means of (1) cilia (2) tentacles (3) pseudopods (4) nematocysts.
2. Paramecium is thought to be a more advanced type of life than ameba because the paramecium (1) has more specialization within the cell (2) is larger (3) moves faster (4) has less cell specialization.
3. An organism having characteristics of both plants and animals is (1) ameba (2) euglena (3) earthworm (4) paramecium.
4. A coelenterate whose body consists almost entirely of water is the (1) sea anemone (2) coral (3) hydra (4) jellyfish.
5. The tapeworm lives in the intestines of man as (1) a saprophyte (2) a symbiont (3) a parasite (4) an independent organism.
6. A roundworm which enters man's body through the soles of his feet is the (1) tapeworm (2) leech (3) trichina (4) hookworm.
7. A segmented invertebrate that helps in restoring soil fertility is the (1) earthworm (2) leech (3) garden slug (4) planaria.
8. A phylum of animals characterized by an exoskeleton and jointed appendages is (1) arthropoda (2) echinodermata (3) annelida (4) chordata.
9. Gills are used in the life process of (1) digestion (2) circulation (3) reproduction (4) respiration.

10. An insect economically important because it carries pollen from flower to flower is the (1) fly (2) bee (3) mosquito (4) praying mantis.

11. The three body parts of the grasshopper are the head, the abdomen and the (1) antennae (2) maxillae (3) thorax (4) tracheae.

12. All vertebrates have (1) an exoskeleton (2) a spinal column (3) lungs (4) a four-chambered heart.

13. An example of a cold-blooded animal is the (1) penguin (2) salmon (3) polar bear (4) whale.

14. A structure of the frog specialized for food-getting is its (1) tentacles (2) sticky foot (3) forked tongue (4) cloaca.

15. The dinosaur is classified as (1) an amphibian (2) a fish (3) a mammal (4) a reptile.

16. An animal that does not belong to a group of mammals is the (1) ape (2) ostrich (3) bat (4) horse.

17. A rodent that spreads disease and destroys man's food crops is the (1) beaver (2) squirrel (3) rat (4) muskrat.

18. The whale is classified as a mammal because it (1) breathes air (2) feeds its young on milk (3) has a backbone (4) has a circulatory system.

19. The American pouched mammal is the (1) opossum (2) beaver (3) porcupine (4) skunk.

20. Man differs from birds in that man has (1) a four-chambered heart (2) hair (3) warm blood (4) a cerebrum.

Essay Questions

1. *a.* Name any protozoan you have studied and state in outline form (1) its food, (2) one of its waste products, (3) one stimulus to which it responds, (4) one way in which it protects itself.

   b. Draw the organism you named in answer to *a*, and label three important structures. State the function of each structure labeled.

   c. Write a brief description of the method of locomotion of some protozoan.

2. Compare a spirogyra cell with a paramecium as follows:

   a. Shape and covering of each.

   b. A structure that is common to both.

   c. A process common to both.

    d. A structure found only in spirogyra.
    e. A structure found only in paramecium.
    f. A process carried on only in spirogyra.
    g. A waste product given off by the spirogyra, but not by the paramecium.
    h. A gas used by both in energy release.
    i. One product of each that may be used by the other.
3. For each of the following statements, mention one fact to support it:
    a. Some living things cannot be definitely classed as either plant or animal.
    b. The jellyfish is not a fish.
    c. A parasitic animal may have lost its ability to move freely and yet it may be successful in its struggle for existence.
    d. The housefly and the crab are related.
    e. Man is a mammal.
4. Although a paramecium is composed of only one cell, it carries on many of the same activities that man does, such as *(a)* food-getting, *(b)* obtaining oxygen, *(c)* movement, *(d)* reproduction, *(e)* excretion, and *(f)* protecting itself.
    For each of any five of these activities *(a)* describe how the activity is carried on by the paramecium, and *(b)* name the structure involved.
5. In a biology class, a pupil noticed a number of similarities between the skeleton of a frog and that of a cat.
    a. Mention two such similarities.
    b. State why these animals have similar skeletal structures.
    c. Which of these skeletons would a human skeleton more closely resemble?
6. *a.* Name a cell that contains contractile vacuoles and cilia.
    b. Mention two major changes in structure that take place as the tadpole develops into an adult frog.
    c. Explain the following facts:
        (1) A tapeworm does not have a digestive system.
        (2) A whale is not a fish.
        (3) Developing kittens are not found in the mother's stomach.

Chapter IX

THE HUMAN SKELETAL SYSTEM

The Organization of Man. Man is made up of cells, tissues, organs, organ systems. The organ systems do *not* function independently. All work together harmoniously for the welfare of the body as a whole. Therefore, in our study of the human organ systems in this and the following chapters, we shall consider not only the structures and functions of each system, but also the close relation of one system to other systems.

The Skeletal System. The skeletal system consists of (1) the *skeleton,* which is the bony framework of the body, (2) the *joints* that permit movement, (3) the *muscles* that move the bones, and (4) the *skin* that covers the body.

The Human Skeleton. The hard, bony framework of the body is the *skeleton.* It consists of 206 separate bones. The functions of the skeleton are (1) to support and give shape to the body, (2) to aid the body in movement and motion, and (3) to protect the delicate internal organs of the body.

Regions of the Skeleton. The skeleton is divided into three main regions: the *skull,* the *spine,* the *limbs.*

1. *The Skull.* Several bones unite together to form the skull, which houses and protects the brain. The skull bones form cavities for the two *eyeballs,* the framework of the *nose,* and the framework for the two *internal ears.* The upper and lower jaw bones form the *mouth.* The skull rotates on the spine, thus making more acute man's senses of seeing, smelling and hearing as the skull is moved in a particular direction.

2. *The Spine.* The spine, or backbone, is comprised of numerous bones, called *vertebrae.* Elastic tissue between the vertebrae permit of some flexibility of the spine. The spinal column helps keep the body and head erect, and houses and protects the spinal cord. Attached to the spine are the *ribs,* which run circularly around the body and meet in front at the *breastbone.* The ribs aid in respiration, and form the chest cavity which houses the heart and lungs.

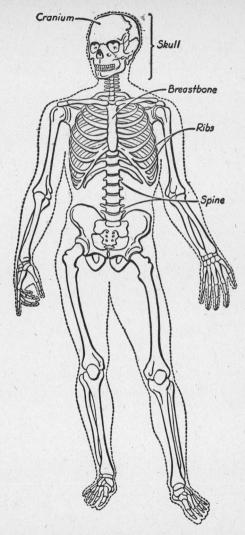

Fig. 46. The Human Skeleton

3. *The Limbs.* Each of the two upper limbs terminates in a hand with five fingers. Each of the two lower limbs terminates in a foot with five toes. The lower limbs help the body to stand erect and to move about. The upper limbs have great and easy movement, and therefore give man the ability to seize and hold objects, and to manipulate tools, instruments and utensils. The fact that man can stand erect and walk on his two lower limbs, thus releasing his two upper limbs for manipulation, gives him great superiority over the animals that require all four limbs for standing and walking.

The Joints. Where two bones meet, there is a *joint.* Where nature demands the greatest amount of movement, there is the *ball and socket joint.* This is the freest type of joint and is found at the shoulders and hips. Where rigidity and stability are needed, a *fixed joint* is found. Fixed joints are between the toothed edges of the skull bones. Where a great amount of movement with leverage in one direction is required, there is a *hinge joint.* Examples of this type are the knee and the elbow joints.

The Muscles. Muscles act as manipulators for the bony levers. Muscles are attached to the bones they move by means of *tendons.* The muscles that move the body framework are made up of *striated muscle tissue* (see page 29) and act voluntarily, that is, according to the human desire.

Muscles act in pairs. When one muscle to a bone contracts (shortens), its opposite muscle relaxes (lengthens). This simultaneous action of the muscles produces precise movement of the bones. For example, flexing the finger causes the under muscles to contract and the upper muscles to relax. Returning the finger to a straightened position, the upper muscles contract and the lower muscles relax.

Bone. In the embryo there are no bones, but cartilage tissue. Shortly before birth, bone structure is present. After the child is born, the bones begin to grow and become harder. Bony matter replaces the soft cartilage. The growth and hardening of the long bones are due to deposits of the minerals calcium phosphate and calcium carbonate. These minerals are secreted by the living bone cells.

The ends of the bone are soft and continue to grow until full development is reached. The mineral matter in the fully-developed bone gives maximum rigidity and support to the skeleton. All bone has an outer protective layer, known as the *periosteum.*

The inner portion of the long bones is a cavity containing a soft, spongy substance known as *bone marrow.* There are two types of bone marrow: Red marrow manufactures red and white corpuscles of the blood, and yellow marrow serves as a nutrient for the bone itself.

Between the bone cells are the *Haversian canals,* through which blood circulates to nourish the bone cells and carry away wastes.

The Skin. The skin is the external covering of the body. The skin consists of two layers: the *epidermis,* or outer layer; and the *dermis,* or inner layer.

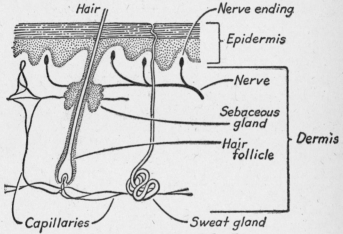

Fig. 47. Structures of the Skin

The Epidermis. The epidermis, although thin, serves to protect the underlying dermis. The uppermost layers of the epidermis are made up of dead cells, or scales, which are continually being shed from the body. As the dead cells fall off, they are replaced by new living cells from below, which in turn die. In the outer layer are numerous tiny openings, called *pores.* Through these pores the underlying sweat glands excrete perspiration to the outside. Both nails and hair develop from the epidermis.

The Dermis. The dermis is a thick layer of skin, and contains the following structures:

1. *Capillaries* (or tiny blood vessels), which nourish the cells of the skin.

2. *Nerve endings,* which receive sensations of pain, heat, cold, touch, etc.

3. *Hair follicles,* from which the hairs start their growth.

4. *Sebaceous glands,* which secrete oil to lubricate the hair and skin.

5. *Sweat glands,* which secrete perspiration (or sweat) and help regulate body temperature. (See also page 158.)

Hygiene of the Skeletal System:

1. *Bone Growth.* In the young growing child, bone growth is aided by the intake of calcium, phosphorus and Vitamin D. Calcium and phosphorus are secured from milk and other mineral foods; Vitamin D is obtained from both foods and sunshine. A lack of Vitamin D results in a deformity of bone in the growing child, a disease known as *rickets.* A lack of calcium and phosphorus results in brittle bones, which are easily fractured.

2. *Posture.* Proper posture affords the maximum correct growth. In standing, the shoulders should be thrown backwards, the chest out, eyes looking forward, abdomen held in, the toes straight. In sitting, the positions are relatively the same as in standing. When reading, hold the book at eye level, with the light coming from behind and over the left shoulder.

3. *Flat Feet.* Improper walking and standing cause a flattening of the arches of the feet, giving rise to pain and discomfort in the lower limbs. This condition can be corrected by proper exercises, or by the use of mechanical arches.

4. *Muscle Exercise and Relaxation.* All muscles must be exercised for proper circulation of blood, for the nourishment and growth of muscle tissue, and for the limbering of muscles. Yet, all muscles must be relaxed at times in order to regain expended energy.

5. *Proper Sleep.* For complete relaxation, the body needs at least eight hours of restful sleep. This can be attained only by (*a*) going to bed with a worry-free mind, (*b*) sleeping in a bed of full size for the body, (*c*) using a mattress hard enough to avoid kinking of the body.

6. *Care of the Skin, Hair and Nails.* The skin must not only look fresh, but also must be clean. Therefore, wash your hands and face frequently, and bathe daily. Washing the skin with soap and water keeps the pores open. Keeping the skin clean prevents the appearance of pimples and blackheads. Do not squeeze pimples or black-

heads, and do not pull hair from any part of the body, particularly from the nose. Cuts of the skin, especially if caused by a rusty object, should be treated with an antiseptic. But if a swelling appears, or if pus forms, seek medical attention.

To prevent irritation of the skin, wear clothing that is loose, not tightly fitting. This is especially true of shoes. Moreover, in warm weather, clothing should be light, so as not to increase body temperature. In cold weather, clothing should be warm enough to retain body heat.

Hair, too, should be washed periodically. Dandruff, which is dead cells of the scalp, should be brushed or washed from the hair. Occasional shampooing of the hair and massaging of the scalp will help keep the hair healthy.

Nails must also be kept clean, and should not be bitten off.

Multiple-Choice Questions

1. The bony framework of the body is the (1) periosteum (2) vertebrae (3) skeleton (4) tendon.
2. The brain is protected by the (1) spine (2) skull (3) ribs (4) muscles.
3. The body is kept erect by the (1) backbone (2) ball and socket joints (3) striated muscles (4) Haversian canals.
4. The ribs are attached to the spine and meet in front of the body at the (1) skull (2) limbs (3) joints (4) breastbone.
5. The vertebrae make up the (1) ribs (2) limb bones (3) backbone (4) joints.
6. The ribs protect the (1) stomach (2) brain (3) spinal cord (4) lungs.
7. The type of joint found at the knee and elbow is the (1) hinge joint (2) ball and socket joint (3) fixed joint (4) double joint.
8. Muscles are attached to bones by means of (1) the periosteum (2) tendons (3) joints (4) marrow.
9. The hollow interior of the long bones is filled with (1) marrow (2) minerals (3) red and white corpuscles (4) Haversian canals.
10. All of the following are necessary for proper bone formation *except* (1) calcium (2) phosphorus (3) Vitamin D (4) starch.

Chapter X

Nutrition in Man

FOODS ARE NECESSARY TO MAINTAIN LIFE

The Nature of Nutrition. Every cell of our body must be supplied with food. But the food used by our cells is quite different in physical and chemical form from the food we originally eat. Ingested food must be broken down into substances that can be used by the cells of the body. This is the process of *digestion*. Digested food diffuses into the bloodstream for delivery to the cells. This is the process of *absorption*. The cells convert the food into protoplasm. This is the process of *assimilation*. The life processes concerned with the obtaining and using of foods are called *nutrition*.

The Nutrients. All foods contain *usable* substances known as *nutrients*. There are six kinds of nutrients. *Carbohydrates, fats* and *proteins* provide the body with energy. In addition to supplying energy, proteins furnish cells with the material for growth and repair. *Water, mineral salts* and *vitamins* aid in regulating the body functions.

Roughage. In addition to usable nutrients, most foods also contain a certain amount of *non-usable* substances, called *roughage*. The main type of roughage is indigestible cellulose, the substance making up the walls of plant cells. Although roughage cannot be digested and absorbed by the body, a certain amount is necessary in the human diet. Roughage aids the process of digestion by providing the bulk which stimulates the intestines to move the food matter along its course through the alimentary canal.

ENERGY-PRODUCING NUTRIENTS

1. Carbohydrates. The carbohydrates include various types of *sugar* and *starch*. They are chemical compounds composed of the elements carbon, hydrogen and oxygen. The carbohydrates are the chief source of the energy we need to carry on our life functions.

Green plants and products made from green plants supply us with most of our carbohydrates. We obtain sugar from fruits, sugar cane and sugar maple. We obtain starch from bread, potatoes and cereal grains.

About 60 per cent of our diet should consist of foods high in sugar and starch. Excellent sources of quick energy are candy and ice cream. These foods contain simple sugar that can be immediately oxidized in our cells.

When carbohydrates are ingested, a portion is used immediately. Most of the remainder is taken to the liver and converted by that organ into *glycogen*, or animal starch. When the body needs energy, the liver reconverts the glycogen into sugar. A small portion of the carbohydrates is converted into fat and stored in the tissues.

Test for Simple Sugar. Place some molasses and water in a test tube. Add a tablespoonful of Fehling's (or Benedict's) solution. Boil. A yellow-orange color indicates the presence of simple sugar.

Test for Starch. Place some cornstarch and water in a test tube. Add a few drops of iodine solution. A blue-black color indicates the presence of starch.

2. Fats and Oils. Fats and oils are chemical compounds composed of the same elements as the carbohydrates, namely, carbon, hydrogen and oxygen—but in different proportions. Oils are fats which are liquid at room temperature. Fats yield twice as much energy as do the carbohydrates. But the processes in breaking down fats are so complex that the energy is not readily available to the body. Therefore, approximately twice as much carbohydrates as fats should be ingested.

We obtain most of our fats from both plant and animal products. Butter, lard, olive oil and bacon yield large amounts of fats. Excess fats are stored in the tissues, mainly just below the surface of the skin, and also around internal organs. The fatty tissue serves as protection for the delicate organs and as a storehouse of energy. Fatty tissue may become superfluous, as noted in obese (fat) people.

Test for Fat. Shake a piece of fatty bacon in carbon tetrachloride to dissolve out the fat. Pour some of the resulting solution on unglazed paper. Let the solution evaporate. The appearance of a grease spot indicates the presence of fat.

3. Proteins. Although proteins provide some energy, their main use is to furnish the body with the materials for building and repairing protoplasm. The proteins are the only nutrient that can be converted by the body into living matter, because only proteins contain the element nitrogen. In addition to nitrogen, other elements present in proteins are carbon, hydrogen, oxygen and a few others in small quantities. The various types of proteins break down to *amino acids* (nitrogen compounds), which the cells can assimilate.

Plant and animal foods rich in proteins are milk, eggs, cheese, nuts and meat. Since plant and animal proteins are complex in chemical make-up, humans must break down these proteins into simple amino acids. Then, the human body forms its own protein matter by re-combining the amino acids.

Test for Protein. Place a small quantity of lean meat in a test tube and cover with nitric acid. Heat gently to boiling. Rinse off the acid with water and add a tablespoonful of ammonium hydroxide. An orange color indicates the presence of protein.

NON-ENERGY NUTRIENTS

1. Water. Water is a chemical compound composed of the elements hydrogen and oxygen. We must have water in order to live. About two-thirds of the weight of the human body is water. By volume, water makes up about 70 to 80 per cent of our cellular tissue. The largest part of our blood is water. Water acts as a solvent for some of the other nutrients. (A *solvent* is a substance which is capable of dissolving other substances in it.)

We obtain most of our supply of water from drinking water and other beverages, and from foods, particularly fruits and vegetables. The average person requires the equivalent of from six to eight glasses of water a day.

Test for Water in Food. Place some food, such as a piece of fruit or vegetable, in a dry test tube. Heat. Moisture collecting on the inside of the tube indicates the presence of water in the food.

2. Mineral Salts. We require certain minerals for building body tissue and controlling some of our body processes. Most of these minerals are in the form of chemical compounds known as *mineral salts*. Sodium chloride, which is ordinary table salt, is a mineral salt composed of the elements *sodium* and *chlorine*. Sodium is necessary for the building of protoplasm, and chlorine for digestion in the stomach.

Other important mineral salts are those containing the elements *calcium, phosphorus, fluorine, iron* and *iodine*. Milk is an excellent source of calcium and phosphorus, which are needed to build strong bones and teeth. Fluorine is believed to diminish tooth decay. It is found naturally in the drinking water of some regions and is being added to the water in other places. Iron forms hemoglobin, which carries oxygen in the blood. Iodine is necessary for the proper functioning of the thyroid gland.

Test for Mineral Salts. Place some food, such as a piece of apple or potato, in an iron spoon. Heat until the food is completely burned. The grayish ash remaining in the spoon is mineral matter.

3. **Vitamins.** Vitamins are essential in maintaining the health and vigor of the body. Vitamins act as catalysts in various chemical reactions taking place in the body. Vitamins also prevent diseases. If the diet lacks a vitamin for an extended period of time, a deficiency disease is likely to result. (See pages 110-111.)

Vitamins were not discovered until the 20th century. Previously, fatalities ran high from certain diseases that today are easily prevented. One such disease, *scurvy*, was common among early sailors on long sea voyages. In the 16th century, it was found that a small amount of lime juice taken frequently would prevent scurvy. However, the biologic explanation and significance of this finding were not understood then. Today, we know that scurvy results from a lack of Vitamin C found in fresh fruits and vegetables. This was the vitamin furnished the sailors through the lime juice.

The first person to extract a vitamin from food was a Polish biochemist, *Dr. Casimir Funk*, in 1912. This led investigators to the discovery of other vitamins. To distinguish one vitamin from another, scientists at first called them Vitamin A, Vitamin B, etc. Later, when scientists discovered that vitamins are actually different types of organic compounds, they then gave chemical names to the vitamins. For example, *Vitamin C* became known as *ascorbic acid*. However, we continue to refer to vitamins by letters as well as by chemical names. At least fifteen vitamins are now known. Some of the more important ones are vitamins A, B-complex (B_1, B_2, P-P, B_{12}), C, D, E and K. For a summary of these vitamins, see the chart on pages 110-111.

Your body requires only small amounts of all the essential vitamins. You will obtain enough vitamins from the foods you daily eat if your diet is varied and your Calorie intake is ample. If you lack a sufficient amount of any vitamin, you may obtain that vitamin from a synthetic vitamin preparation. However, it is inadvisable to take synthetic vitamins without the advice of a physician, because the vitamins contained in such a preparation may be of no use to you. A preparation may contain vitamins your body already sufficiently possesses, while not providing the certain vitamins your body needs. In other words, each vitamin has a specific function, and one vitamin cannot be substituted for another vitamin.

Vitamin	Source of the Vitamin	Result of Vitamin Deficiency
A	Carrots and other yellow vegetables. Whole milk, butter, eggs. Leafy green vegetables. Fish liver oils. Peas.	Xerophthalmia (an eye infection). Night-blindness (inability to see in dim light). Infections of the nose and throat. Skin diseases.
B_1 (Thiamin)	Whole grain cereals and enriched bread. Beans and peas. Leafy green vegetables. Fruits and nuts. Eggs. Lean meat, liver, pork.	Loss of appetite. Limited growth. Improper oxidation of foods, especially of carbohydrates. Beri-beri (exhaustion, paralysis, heart disease).
B_2 or G (Riboflavin)	Yeast. Lean meat, liver. Milk, eggs. Green vegetables. Whole wheat. Prunes.	Cracked lips. General weakness. Weak eyes. Digestive upset. (Note: Deficiency of riboflavin is often associated with pellagra.)
P-P Factor (Niacin or Nicotinic Acid)	Lean meat, liver. Milk, eggs. Tomatoes. Leafy green vegetables. Yeast.	Pellagra (skin irritation, tongue inflammation, digestive and nervous disturbances). (Note: P-P means pellagra preventative.)
B_{12}	Liver extract. Synthetic vitamin preparations.	Pernicious anemia. Retarded growth. Disorders of the nervous system.

B-complex

Vitamin	Source of the Vitamin	Result of Vitamin Deficiency
C (Ascorbic Acid)	Citrus fruits (oranges, grape-fruits, lemons, limes). Leafy green vegetables, tomatoes.	Scurvy (soft and bleeding gums, loose teeth, swollen painful joints, bleeding under the skin).
D (Calciferol)	Fish liver oils. Milk, eggs. (Not commonly found in foods. Some foods are irradiated to increase their Vitamin D content.) (If directly exposed to sunlight, the body is able to manufacture Vitamin D. For this reason it is called the "Sunshine Vitamin.")	Rickets (Improper assimilation of calcium and phosphorus results in bow legs, misshapen limbs, swollen joints, especially wrists and ankles.) Unhealthy bones and teeth.
E (Tocopherol)	Wheat germ oil. Leafy green vegetables. Milk, butter. Meat.	Sterility (inability to reproduce) in rats, and possibly in humans.
K	Leafy green vegetables, tomatoes. Egg yolk. Synthetic preparations.	Hemorrhage (excessive bleeding due to the inability of the body to make prothrombin, a protein necessary for the normal clotting of blood).

Conserving the Vitamin Content of Food. Some foods lose all or part of their vitamin content during processing, and therefore require that their vitamin content be artificially increased. Any food whose vitamin content has been artificially increased is called an *enriched* food. For example, when thiamin (B_1), riboflavin (B_2) and niacin (P-P) are added to bread, it is called enriched bread. To increase the Vitamin D content of milk, synthetic vitamins may be added or the milk may be *irradiated*, that is, exposed to ultra-violet light.

Foods lose some vitamins if cooked or prepared improperly. When preparing foods at home, follow these few simple rules to conserve vitamins:

1. Cook green vegetables in only a small amount of water, since many vitamins, especially B-complex vitamins, are soluble in water.

2. Cook potatoes in their skins, because the skins contain many vitamins.

3. Cook foods containing Vitamin C in covered pots and as quickly as possible, since this vitamin is easily destroyed by heat. Do not use baking soda, because baking soda chemically destroys Vitamin C. In preparing Vitamin C foods, a pressure cooker will save both time and vitamins.

4. Fix salads immediately before eating. This prevents a loss of vitamins.

What Is a Calorie? The energy which our body gets from food is *heat energy*. The unit for measuring heat energy is the *Calorie*. A Calorie is *the amount of heat required to raise the temperature of one kilogram* (approximately one quart) *of water one degree centigrade.*

To release the energy stored in food, the food must be oxidized in the cells. In the process of oxidation, heat is liberated. To determine the amount of potential energy in a food, we burn a given portion of that food and measure the number of heat units, or Calories, given off. To do this, an instrument, called a *bomb calorimeter,* is used. The food is placed in a chamber surrounded by water. As the food is burned, the water absorbs the heat given off. From the temperature increase of the water, we are able to determine the number of Calories released from the food.

Caloric Requirements Vary. The amount of energy a person must obtain from foods is called the *Caloric requirement.* The Caloric requirement of a person depends upon that individual's *occupation, age, size, sex* and *glandular stability*. Another important factor is *climate*.

1. *Occupation.* This is the most important single factor in determining Caloric requirements. An individual who is very active, or performs heavy labor, requires more Calories than an individual who is less active, or performs light work. Some of the average daily requirements of people performing different tasks are listed below:

The Individual	Calories Per Day
Woodcutter	5000
Athlete or laborer	4500
Man doing little manual work	2500
Woman working at a desk	2100
Average high school boy	3200-3800
Average high school girl	2400-2800

2. *Age.* A young person, being more active, requires more Calories than an elderly person.

3. *Size.* A large person normally requires more Calories than a small person doing the same work, because the larger person has more body cells which require food for energy.

4. *Sex.* Males generally require more Calories than females, since males are usually engaged in heavier work.

5. *Glandular Stability.* A person's Caloric requirements would vary from the normal if suffering from some disturbance of a gland, such as an underactive or overactive thyroid gland.

6. *Climate.* A person needs more Calories in periods of cold weather than in periods of warm weather, while doing the same amount of work. In cold weather, the body requires the added heat for warmth. People living in the tropics need fewer Calories per day than do people living in cold regions, because less heat is required to maintain normal body temperature.

What Is a Balanced Diet? A diet containing a sufficient number of Calories and the proper amounts of all the nutrients is a *balanced diet*. A balanced diet actually means variety and quantity of the right kinds of food. In a guide to good eating published by the Department of Agriculture, this agency says:

"All kinds of food are good, but for health we need variety. Our bodies are made of many materials which must be supplied in the food we eat. We must have foods that yield energy, foods that supply the materials for growth and upkeep, and foods to keep our bodies in good running order."

Well-balanced meals can be planned around seven groups of foods, known as the *basic seven*. Here is what the Department of Agriculture recommends:

"You can get all the right kinds of food needed for health by using this simple guide—the Basic 7. Be sure to include in your meals each day at least the minimum number of servings from each group shown on the chart. And make it a point to provide extra large servings to teen-agers and very active adults."

THE BASIC 7 FOOD GROUPS

GROUP 1—Leafy, Green, and Yellow Vegetables

One or more servings daily of: asparagus, beans, broccoli, cabbage, carrots, lettuce, peas, peppers, spinach, squash, sweet potatoes, turnip greens.

GROUP 2—Citrus Fruits, Tomatoes, Raw Cabbage

One or more servings daily of: cabbage, cantaloups, grapefruit, lemons, limes, oranges, peppers, pineapples, strawberries, tangerines, tomatoes, turnips.

GROUP 3—Potatoes and Other Vegetables and Fruit

Two or more servings daily of: apples, apricots, bananas, beets, cauliflower, celery, corn, cucumbers, lettuce, onions, peaches, pears, potatoes, radishes, watermelons.

GROUP 4—Milk, Cheese, Ice Cream

Children: three to four cups daily.
Adults: two or more cups daily.
Milk: buttermilk, condensed, dried, evaporated, skim, whole.
Cheese or ice cream may be substituted for milk.

GROUP 5—Meat, Poultry, Fish, Eggs, Dried Beans and Peas, Nuts

Meat, Poultry, Fish: one serving daily of beef, chicken, duck, fish, kidneys, lamb, liver, mutton, pork, shellfish, turkey, veal.
Eggs: four or more a week.
Dried Beans and Peas, Nuts: two or more servings a week.

GROUP 6—Bread, Flour, and Cereals
Every day.
Bread (enriched white, rye, whole wheat), Flour, Rolls, Crackers, Cereal.

GROUP 7—Butter and Fortified Margarine
Some daily.

A SUMMARY OF THE NUTRIENTS

ENERGY-PRODUCING NUTRIENTS

Nutrient	Composition	Uses in the Body	Source
Carbohydrates (Sugars and Starch)	Carbon, hydrogen and oxygen.	The chief source of energy. Excess carbohydrates are stored for future use.	Sugars: fruit, honey, candy and ice cream. Starch: cereal grains, potatoes, bread and pastries.
Fats and Oils	Carbon, hydrogen and oxygen.	Supply energy. Excess fats and oils are stored for future use.	Butter, lard, cream, cheese, bacon, meat, olive oil and nuts.
Proteins	Nitrogen in addition to carbon, hydrogen and oxygen. Some proteins also contain sulfur, iron, phosphorus and other elements.	Promote growth and repair of all body cells; and supply small amounts of energy.	Milk, cheese, eggs, meat, liver, fish, peas, beans, and nuts.

Non-Energy Nutrients

Water	Hydrogen and oxygen.	Water makes up 70 to 80 per cent of protoplasm; and constitutes the largest part of the blood.	Drinking water, milk and other beverages; and most foods, particularly fruits and vegetables.
Mineral Salts	Chiefly calcium, phosphorus, fluorine, iron, iodine, sodium and chlorine.	Calcium and phosphorus build strong bones and teeth.	Milk, eggs, cheese.
		Iron makes up part of the hemoglobin in the blood.	Liver, eggs, beef, green vegetables.
		Iodine constitutes a large part of the secretion of the thyroid gland.	Sea foods, iodized table salt.
		Fluorine prevents tooth decay.	Some in natural water, but often added.
		Sodium is useful in building protoplasm.	Table salt.
		Chlorine forms a part of hydrochloric acid, which is necessary in digestion.	Table salt.
Vitamins	Carbon, hydrogen, oxygen, nitrogen and other elements.	See the vitamin table on pages 110-111.	

FOODS ARE DIGESTED IN THE BODY

The Nature of Digestion. By the process of digestion, food is changed from its natural complex form to simple end products which can be utilized by the body. Digestion occurs in two ways, mechanically and chemically.

1. In *mechanical digestion,* the physical nature (size, shape, etc.) of foods is changed. For example, the teeth break up solid foods into small particles by chewing. Chewing prepares the food for chemical digestion.

2. In *chemical digestion,* foods are changed from complex substances to simple soluble substances able to pass through cell membranes by osmosis. Chemical digestion is brought about by the action of *enzymes* on foods. Enzymes are secreted by the digestive glands. Since enzymes are catalysts, they do not enter into the chemical reaction.

The Digestive System. Man's digestive system consists of the *alimentary canal* and various *glands* whose secretions of enzymes take part in the digestive process. The alimentary canal is made up of the *mouth, pharynx, esophagus, stomach, small intestine* and *large intestine.* Digestion takes place as food passes through these organs.

The Mouth. Food enters the alimentary canal at the *mouth.* There are three important parts of the mouth, namely: the *teeth* and the *tongue,* which start the process of mechanical digestion, and the *salivary glands,* which start the process of chemical digestion.

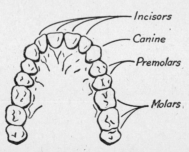

Incisors

Canine

Premolars

Molars

Fig. 48. The Permanent Teeth

1. *The Teeth.* By chewing food into small pieces, the teeth prepare the food for chemical digestion. There are 32 adult, or permanent, teeth—16 in the upper jaw and 16 in the lower jaw. Each jaw has 4 *incisors* for biting, 2 *canines* for tearing, 4 *premolars* (or bicuspids) and 6 *molars* for crushing and grinding. Sometimes the last two molars, the "wisdom teeth," do not break through the gums. The permanent teeth replace the temporary teeth, or *milk teeth,* of childhood.

Although teeth are shaped differently, they are fundamentally the same in structure. A typical tooth consists of three parts: The crown, the neck, the root. The *crown* is above the gum. The *neck* is the part where the tooth meets the gum. The *root,* which is below the gum, holds the tooth in place in the jawbone.

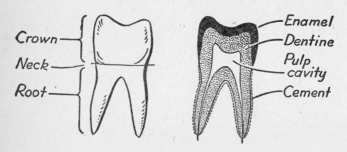

Fig. 49. Structures of a Tooth

In the center of the tooth is the *pulp cavity.* It contains blood vessels and nerves, which enter through the root. The blood vessels supply the tooth with food and oxygen, and remove waste products. The nerves are the means by which we receive the sensation of pain when the tooth is diseased or injured. The nerves also maintain the life of the tooth. If a nerve dies or is removed, the tooth will die. Surrounding the pulp cavity is the *dentine,* a bone-like material making up the greater part of the tooth. On the crown, the dentine is covered with *enamel,* the hardest substance in the body. The enamel protects the tooth. On the root, the dentine is covered with *cement,* which aids in anchoring the tooth to the jawbone.

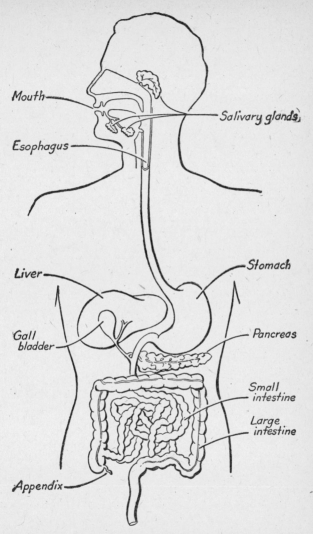

Fig. 50. The Digestive System

2. *The Tongue.* We use the tongue for tasting and swallowing food. The upper surface of the tongue is covered with *taste buds,* with which we taste sweet, sour, bitter and salt. The tongue, being muscular, turns the food around in the mouth and pushes the chewed food back into the throat, or *pharynx.* From there the food passes into the *esophagus.*

3. *The Salivary Glands.* The process of chemical digestion in the alimentary canal is started by the secretion of the salivary glands. These are three pairs of glands which secrete *saliva,* a digestive juice (or fluid). Saliva contains the enzyme *ptyalin,* which chemically begins to change starch into malt sugar (*maltose*). But saliva does not affect proteins and fats. Saliva also aids mechanical digestion by moistening the food and thus making it easier to swallow.

To Prove That Saliva Digests Starch. Make a suspension of starch. Test with Fehling's (or Benedict's) solution to make sure no sugar is present. Add saliva, and shake the mixture. Keep at body temperature (98.6°F.) for twenty minutes. Again add Fehling's (or Benedict's) solution and heat to boiling. An orange color shows that sugar is present. We can therefore conclude that the saliva (which contains ptyalin) digested the starch to sugar.

The Esophagus (Gullet). Food passes from the mouth to the stomach through the *esophagus,* or *gullet.* The esophagus is a long tube-like structure with two sets of muscles in its walls. One set of muscles is circular, the other longitudinal. These muscles contract regularly, causing wavelike motions known as *peristalsis.* Peristaltic waves occur throughout the alimentary canal, except in the mouth. It is by means of these waves that food is pushed downward through the alimentary tract. The passage of food is further aided by a slimy *mucus* secreted from *mucous glands* in the wall of the esophagus. No chemical digestion takes place in the esophagus, except for the continuing action of ptyalin on starch, which started in the mouth.

The Stomach. Lying in the upper left half of the abdominal cavity, just under the diaphragm, is the *stomach.* This digestive organ is shaped like the letter J, with an opening, or valve, at either end. The upper valve is at the junction with the esophagus; the lower valve is at the junction with the small intestine. As food enters the stomach, both valves close in order to retain the food in the stomach. Then peristaltic waves begin. These waves (1) churn the food and mix it with the digestive juice of the stomach, and (2) push the food from the upper to the lower end of the stomach. The action of digestive juices on foods is described on the pages that follow.

The Gastric Glands. The inner lining of the stomach contains numerous tiny structures known as the *gastric glands.* They secrete *gastric juice,* the digestive fluid of the stomach. Gastric juice contains *pepsin* and *rennin,* which are enzymes, and *hydrochloric acid,* which is not an enzyme. The chief function of these substances is the digestion of proteins, which occurs as follows:

1. Pepsin digests proteins into simpler protein substances, known as *peptones* and *proteoses,* which are intermediate products between proteins and amino acids.

2. Rennin acts on milk protein (*casein*), making the protein ready for digestion by pepsin.

3. Hydrochloric acid does not effect a change in the nature of proteins, but it must be present in order for pepsin to act on proteins. Hydrochloric acid also dissolves out the minerals in food and destroys any bacteria which might cause decay of food in the stomach.

As a result of the constant churning of food by the stomach muscles, and the mixing of food with gastric juice, a mass of liquid food, called *chyme,* is produced. When the lower, or *pyloric* valve, relaxes, the chyme passes from the stomach to the small intestine, there to undergo further digestion. The valve then contracts, preventing the flow of the partially digested food back into the stomach.

To Prove That Gastric Juice Digests Proteins. Label three test tubes A, B and C. Place water and a few drops of hydrochloric acid into tube A. Place water and some pepsin into tube B. Place water, a few drops of hydrochloric acid, and some pepsin into tube C. To each tube add a small piece, each the same size, of boiled egg white (protein). Place the tubes in a warm place (at about body temperature) and allow to stand overnight. On the following day it will be seen that only the egg white in tube C has disappeared (been digested). We can therefore conclude that, in the presence of hydrochloric acid, pepsin digests proteins.

The Small Intestine. In the lower half of the abdominal cavity is the *small intestine.* This is a coiled tube about 20 feet in length and a little more than an inch in diameter. The small intestine functions as follows: (1) It completes the digestion of all foods. (2) It absorbs digested foods into the bloodstream. (3) By peristalsis, it moves the undigested parts of food matter along to the large intestine.

Digestion in the small intestine is brought about by secretions of the *pancreas*, the *liver* and the *intestinal glands*. The work of these three glands is described below.

1. *The Pancreas*. This elongated gland lies behind and beneath the stomach. When stimulated, the pancreas secretes *pancreatic juice*, which flows through a tube, or *duct*, into the small intestine. Pancreatic juice contains three important enzymes: *amylase, trypsin* and *lipase*. These enzymes act on food as follows:

a. Amylase digests starch into malt sugar (maltose), completing the work done by the ptyalin in saliva.

b. Trypsin digests peptones and proteoses (the results of stomach digestion of proteins) into simple amino acids. Trypsin also digests some of the proteins that the stomach did not act upon.

c. Lipase digests fats into fatty acids and glycerol.

To Prove That Pancreatic Juice Digests Fats. Label two test tubes A and B. Place some water and a few drops of salad oil into tube A. Place water, pancreatin (artificial pancreatic juice) and a few drops of salad oil into tube B. Place the tubes in a warm place (at about body temperature) and allow to stand overnight. On the following day it will be seen that only the oil in tube B has disappeared (been digested). We can therefore conclude that pancreatin contains an enzyme (lipase) able to digest fats.

2. *The Liver*. This is the largest gland in the human body, situated to the right of the stomach. The liver produces a secretion, called *bile*, which enters the small intestine along with the pancreatic juice. Bile, although containing no enzyme, is essential to the digestion and absorption of fats. Bile *emulsifies* the fat, that is, breaks it up into minute particles, thus enabling the fat to be more easily digested by lipase. Bile first goes to the *gall bladder*, which stores the bile until needed by the small intestine.

3. *The Intestinal Glands*. The lining of the small intestine contains numerous glands. These glands secrete *intestinal juice*, which consists of four important enzymes: *erepsin, maltase, lactase* and *sucrase*. These enzymes complete the digestion of substances which had not been acted upon by the pancreatic juice, as follows:

a. Erepsin digests peptones, proteoses and any remaining proteins into amino acids, thus completing the digestion of proteins.

b. Maltase, lactase and sucrase digest different kinds of sugars into simple sugar (glucose). Maltase acts on malt sugar (maltose); lactase on milk sugar (lactose); and sucrase on cane sugar (sucrose).

THE SECRETIONS OF THE DIGESTIVE GLANDS

Glands	Secretions	Enzymes
salivary glands	saliva	ptyalin
gastric glands	gastric juice	pepsin and rennin (hydrochloric acid—not an enzyme but needed for digestion)
pancreas	pancreatic juice	amylase, trypsin and lipase
liver	bile	
intestinal glands	intestinal juice	erepsin, maltase, lactase and sucrase

How Does Food Get to the Cells?

End Products of Digestion. In the process of digestion, as we have seen, the energy-producing nutrients break down into usable *end products* as follows:

Nutrients	End Products
Carbohydrates (sugars and starch)	Glucose
Fats	Fatty acids and glycerol
Proteins	Amino acids

The end products of digestion differ from the original ingested food in these two ways: (1) The end products are simple and therefore can be used by the cells. (2) The end products are carried in solution and therefore can be absorbed into the bloodstream.

Absorption. In the process of absorption, the end products, along with the non-energy nutrients, diffuse through the membrane of the alimentary canal into the bloodstream. The blood then carries the nutrients to the cells for nourishment. The greatest part of absorption takes place in the small intestine.

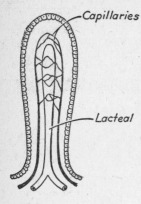

Fig. 51. A Villus

The Villi. The small intestine is well-adapted for absorption. The inner lining contains numerous fingerlike structures, known as *villi.* The villi greatly increase the area of absorption. In the center of each villus are *capillaries* (microscopic blood vessels) surrounding a lymph vessel, the *lacteal.* By the process of osmosis, simple sugars and amino acids diffuse into the capillaries and are carried by the blood to the cells; fatty acids and glycerol diffuse into the lacteals and eventually into the bloodstream to the cells.

The Large Intestine (Colon).   Undigested matter passes from the small intestine into the *large intestine,* or *colon.* This organ is a tube-like structure about five feet in length and over two inches in diameter. In shape, it resembles an inverted U.

Most of the bulk which moves into the large intestine consists of indigestible matter (wastes) and water. As peristaltic waves push the wastes downward, some of the water is removed and absorbed. The wastes then pass into the lower part of the large intestine, called the *rectum,* and are eliminated from the body through the *anus.* It takes 12 to 14 hours for the bulk to pass through the large intestine.

Appendicitis.   Attached to the large intestine, just below the point where it meets with the small intestine, is the *appendix.* The appendix is normally found in the lower right side of the abdomen. The appendix is a small, tubular structure, apparently of no use to the body. An inflammation of the appendix, known as *appendicitis,* usually necessitates its removal by surgery. The symptoms of appendicitis almost always are: (1) a sharp, knife-like pain in the lower right side of the abdomen, (2) nausea or vomiting, and (3) a rising temperature. These symptoms must not be neglected; medical advice should be sought immediately.

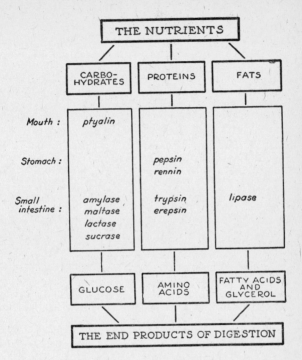

Fig. 52. Enzyme Action on the Nutrients

Hygiene of the Digestive System:

1. *Eat a balanced diet, and do not overeat.* A balanced diet is essential to health. Overeating causes a strain on the digestive, nervous and circulatory systems. Obesity (fatness) resulting from overeating, or eating an unbalanced diet, can be detrimental to health.

2. *Eliminate wastes regularly.* The wastes of digestion must be eliminated from the body. For regular bowel movements, drink plenty of water, eat a proper amount of roughage, and acquire the habit of eliminating at a fixed time.

3. *Avoid rapid eating, and chew food thoroughly.* Rapid eating does not allow sufficient time for proper chewing, or for the moistening of the food with saliva. This hinders digestion, since it places a burden upon the stomach. Over a period of time, this practice may result in serious ailments of the digestive tract.

4. *Take care of your teeth.* A full set of healthy teeth not only adds to one's charm, but also aids digestion. Teeth and gums must be kept free of food particles. Decay must be removed, and cavities filled. Missing teeth (except wisdom teeth) should be replaced. The best procedure for the care of the teeth is the oft-told advice, "Brush your teeth twice a day, and visit your dentist twice a year."

5. *Eat in a pleasant environment.* Pleasant surroundings and congenial associates are relaxing. Relaxation assists in digestion by stimulating the flow of digestive juices. On the other hand, arguing heatedly while eating, not only deprives one of the pleasure of eating, but also interferes with the process of digestion.

6. *Rest after eating.* During and after eating, the blood normally flows to the digestive system to assist in the functions of digestion and absorption. It is therefore advisable to rest for about a half hour after eating in order to allow the blood to serve the digestive system. Exercise would tend to divert the blood to the muscles, and thus hamper digestion and absorption.

7. *Consult a physician regarding digestive disturbances.* Disturbances of the digestive system may be simple in nature, but not always. In case of persistent discomfort, it is wise to consult a physician. He will determine whether the disorder is due to faulty glandular secretion, faulty metabolism, or a structural defect of the digestive tract.

Completion Questions

1. The usable parts of foods are called _____.
2. The non-usable parts of foods that aid digestion are called
_____
3. Sugars and starch are forms of a nutrient called _____.
4. The liver stores excess carbohydrates in the form of _____.
5. Benedict's solution is used to test for the presence of _____.
6. The element present in proteins but not in carbohydrates is
_____.
7. The primary function of amino acids in the body is to
_____.

8. The test for proteins involves the use of _____ acid.
9. The non-energy nutrient which carries the other nutrients in solution is _____.
10. A disease for which citrus fruits provide a cure is _____.
11. Milk is irradiated principally to increase the amount of Vitamin _____.
12. The energy value of food materials is expressed in terms of units called _____.
13. The chemical change in foods that prepares them for use by the body is _____.
14. Digestive fluids contain catalytic agents called _____.
15. Digestion in the human body begins in the _____.
16. If the gastric juice in the stomach contained no pepsin, a nutrient whose digestion would be slowed is _____.
17. The longest section of the alimentary canal is the _____.
18. A gland whose secretion contains three kinds of digestive enzymes is the _____.
19. That part of the human body in which bile is stored is the _____.
20. The absorbing surface of the small intestine is greatly increased by the _____.

Multiple-Choice Questions

1. Nutrition includes all of the following life functions *except* (1) digestion (2) assimilation (3) reproduction (4) absorption.
2. If equal weights of the following substances are oxidized, the largest amount of energy is released by (1) fats (2) proteins (3) starch (4) sugars.
3. A complex substance made by plants and used by animals to build protoplasm is (1) sugar (2) protein (3) fat (4) roughage.
4. Two elements necessary for the formation of strong bones and teeth are calcium and (1) phosphorus (2) gold (3) mercury (4) chlorine.
5. A food rich in iron is (1) carrots (2) liver (3) milk (4) tomatoes.
6. Deficiency diseases are caused by (1) germs (2) insufficient exercise (3) lack of vitamins (4) undersecretion of hormones.
7. A vitamin that affects the ability to see at night is (1) A (2) B_{12} (3) C (4) D.

8. Vitamin D is found plentifully (1) in all vegetables (2) in meat (3) only in manufactured products (4) in fish oils.

9. A calorimeter is used to test foods for (1) vitamin content (2) protein content (3) energy content (4) sugar content.

10. Calorie requirements vary according to all of the following *except* (1) age (2) intelligence (3) occupation (4) climate.

11. The best source of vitamins for high school pupils is (1) cod-liver oil (2) a properly varied diet (3) vitamin injections (4) vitamin pills.

12. The part of the tooth which contains the hardest substance in the body is the (1) root (2) dentine (3) cement (4) enamel.

13. The enzyme found in the salivary juice that begins carbohydrate digestion is (1) ptyalin (2) pepsin (3) rennin (4) hydro-chloric acid.

14. Contraction of the smooth muscle of the alimentary canal is called (1) peristalsis (2) digestion (3) absorption (4) as-similation.

15. A secretion of the gastric glands without which protein digestion would not take place in the stomach is (1) hydrochloric acid (2) sucrase (3) maltase (4) erepsin.

16. The test for fat digestion requires pancreatin because it con-tains the enzyme (1) amylase (2) trypsin (3) lipase (4) lactase.

17. The digestion of food occurs principally in the (1) stomach (2) small intestine (3) mouth (4) large intestine.

18. Bile is necessary for the proper digestion of (1) fat (2) pro-tein (3) starch (4) sugar.

19. The part of the food that has not been digested is eliminated from the body through the (1) small intestine (2) large in-testine (3) esophagus (4) pharynx.

20. Protein is absorbed in the small intestine principally as (1) amino acids (2) carbonic acid (3) fatty acids (4) glycerol.

Modified True-False Questions

1. *Insoluble* substances pass through cell membranes by osmosis.

2. Most of the indigestible parts of vegetables are composed of starch.

3. The appearance of a grease spot on unglazed paper shows the presence of *sugar*.

4. Iodine is used to test a food for the presence of *protein*.

5. Soybean products are particularly useful in the diet because they contain large amounts of *sugar*.
6. An example of a food that is rich in calcium is *cabbage*.
7. Enriched margarine (butter substitute) contains large amounts of *Vitamin A*.
8. Milk is irradiated principally to increase the amount of *Vitamin C*.
9. Digested proteins and carbohydrates pass into the *lacteals* of the villi.
10. A structure believed to be useless to the body, and located approximately where the small and large intestines meet, is the *appendix*.

Essay Questions

1. Write an explanation of each of the following:
   a. The Calorie requirements of individuals differ.
   b. Cheese and eggs, rather than bread and potatoes, are good substitutes for meat.
   c. Dried foods may need added vitamins.
   d. Enriched bread has greater value in the diet than has ordinary white bread.
   e. Milk should be part of the diet of all children of school age.
   f. The water in which vegetables are cooked should be saved and used.
   g. The cost of a food is not an indication of its value in the diet.
   h. A diet entirely free of fats may result in a deficiency disease.
   i. If rice is the principal food in the diet, it should be brown rice.
   j. The diet of every person must include some protein.
2. During the past 20 years, our food habits have undergone many changes. Give one biologic reason for each of the following dietetic changes:
   a. Increased popularity of yellow vegetables.
   b. Increased use of salads, of raw fruits and vegetables.
   c. The great demand for liver.
   d. Cooking vegetables in their skins.
   e. Feeding babies orange or tomato juice.
   f. Preference shown for whole-wheat bread and cereals.
   g. Children born in November and kept indoors during the winter months should have synthetic vitamins added to their diets.

    h. Greater emphasis is being placed on properly balanced diets.

    i. People have become more concerned about the vitamin content of foods.

    j. Food processing companies have been seeking ways of preparing their products to save vitamins.

3. The lettered expressions below relate to the functions of these six organs: *gullet, liver, mouth, pancreas, small intestine, stomach.* Write the name of the organ to which the corresponding expression is most closely related.

    a. The organ in which most of the digested food is absorbed.

    b. An organ through which food does not pass during digestion.

    c. Contains the gastric glands.

    d. A region through which food passes but which does not secrete a digestive juice.

    e. The region in which pancreatic juice acts on food.

    f. The region into which the salivary glands open.

    g. Produces bile.

    h. Has many villi on its walls.

4. *a.* State one important function of the saliva.

    b. Describe three different functions of the small intestine that make it such an important organ of the digestive system.

5. *a.* What biologic process would be interrupted if the lining epithelium of the stomach is totally removed?

    b. What is the function of glycogen in the human body? Where is glycogen stored?

6. Describe a properly controlled experiment to determine the truth of the following statements:

    a. Starch digestion takes place in the mouth.

    b. Pepsin will not digest protein unless hydrochloric acid is present.

Chapter XI

RESPIRATION IN MAN

What is Respiration? We are constantly taking in oxygen from the air we breathe. Oxygen is an element comprising about 21% of the atmosphere. Oxygen along with food nutrients is transported by the blood to every cell of the body. In the cells, the oxygen combines with the food, the food actually being burned and heat energy being released. This is the process of *oxidation*. As a result of oxidation, carbon dioxide and water are given off. These waste products are carried away from the cells by the blood.

The above process of taking in oxygen from the air and giving off carbon dioxide and water vapor to the air is called *respiration*. In its fullest sense, respiration includes: (1) breathing in air containing oxygen, (2) using the oxygen to oxidize food in the cells, *thus releasing energy* (the chief purpose of respiration), and (3) giving off air containing the waste products of oxidation, namely, carbon dioxide and water vapor.

Laboratory Experiments on Respiration:

1. *To Prove that Oxygen Is Needed for Respiration.* Soak some seeds overnight, and plant half of them in each of two jars. Place the cover on one jar to keep out the air. Leave the other jar uncovered. The seeds in the uncovered jar will sprout, while those in the covered jar will die for want of oxgyen.

2. *To Prove that Heat Is Produced in Respiration.* Place a few live sprouting beans in vacuum bottle A. Kill a few sprouting beans by boiling, and then place them in vacuum bottle B. Into each bottle, fit a stopper bearing a thermometer. A few hours later it will be found that the temperature of bottle A is higher than the temperature of bottle B. The increase in temperature is due to the heat produced by the respiration of the live sprouting seeds.

3. *To Prove that Carbon Dioxide Is Produced in Respiration.* Blow through a straw into a beaker of limewater for several minutes. The limewater becomes cloudy, thus proving that carbon dioxide is exhaled from the lungs.

4. *To Prove that Water Is Produced in Respiration.* Breathe against a cold glass. Droplets of moisture condense on the glass, thus proving that water vapor is exhaled from the lungs.

131

The Respiratory System. The respiratory system consists of the following organs: the *nose, pharynx, trachea, bronchi* and *lungs.* The process of respiration is aided by the *ribs,* as well as by certain muscles lying outside the respiratory system, namely, the *rib muscles* and the *diaphragm.*

Oxygen on its way to the bloodstream passes through the respiratory tract as follows:

The Nose. Air enters our body through the *nose.* This organ is well equipped to aid breathing. It has two openings, the *nostrils,* which lead into long curved passageways called the *nasal passages.* Air passing through the nostrils is filtered. Coarse hairs that line the nostrils prevent dust and other foreign matter from passing through. Air in its course through the nostrils and nasal passages is warmed by the numerous blood vessels which lie immediately below the thin mucous membrane. The mucous membrane lining the nostrils and nasal passages is composed of a layer of flat epithelial cells which produce a secretion that catches dust and germs.

The Pharynx. Air leaving the nasal passages goes into the *pharynx,* the throat cavity in back of the mouth. The mucous membrane lining the pharynx moistens passing air.

The Trachea (Windpipe). As air leaves the pharynx, it enters the *trachea,* or *windpipe.* This is a tube about 4 inches long and 1 inch in diameter. It is located in front of the esophagus. The trachea is kept fairly rigid by its structure of rings of cartilage. The trachea is thus kept open for the passage of air. In the mucous membrane that lines the trachea are cells equipped with *cilia.* The cilia sweep dust and germs upward into the throat for elimination from the body. Similarly, ciliated cells in the nasal passages and bronchi help to eliminate foreign particles.

The upper part of the trachea forms the voice box, or *larynx,* which contains the vocal cords. The opening into the trachea is the *glottis.* A cartilaginous lid, the *epiglottis,* is an important organ at this site. During respiration, it permits air to enter the trachea; during swallowing of food, it closes off the entrance of the trachea. Thus, food can flow only to the esophagus and cannot enter the breathing apparatus.

The lower part of the trachea divides, forming two main branching tubes, called the *bronchi.* Each bronchus enters a lung.

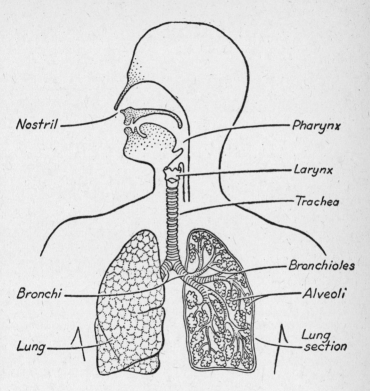

Fig. 53. The Respiratory System

The Lungs. Air passing through the trachea and the bronchi enters the lungs. The lungs are two spongy organs which occupy the greater portion of the chest cavity (*thorax*). Each lung is covered with an elastic protective membrane called the *pleura*, which separates the lung from the chest wall. The pleura has two layers, between which a secretion is normally found that prevents friction when the lungs expand and contract.

Within the lungs, the bronchi divide many times, forming numerous small tubes barely visible to the eye. These tubes, known as the *bronchial tubes* (or bronchioles), end in groups of microscopic air sacs, known as *alveoli*. Each alveolus is surrounded by a network of blood vessels, the capillaries. Thus, the alveoli are specially adapted for the exchange of gases between the lungs and the blood.

In addition to bringing oxygen to the cells, the blood takes on the wastes of oxidation, which are carbon dioxide and water. The blood, now impure, is carried back to the alveoli in the lungs to exchange the wastes for fresh oxygen.

The Exchange of Gases.   Oxygen is the only part of the inspired air that can be utilized by the body. The oxygen combines with the hemoglobin in the red blood cells to form the compound *oxyhemoglobin*. This freshly oxygenated blood, or pure blood, circulates through the body carrying oxygen to the cells for oxidation.

After releasing the oxygen, the hemoglobin unites with the waste of oxidation, which is carbon dioxide, to form the compound *carboxyhemoglobin*. This impure blood is carried back to the alveoli in the lungs for the exchange of the waste, carbon dioxide, for fresh oxygen.

The exchange of gases is a continuous process, for the cells must be constantly supplied with fresh oxygen and the gaseous wastes carried away.

Lung Respiration.   The walls of the alveoli are only one cell in thickness. Oxygen from the inhaled air diffuses through the thin walls of the alveoli into the blood in the surrounding capillaries. Carbon dioxide and water diffuse from the blood into the air in the alveoli. This oxygen-carbon dioxide exchange between the air and the blood in the alveoli is called *external respiration*.

Cellular Respiration.   After obtaining oxygen in the capillaries surrounding the alveoli, the oxygenated blood is circulated throughout the body. In all tissues, oxygen diffuses from the blood into the cells; carbon dioxide and water pass from the cells into the blood. This gas exchange between the cells and the blood is called *internal respiration*.

How Do We Breathe?   The mechanical act of breathing involves inhaling and exhaling. When we *inhale*, we take into our lungs air that is high in oxygen. When we *exhale*, we expel air that is high in carbon dioxide and water vapor. During breathing, the lungs expand and contract rhythmically, somewhat in the manner of a bellows.

Since they have no muscles, the lungs do not cause their own expansion and relaxation. Instead, breathing is caused by a change in the size of the chest cavity surrounding the lungs. This change is brought about by the movement of the ribs as well as of certain muscles, namely, the *rib muscles* and the *diaphragm*. The diaphragm is the arched, muscular wall separating the chest cavity from the abdominal cavity. The action of the rib muscles and the diaphragm, with their effects on the chest cavity and the lungs, is as follows:

Inspiration. This is the act of *inhaling*, or taking air into the lungs. When we inhale: (1) the rib muscles contract, causing the ribs to move up and outward, and (2) the diaphragm contracts, moving from its normal arched position to a flatter position. These simultaneous movements increase the size of the chest cavity. Thus, air rushes into the lungs, filling them and making them expand.

Expiration. This is the act of *exhaling*, or expelling air from the lungs. When we exhale, the rib muscles and the diaphragm relax and return to their normal positions. Thus, the size of the chest cavity is decreased, causing the lungs to contract and expel air.

An Experiment to Illustrate the Function of the Diaphragm in Breathing. In Fig. 54 on page 136, the bell jar represents the human *chest cavity;* the balloons represent the *lungs;* and the rubber membrane corresponds to the *diaphragm.*

When the rubber membrane (or diaphragm) is moved downward, a partial vacuum results within the bell jar (chest cavity). As a result, atmospheric pressure forces air into the balloons (lungs). (This is the process of *inspiration*, or breathing *in.*)

When the rubber membrane (diaphragm) returns to its original position, air is forced out of the balloons (lungs). (This is *expiration*, or breathing *out.*)

How Breathing Is Controlled. We know that we do not order our body to perform the act of breathing. We breathe at all times of the day and night without being conscious of the act. This is because breathing is an *involuntary* act, that is, it is not controlled by our will. Instead, breathing is automatically controlled by a part of our brain called the *medulla.* In the medulla is the *respiratory center,* formed by certain nerve cells, which sets up nervous impulses. The impulses travel along a chain of nerves (like electricity flowing through a copper wire) to the rib muscles and the diaphragm, causing their rhythmic contraction and relaxation—which bring about the process of breathing.

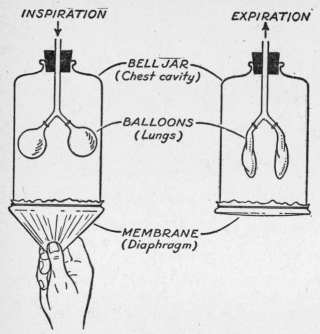

INSPIRATION   EXPIRATION

BELL JAR
(Chest cavity)

BALLOONS
(Lungs)

MEMBRANE
(Diaphragm)

Fig. 54. The Mechanics of Breathing

Our Rate of Breathing. The amount of carbon dioxide in our blood regulates our rate of breathing. The average normal rate of breathing is eighteen times per minute. As we engage in added activity, this rate increases, due to an increase of carbon dioxide in our blood. How does this occur? The increased activity demands more energy output. The added energy is obtained by burning more food in our cells. As a result of the increased oxidation in our cells, a greater amount of carbon dioxide is given off to the blood. The excess carbon dioxide stimulates the respiratory center, causing the nerve cells to send out more than the usual number of nervous impulses. Therefore, we breathe faster. Conversely, our rate of breathing falls below normal in times of rest or sleep, because we are expending less energy.

It is possible to breathe *voluntarily*, that is, control our own breathing, as when we hold our breath. However, we can do this only for a short time, because cellular respiration is going on and is releasing carbon dioxide to the blood. When the carbon dioxide content builds up to such an extent as to stimulate the respiratory center, involuntary breathing starts again.

To Determine the Effect of Exercise on Breathing Rate. Count the number of your inspirations per minute while at rest. Engage in vigorous exercise for a short time and make another count. Exercise will cause the breathing rate to increase in order to supply the cells' sudden demand for more oxygen.

Common Diseases Affecting the Respiratory System:

1. The *common cold* is a virus infection that weakens the body and leaves it open to attack by other disease-causing organisms.

2. *Bronchitis* is an inflammation of the bronchi.

3. *Pneumonia* is an inflammation of the lungs themselves.

4. *Tonsilitis* is an inflammation of the tonsils.

5. *Diphtheria, pleurisy* and *tuberculosis* are bacterial diseases that affect the respiratory system.

6. *Asthma* is an allergy that causes an irritation of the lungs and impairs breathing.

Carbon Monoxide Poisoning. Carbon monoxide is a poisonous gas present in automobile exhaust fumes. If inhaled, the carbon monoxide readily combines with the hemoglobin of the blood, thus preventing the blood from carrying sufficient oxygen to the tissues. When a person has been overcome by carbon monoxide, he must be placed in the open air and given artificial respiration. Otherwise, the sufferer of carbon monoxide poisoning will die.

Hygiene of the Respiratory System:

1. *Breathe plenty of fresh air* in order to obtain oxygen free of injurious substances, such as dust or smoke. Spending at least two hours each day in the open air is desirable. While indoors, care should be taken to have proper ventilation, that is, an adequate supply and circulation of air.

2. *Breathe deeply* in order to get air into the lower parts of the lungs. A brisk walk or some other daily exercise helps to develop the habit of breathing deeply.

3. *Breathe through the nose, not through the mouth.* The nose is adapted for warming the air and removing dust particles. The mouth is not similarly adapted.

4. *Consult a physician for any abnormality of the respiratory tract.* Infected tonsils or adenoids may, by their position, mechanically block the respiratory tract.

5. *Have an annual X-ray of the chest* in order to detect tuberculosis, or any other disease, at an early stage.

Completion Questions

1. Respiration is the process by which _____ is released for cell activity.

2. The combining of foods with oxygen in the cells is the process called _____.

3. The waste products of respiration include carbon dioxide and _____.

4. Sprouting seeds kept in a closed container die, thus indicating that _____ is needed for respiration.

5. By measuring the temperature increase of sprouting seeds kept in a vacuum bottle, we can show that _____ is produced in respiration.

6. After blowing through a straw in a beaker of limewater, the limewater turned cloudy. This proves that _____ is given off as a result of respiration.

7. Dust is filtered from inhaled air by _____ in the nostrils.

8. The throat cavity in back of the mouth is the _____.

9. The trachea is composed of rings of _____.

10. The lower end of the trachea branches into two _____.

11. In the lungs, each alveolus is surrounded by a network of _____.

12. The walls of the alveoli are _____ in thickness.

13. In respiration, the only atmospheric gas of use to man is _____.

14. The carbon dioxide-oxygen exchange between the cells and the blood is called _____ respiration.

15. The muscular wall that aids us in breathing is the _____.

Multiple-Choice Questions

1. The essential purpose of respiration is (1) to furnish oxygen for the body (2) to provide energy (3) to get rid of carbon dioxide (4) to purify the blood.

2. The cells lining the trachea are adapted to catch dust and germs because they are equipped with (1) alveoli (2) villi (3) cilia (4) capillaries.

3. The windpipe is located (1) in front of (2) behind (3) to the left of (4) to the right of   the esophagus.

4. The (1) pharnyx (2) larynx (3) glottis (4) bronchus contains the vocal cords.

5. Between the lungs and chest wall is an elastic membrane called the (1) pleura (2) alveolus (3) thorax (4) glottis.

6. The tiny tubes in the lungs which conduct air from the bronchi to the air sacs are called (1) nasal passages (2) nostrils (3) capillaries (4) bronchioles.

7. The compound produced by the union of oxygen and the material in the red blood cells is (1) oxyhemoglobin (2) carbon dioxide (3) water vapor (4) carbon monoxide.

8. The carbon dioxide-oxygen exchange with the atmosphere occurs in the (1) nose (2) trachea (3) lungs (4) bronchi.

9. Blood is oxygenated in the capillaries of (1) the air sacs (2) the heart (3) the muscles (4) the liver.

10. The red blood cells carry (1) antibodies (2) oxygen (3) hormones (4) urea.

11. During inspiration, the ribs (1) do not move (2) move downward (3) move inward (4) move upward.

12. In breathing, air is forced into the lungs by (1) the ribs (2) the pleura (3) atmospheric pressure (4) the blood.

13. The part of the brain that controls respiration is the (1) medulla (2) cerebellum (3) cerebrum (4) spinal cord.

14. The average normal breathing rate for an adult is (1) 18 times per minute (2) 72 times per minute (3) 120 times per minute (4) 72 times per hour.

15. Exercise increases the rate of breathing because it causes, in the blood, an increase of (1) oxygen (2) carbon monoxide (3) nitrogen (4) carbon dioxide.

Modified True-False Questions

1. *Carbon monoxide* is a waste product of respiration.
2. The air exhaled by an individual contains *the same amount of* nitrogen as is contained in the air which he inhaled.
3. A disease of the respiratory system that calls for a great deal of rest, fresh air and sunshine is *tuberculosis*.
4. A disease resulting from an allergic condition and which makes breathing difficult is *diphtheria*.
5. *Carbon dioxide* is a poisonous gas found in automobile exhaust fumes.

Essay Questions

1. Describe the movements of the ribs and diaphragm when inhalation is taking place, and explain why these movements result in inhalation.
2. In short paragraphs, explain the following:
   a. Vigorous exercise increases the amount of carbon dioxide given off from the body.
   b. Although it is called a waste product, carbon dioxide is essential to the body of man.
3. *a.* Give the changes that take place in the blood during cell respiration.
   b. Prove that water vapor is a waste product of respiration.
4. Describe the structure and give one function of each of the following: mucous membrane, epiglottis, alveolus, trachea.
5. Define: respiration, breathing, external respiration, internal respiration.

Chapter XII

HUMAN CIRCULATION

The Circulatory System. In order to carry on the life activities, all cells in the body must receive food and oxygen, and must dispose of the waste products of oxidation. Blood is the fluid medium which supplies the body cells with the food and oxygen, and carries away the wastes. Blood is transported to every cell in the body by means of the *circulatory system,* which consists of the *heart, blood vessels, blood* and *lymph system.*

THE HEART

The Four Chambers. The heart is a four-chambered muscular organ for pumping blood to all parts of the body. The heart is composed of a right side and a left side. Each side consists of two chambers, an auricle and a ventricle. The *auricle* is a thin-walled *upper* chamber which receives blood. The *ventricle* is a thick-walled *lower* chamber which pumps blood.

Functions of the Four Heart Chambers. Blood circulates through the heart and lungs in the following manner: The *right auricle* receives impure blood from the body by means of the veins; the *left auricle* receives pure blood from the lungs. The auricles contract simultaneously, pumping blood to the ventricles. The ventricles then contract simultaneously—the *right ventricle* pumping impure blood to the lungs for aeration, and the *left ventricle* pumping pure blood through the arteries to all parts of the body. Thus, whenever the blood passes from the right side of the heart to the left side, the blood must first flow through the lungs, where the blood is oxygenated.

Right Side	Left Side
Auricle is the *receiving* chamber for *impure* (deoxygenated) blood from the body.	*Auricle* is the *receiving* chamber for *pure* (freshly oxygenated) blood from the lungs.
Ventricle is the *pumping* chamber of *impure* blood to the lungs for the exchange of gases.	*Ventricle* is the *pumping* chamber of *pure* blood to all parts of the body.

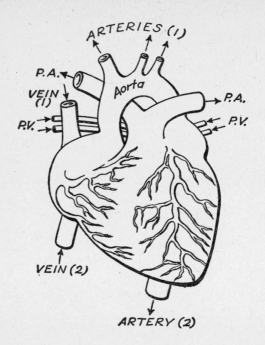

ARTERIES (1) — *from heart to upper region of body*
ARTERY (2) — *from heart to lower region of body*

VEIN (1) — *to heart from upper region of body*
VEIN (2) — *to heart from lower region of body*

P.A. — *pulmonary arteries from heart to lungs*
P.V. — *pulmonary veins to heart from lungs*

Fig. 55. The Heart (External View)

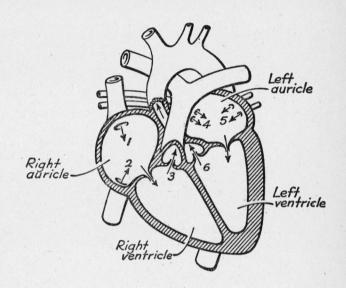

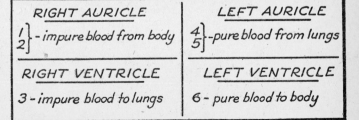

RIGHT AURICLE	LEFT AURICLE
$\left.\begin{matrix}1\\2\end{matrix}\right\}$ – impure blood from body	$\left.\begin{matrix}4\\5\end{matrix}\right\}$ – pure blood from lungs
RIGHT VENTRICLE	LEFT VENTRICLE
3 – impure blood to lungs	6 – pure blood to body

Fig. 56. The Heart (Sectional View)

Valves of the Heart. Between the auricles and ventricles are valves which open as blood flows from the auricles to the ventricles. When the ventricles contract, the valves close so that blood cannot flow back into the auricles. The faulty functioning of a valve results in a condition called "leaky valve."

Differences in the Walls. The walls of the heart chambers differ in thickness according to the different work they do. The walls of the auricles are thin; they pump blood only a short distance, namely, to the ventricles. The walls of the ventricles are more muscular and therefore thicker, because of the more difficult work they do. The left ventricle is thicker than the right ventricle, because it drives the blood to all parts of the body, from head to toes, whereas the right ventricle pumps blood only to the lungs.

Beat of the Heart. The rhythmic contraction of the heart is known as the *heart beat*. Between beats, the heart gets its rest. The average normal heart beat is 72 times per minute. But in times of increased activity, or in an emergency, the heart beats more rapidly, since the body is burning up energy faster.

THE BLOOD VESSELS

Arteries, Veins and Capillaries. The blood vessels are the arteries, veins and capillaries. *Arteries* originate at the heart and carry blood to the capillaries. The *capillaries* communicate directly with every cell in the body. *Veins* carry blood from the capillaries back to the heart. Thus, blood circulates in a closed system of blood vessels.

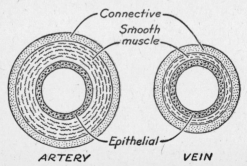

Fig. 57. **The Three Tissues of the Artery and Vein**

1. *Arteries.* Blood is pumped from the left ventricle through the *aorta,* the largest artery, and then through the arterial system. This system consists of the many arteries going to all organs of the body. Arteries branch out again and again, getting smaller and smaller, terminating in capillaries. The walls of arteries are thick and elastic. Arteries carry blood rich in food and oxygen. An exception is the pulmonary artery, which carries blood low in oxygen.

2. *Veins.* The veins return blood to the heart. In the course back to the heart, veins unite many times, becoming larger and larger. Veins are thin-walled and only slightly elastic. They are equipped with valves to prevent a backward flow of blood. Veins carry blood high in carbon dioxide and low in oxygen. Exceptions are the pulmonary veins, which carry blood rich in oxygen.

3. *Capillaries.* Connecting the arteries with the veins are the capillaries, a network of microscopic blood vessels. The walls of capillaries are only one cell in thickness. It is through the capillaries that an exchange of materials between the bloodstream and the cells in a tissue takes place. Capillaries join together to form veins.

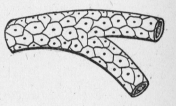

Fig. 58. A Capillary

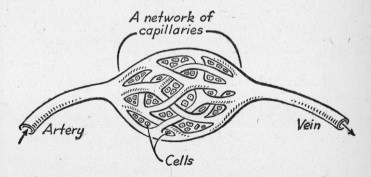

Fig. 59. Capillaries Communicate With Tissue Cells

ARTERIES, VEINS AND CAPILLARIES COMPARED

Arteries	Veins	Capillaries
Leave ventricles, carrying blood away from the heart.	Enter auricles returning blood to the heart.	Connect arteries with veins.
Become smaller and smaller as they get farther from the heart, and finally subdivide into capillaries.	Become larger and larger as they get nearer the heart.	Microscopic and threadlike, and recombine to form veins.
Walls are thick and elastic.	Walls are thin and only slightly elastic.	Walls consist of a single layer of cells.
No valves (except at the point of origin of the large blood vessels at the heart).	Equipped with valves.	No valves.
Carry blood rich in oxygen and low in carbon dioxide. (An exception is the pulmonary artery, which leaves the right ventricle carrying blood to the lungs that is high in carbon dioxide and low in oxygen.)	Carry blood high in carbon dioxide and low in oxygen. (Exceptions are the pulmonary veins, which enter the left auricle carrying blood high in oxygen and low in carbon dioxide.)	Communicate directly with cells in a tissue.

The Pulse. As the heart contracts, blood is pumped in waves, or spurts, through the arterial system. Each spurt is felt as a bounding pressure in all arteries situated near the skin surface. This is called the *pulse*. Normally, the pulse rate is the same as the heart beat.

Blood Pressure. The resistance of the arterial wall to the forward drive of the blood creates what is called *blood pressure*. Normally, it remains within safe limits. Due to certain diseases, however, variations, known as *low* blood pressure or *high* blood pressure, may occur.

The Course of Circulation. In the 17th century, the English physician William Harvey discovered that blood flows through the body in a closed circulatory system. The circulatory system is divided into three pathways, called *circulations,* as follows:

1. *The Pulmonary Circulation.* The blood entering the right auricle is richly laden with foods absorbed from the small intestine. But the blood is deoxygenated, having given up its oxygen to the body cells. The blood flows from the right auricle into the right ventricle, which contracts, sending the blood through the pulmonary artery to the lungs. In the capillaries of the lungs, the blood gives off water and carbon dioxide and absorbs oxygen. The blood, now laden with food and oxygen, passes through the pulmonary veins to the left auricle.

2. *The Systemic Circulation.* Contraction of the left auricle sends blood, rich in food and oxygen, into the left ventricle. Contraction of the left ventricle forces the blood through the aorta. This artery subdivides many times, becoming smaller and smaller, ending in capillaries. Through the capillaries, food and oxygen pass to the cells and waste products are taken away from the cells. Finally, the blood passes through the veins, which become larger and larger,

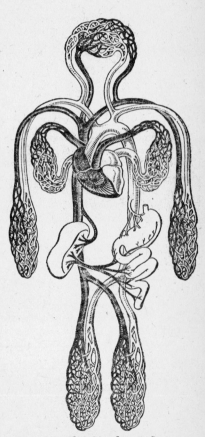

Fig. 60. The Circulatory System

until the largest veins, the *vena cavae,* pour the blood back to the right auricle. The systemic is the largest circulation in the body.

3. *The Portal Circulation.* This is a subdivision of the systemic circulation, whereby the blood circulates through the organs of the digestive system. The digested nutrients which are absorbed into the blood are carried to the capillaries in the liver by means of the *portal vein.* The portal vein, in a sense, acts in the manner of an artery, since it is the supplier of highly nutritious blood to the liver. Excess glucose in the blood is changed to glycogen in the liver and stored there until called for by the body. The blood, rich in nutrients, flows from the liver, by means of the *hepatic vein,* into the lower vena cava, which returns the blood to the heart.

THE BLOOD

The Composition of Blood. Blood is a fluid tissue. It consists of a liquid, the *plasma,* in which float three different kinds of cells: *red corpuscles, white corpuscles, blood platelets.*

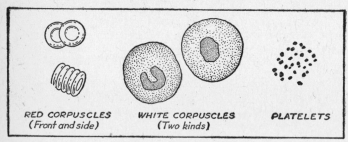

RED CORPUSCLES   WHITE CORPUSCLES   PLATELETS
(*Front and side*)   (*Two kinds*)

Fig. 61. Blood Cells

Plasma. The plasma is a straw-colored liquid, about 90% of which is water. Plasma serves as a medium for transporting the blood corpuscles and platelets. Dissolved in the plasma are:

1. *Digested nutrients*—glucose, amino acids, fatty acids and glycerol absorbed from the small intestine, or from storage places in the body. These digested nutrients are given off by the plasma to the tissue cells, wherever needed, as the blood circulates throughout the body.

2. *Wastes*—carbon dioxide, water, urea and uric acid given off by tissue cells and carried in the plasma to organs of excretion.

3. *Antibodies*—substances manufactured by the cells of the body to counteract germs, or poisons produced by germs.

4. *Hormones*—chemicals secreted by the ductless glands and carried by the plasma to certain organs for regulation of the body activities.

5. *Fibrinogen*—a protein material which is necessary in the formation of a clot in case of bleeding.

6. *Vitamins*—non-energy nutrients transported in the plasma to all tissues of the body to prevent certain diseases.

7. *Mineral salts*—inorganic materials for building tissue and controlling body processes.

Red Corpuscles. The red blood cells, or red corpuscles, are disc-shaped cells produced in the red marrow of bones. Red corpuscles are so tiny that there may be as many as five million in a drop of blood. Mature red corpuscles are the only cells in the human body without nuclei. The chief function of the red corpuscles is to carry oxygen to all cells of the body. This is accomplished by the red pigment, *hemoglobin,* an iron compound present in the red blood cells. Hemoglobin unites readily with oxygen as the blood flows through the capillaries of the lungs. The hemoglobin releases the oxygen as the blood circulates among the various tissues of the body. Red corpuscles wear out and are then destroyed in the liver and spleen.

In unusual cases, a person's blood may contain too few red corpuscles, or insufficient hemoglobin. Such a condition is called *anemia.* An anemic person looks pale and tires easily. A diet rich in iron often helps those who suffer from iron deficiency anemias.

White Corpuscles. The white blood cells, or white corpuscles, are produced in bone marrow and in lymph nodes (page 152). The white corpuscles have one or more nuclei, and are much larger cells than the red corpuscles, but less numerous. The ratio may be one white cell to as many as a thousand red cells.

The chief function of certain white corpuscles, called *phagocytes,* is to destroy bacteria that invade the body. Resembling tiny amebas, the phagocytes crawl about in the bloodstream, sometimes squeezing through the thin walls of capillaries to migrate among the tissue cells. There the phagocytes engulf not only the bacteria, but also broken-down tissue.

If the bone marrow produces an extraordinary number of white cells in proportion to the number of red cells, that person is suffering from *leukemia.* This disease, commonly called "cancer of the blood," is usually fatal.

Blood Platelets. The platelets are smaller cells than the red or white blood cells. The functions of the blood platelets have not yet been definitely determined. It is believed, however, that they take part in the clotting of blood, a process by which the flow of blood from a cut is checked as follows:

Where bleeding occurs, the platelets disintegrate and the substances liberated in the breakdown go through a complex chemical process. Ultimately, the blood protein, *fibrinogen*, is transformed into *fibrin*. The fibrin forms a mesh network which entangles the blood components, thus forming a *clot*. The clot seals the wound.

In certain cases of abnormally heavy bleeding, Vitamin K is administered to assist in clotting.

There are some people whose blood will not clot sufficiently to stop the flow of blood from even a minor cut. Such persons are called "bleeders." One type of bleeder suffers from a hereditary disease known as *hemophilia*. It is found chiefly in men and transmitted through women to male offspring.

Blood Transfusions. In case of serious bleeding (a condition called *hemorrhage*), or certain diseases (such as anemia), the patient is given a *transfusion*. Blood is transferred from the body of a healthy person (called the *donor*) to the body of the sick person (the *recipient*). However, the recipient cannot accept blood from any willing donor. The donor's blood and the recipient's blood must agree (be compatible) as to type and Rh factor, as explained below.

1. *Blood Types.* There are four blood types: AB, A, B, O. In a transfusion, it is advisable that a person receive blood of his own type. However, in an emergency, O type blood may be given in place of any of the other types. Type O is called the "universal donor," because it may be given not only to O, but also to any other type person. A person having AB is known as the "universal recipient," because he can be given not only his own type, but in an emergency any of the other types. A person having O type blood must be given O only.

COMPATIBLE BLOOD TYPES

AB—may receive from all four types—the "universal recipient"
  A—may receive A or O
  B—may receive B or O
  O $\begin{cases} \text{may } give \text{ to all four types—the "universal donor"} \\ \text{may } receive \text{ O only} \end{cases}$

In a transfusion, a person of A cannot be given B; B cannot be given A; O cannot be given A, B or AB. Blood types that cannot be used in combination are said to be *incompatible*. A mixture of incompatible types may bring fatal results to the recipient. The red corpuscles clump together (*agglutinate*), causing a clogging of blood in the blood vessels, especially in the microscopic capillaries.

Blood type is an inherited characteristic and remains unchanged for the life of an individual. The blood types are not representative of different kinds of people. The same blood groups are found among all peoples, regardless of race or color.

2. *Rh Factor.* The Rh factor is a complex chemical substance found in the red corpuscles of most people. In this country, about 85% of the people have this factor and are called Rh *positive*. The remaining 15% whose blood cells lack this factor are Rh *negative*. For a successful blood transfusion, both the donor and the recipient must have the same Rh.

If an Rh negative patient receives a transfusion of Rh positive blood, the recipient's body produces substances, called *antibodies,* which destroy the red corpuscles containing the Rh factor that has been transfused. The first such transfusion may not prove serious, but a second or a third may be fatal.

The Rh factor is also a consideration in pregnancy. For childbearing, both parents should have the same Rh. If the woman is Rh negative and the man Rh positive, the woman's blood builds up antibodies which destroy the embryo's red corpuscles. This may not occur in the first-born child, but it may in the second or third child.

To avoid fatal consequences, a pregnant woman's blood is tested to determine her Rh. If her blood is Rh negative, her husband's blood is then tested. If his Rh is also negative, no complications due to Rh will be encountered. But if his blood is Rh positive, then upon the birth of the child, the child is immediately given transfusions.

Blood Banks. For emergency use, hospitals store blood in a refrigerated room, called a *blood bank*. It may be *whole* blood, or *plasma*. In the case of whole blood, a chemical is added so as to prevent clotting of the blood from taking place in the bottle. Both kinds of blood serve somewhat different purposes for transfusion. Both, however, are used in treating cases of shock. Whole blood must be kept separated by types; but plasma can be *pooled*, or mixed. Typing of plasma is not necessary because it does not contain red corpuscles, the part of the blood possessing the substances that determine blood groups and Rh factor.

During World War II, blood plasma was dried and packaged in airtight containers for easy transportation to our fighting forces all over the world. In an emergency, the dried plasma was mixed with sterile distilled water and used in cases of hemorrhage and shock. Having blood plasma on hand ready for immediate use saved the lives of countless thousands of people.

THE LYMPH SYSTEM

Lymph. Lymph is the fluid substance found within the lymph channels of the body. Lymph surrounds every body cell. It is the fluid in a "water blister." Before lymph fluid enters the lymph vessels, it is known as *tissue fluid*. Tissue fluid is actually blood plasma without most of the solid substances found in blood plasma. Also in the tissue fluid are the white corpuscles which have passed through the capillaries to devour bacteria. Tissue fluid carries some nourishment to the cells and carries away some cell wastes by means of the lymph vessels.

Lymph Vessels. The lymph vessels, or *lymphatics* as they are also called, start in the tissues as tiny tubes. They become larger and larger along their course to the heart. Finally, two large ducts are formed which terminate in one of the large veins near the heart. In this manner, the lymph again becomes a portion of the blood plasma.

A very small portion of the lymph returns immediately to the blood by way of the capillaries instead of entering the lymph system.

The larger lymph vessels have valves to prevent the backward flow of lymph.

In the center of each intestinal villus is a lymph vessel, the *lacteal,* which absorbs digested fats. (See Fig. 51 on page 124.) By way of the lymph system, digested fats reach the bloodstream.

Lymph Nodes. At frequent intervals along the lymph vessels are spongy structures called *lymph nodes,* or *lymph glands.* These nodes contain countless white corpuscles, which serve to purify the lymph by destroying bacteria. In case of an infection, the lymph nodes enlarge, due to the increased number of lymph cells that have formed to destroy the bacteria. In this condition, the nodes are felt as tender "swollen glands." The tonsils and adenoids are lymph nodes. When they become diseased, they have to be removed.

Hygiene of the Circulatory System:

1. *Get sufficient rest.* A proper amount of rest takes strain off the circulatory system, especially the heart. It should be noted that heart disease is the leading cause of death.

2. *Take a moderate amount of exercise.* Proper exercise is beneficial to the circulatory system. The amount of exercise considered "moderate" depends upon the individual's age, sex and physical condition. Overexercise is harmful to the heart.

3. *Eat a balanced diet.* A correct diet will do much toward keeping the circulatory system in a healthy condition.

4. *Avoid the use of tobacco and alcohol.* These drugs should be avoided, particularly during the years of a person's growth. Damaged blood vessels, high blood pressure, and heart disease are among the results of overindulgence in tobacco and alcohol.

5. *Have an annual physical examination.* Diseases of the heart and blood vessels can be successfully treated when detected in their early stages.

Completion Questions

1. _____ brings food and oxygen to all the cells and removes their wastes.
2. The thick-walled heart chambers are the _____.
3. The heart chamber that pumps blood to all parts of the body is the _____.
4. The _____ purify the blood as the blood flows from the right side to the left side of the heart.
5. 72 times per minute is the average normal heart _____.
6. The _____ is the largest artery in the body.
7. When the blood returns from the tissues, it flows from capillaries into _____.
8. The expansion felt in the artery located in the wrist is called the _____.
9. The blood pathway from the right ventricle to the lungs, and then back to the left auricle, is the _____ circulation.
10. The branch of the systemic circulation, in which the blood carries digested nutrients from the small intestine to the heart, is the _____ circulation.
11. The liquid portion of the blood is called _____.

12. In the capillaries of the lungs, _____ combines with the hemoglobin of the red corpuscles.
13. White corpuscles leave the bloodstream through the walls of the _____.
14. Fibrinogen helps to bring about the _____ of blood.
15. The fluid that surrounds the cells of the body is called _____.

Multiple-Choice Questions

1. The chamber of the heart which pumps oxygenated blood to all parts of the body is the (1) left auricle (2) right ventricle (3) right auricle (4) left ventricle.
2. The heart (1) never rests (2) rests while you sleep (3) rests between beats (4) rests during periods of stress.
3. The blood system of man is (1) closed (2) open (3) open in places (4) open at one end.
4. A blood vessel which carries deoxygenated blood is the (1) aorta (2) pulmonary artery (3) hepatic artery (4) pulmonary vein.
5. The backward flow of blood in the veins is prevented by (1) muscles (2) valves (3) the heart beat (4) lymphatics.
6. Digested food is carried in the blood by the (1) blood platelets (2) plasma (3) red corpuscles (4) white corpuscles.
7. The human red corpuscle has (1) no nucleus (2) one nucleus (3) several nuclei.
8. Worn-out red blood cells are decomposed in the (1) heart (2) lungs (3) kidneys (4) liver.
9. A defense of the body against bacteria is (1) hemoglobin (2) phagocytes (3) red blood cells (4) blood platelets.
10. In transfusions, the blood must be compatible not only in blood type, but also in (1) number of red cells (2) Rh factor (3) number of white cells (4) race of donor and recipient.
11. The disease hemophilia is associated with (1) the bone structure (2) blood clotting (3) the structure of nervous tissue (4) the formation of red corpuscles.
12. The person who can give blood to any other person but can receive only his own type blood, has blood type (1) A (2) O (3) AB (4) B.
13. The liquid that bathes every cell and acts as a medium of exchange is (1) cell sap (2) fibrinogen (3) lymph (4) fibrin.
14. Digested fats are absorbed into the lymph system through the (1) capillaries (2) lacteals (3) marrow (4) platelets.

15. "Swollen glands" means an enlargement of the (1) lymph nodes (2) heart valves (3) vena cavae (4) portal vein.

Essay Questions

1. Certain changes occur in the blood as it flows through the tissue cells.
   a. Name (1) two substances brought by the blood to all cells, (2) two substances taken by the blood from all cells.
   b. For each of the following organs, name two changes in the blood due to the special function of the organ: kidney, liver, lungs, small intestine.

2. a. Describe the structure and give one function of (1) capillaries, (2) red blood cells.
   b. Explain how each of the following protects the human body: (1) fibrinogen, (2) lymph nodes.
   c. One difference between the flow of blood in arteries and that in veins is the direction of flow. State two other differences and give a reason for each difference.

3. a. Write a brief explanation of each of the following:
      (1) Blood does not flow backward in arteries.
      (2) Rapid destruction of red blood cells causes a decrease in energy.
      (3) Nosebleed occurs at unusually high altitudes.
   b. Tell how each of the following is carried in the blood: antibodies, hormones, oxygen, glucose.

4. a. The wall of the right ventricle of the normal heart is thinner than the wall of the left ventricle. Explain how the thickness of the wall is related to the work that each ventricle does.
   b. Tell why some veins contain blood carrying large amounts of oxygen and some arteries contain blood carrying little oxygen.

5. a. Explain how faster heartbeat makes it possible for a person to continue exercising vigorously.
   b. Describe the path that digested fat takes from the small intestine to the bloodstream.

6. The American Red Cross needs blood donations to keep up its supply of plasma.
   a. State two conditions that may require the use of plasma.
   b. Name two parts of the blood that are removed before the plasma is stored for future use.
   c. Name two substances dissolved in the plasma.

Chapter XIII

EXCRETION IN MAN

What Is Excretion? Cellular activity produces wastes in the body. The wastes must be removed. If allowed to accumulate, they would become poisonous. The process of eliminating wastes from the body is called *excretion*. Wastes formed in living cells are picked up by the plasma of the blood and delivered to organs of excretion.

Origin of the Wastes. The metabolism of the end products of digestion (namely, glucose, fatty acids and amino acids) produces carbon dioxide and water as wastes. In addition to these wastes, metabolism of the amino acids produces *nitrogenous wastes*—urea, uric acid, and other nitrogen compounds. Mineral salts and water in excess of the body's needs must also be excreted.

The Organs of Excretion. The *lungs*, the *skin* and the *kidneys* are the organs of excretion of cellular wastes. The *large intestine* and the *liver* also play a vital role in ridding the body of wastes. However, since the wastes they eliminate are *not* the products of metabolism, the large intestine and the liver are not generally considered to be true excretory organs.

The Lungs. As digested foods undergo oxidation in the cells, energy is released and carbon dioxide and water are given off. These wastes diffuse from the tissues into the bloodstream. The blood transports the carbon dioxide and water to the lungs, where the wastes are excreted with the exhaled air as gases.

SUMMARY OF THE METABOLISM OF THE NUTRIENTS

	Nutrients	End Products	Results of Metabolism	Wastes of Metabolism	Organs of Excretion
ENERGY	carbohydrates	glucose	energy release	carbon dioxide and water	lungs — kidneys and skin
ENERGY	fats	fatty acids and glycerol	energy release	carbon dioxide and water	lungs — kidneys and skin
ENERGY	proteins	amino acids	energy release, and the building and repair of protoplasm	carbon dioxide and water and nitrogenous wastes	lungs — kidneys and skin — kidneys and skin
NON-ENERGY	mineral salts		regulate body activities, and build protoplasm	excess salts (those not used by the body)	kidneys and skin
NON-ENERGY	water		maintains body temperature; a solvent for digested foods and wastes; for protoplasm	excess water (that not used by the body)	lungs, kidneys and skin

The Skin. The waste excreted through the skin is called *perspiration*, or *sweat*. Perspiration consists mainly of water, along with some salts and urea. These wastes diffuse from capillaries into *sweat glands*. The perspiration is conducted up the tubular sweat glands from the origin, the *dermis*, through the *epidermis* to tiny openings on the surface of the skin, called *pores*. As perspiration reaches the surface of the skin, the water evaporates, leaving the salts on the skin.

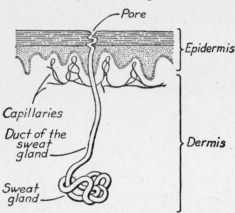

Fig. 62. The Skin As an Excretory Organ

Perspiration. The release of energy in cells warms the body, and thus causes perspiration. Normally, perspiration is not noticeable, except perhaps on the palms of the hands and under the armpits. In hot weather, or when under excitement, or when engaging in vigorous exercise or work, perspiration becomes more apparent. This condition is due to the fact that (1) the rate of oxidation has increased, (2) the quantity of wastes in the blood has increased, and (3) the activity of the sweat glands has increased.

The evaporation of perspiration from the skin requires a certain amount of heat. This heat comes from the body. As heat is removed for the process of perspiration, the body is cooled. Thus, by its cooling effect, perspiration helps to regulate body temperature.

When perspiration is excessive, too much salts are excreted and must be replaced by the intake of salt tablets.

The Kidneys. The two bean-shaped kidneys are each about four inches long, lying in the "small of the back," one on either side of the spinal column. Wastes in the blood diffuse from capillaries inside the kidneys to tiny tube-like structures, called *tubules*. The tubules filter out certain useful substances, such as glucose and water, and return them to the bloodstream. The wastes form into *urine*, which is excess water containing nitrogenous wastes and salts. Tubes, called *ureters* (one from each kidney), carry the urine to the *bladder* for temporary storage. From the bladder, the urine passes out of the body through another tube, the *urethra*.

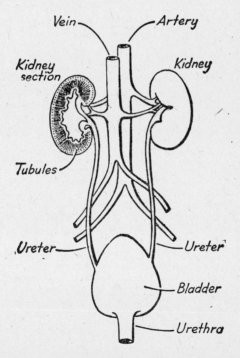

Fig. 63. The Kidneys

The Liver. Amino acids that were not used by the cells for energy release, or for repairing or building new protoplasm, are harmful nitrogenous wastes. The liver breaks down these poisonous wastes into the less harmful urea and uric acid. These are then carried by the blood to the kidneys, and eliminated in the urine.

Worn-out red cells are taken from the blood by the liver and decomposed to form part of bile. The liver secretes the bile into the small intestine for the emulsification of fats. The bile then flows into the large intestine for elimination.

The Large Intestine. Food matter, such as cellulose and cartilage, pass through the alimentary canal without being digested. These wastes empty into the large intestine. There, they mix with the bile and are excreted through the rectum as bulk.

Hygiene of the Excretory System:

1. *Drink plenty of water.* Water is necessary not only for digestion, for building and maintaining protoplasm, and as a part of blood plasma, but also to aid the body in excreting wastes. To maintain the body's needs, a minimum of about eight glasses of water, or some other liquids, should be drunk. This water replaces the water lost by the body through excretion.

Water aids the excretory process by (*a*) flushing the kidneys, thus diluting the poisonous nitrogenous wastes and then washing them away, (*b*) giving a soft consistency to the bulk excreted by the large intestine, thus preventing constipation, and (*c*) forming perspiration, which cleanses the sweat glands and carries away wastes.

2. *Move your bowels daily.* Daily bowel movements are necessary in order to rid the body of wastes. Accumulated wastes mildly poison the body and reduce the body's efficiency. If approximately thirty-six hours have elapsed without having had a bowel movement, a mild laxative should be taken.

3. *Wash the skin with soap and water, and take daily baths.* The pores are thus kept open, permitting the sweat glands to excrete perspiration freely.

Completion Questions

1. _____ is the process by which the body rids itself of wastes.

2. Wastes are transported from the cells to organs of elimination by the _____.

3. A waste product, other than water, given off by every living cell is _____.

4. Urea is a waste material containing the element _____.

5. The organs that excrete cellular wastes are the lungs, the kidneys and the _____.

6. Waste products given off by the lungs are carbon dioxide and _____.

7. The glands that eliminate wastes through the skin are the _____ glands.

8. The waste product eliminated by the kidneys which consists of water, nitrogenous wastes and salts is called _____.

9. Excess amino acids are broken down into urea and uric acid by the _____.

10. Bile is excreted from the body by the _____.

Multiple-Choice Questions

1. Two non-energy nutrients needed by the body, but which are excreted when present in excess, are water and (1) glucose (2) mineral salts (3) urea (4) bile.

2. Two organs which excrete wastes *not* produced by metabolism are the large intestine and the (1) skin (2) lungs (3) liver (4) kidneys.

3. An organ of the human body that excretes urea is the (1) skin (2) anus (3) large intestine (4) lungs.

4. The chief value of perspiration is that it (1) eliminates body odors (2) opens the pores (3) reduces weight (4) regulates body temperature.

5. Urea is removed from the blood as it goes through the (1) bladder (2) pancreas (3) spleen (4) kidneys.

6. The tubes which connect the kidneys with the bladder are known as (1) tubules (2) urethra (3) ureters (4) dermis.

7. Urine is stored in an organ called the (1) diaphragm (2) kidney (3) bladder (4) lung.

8. Excess amino acids are made less poisonous by the action of the (1) skin (2) lungs (3) kidneys (4) liver.

9. The organ which decomposes worn-out red corpuscles is the (1) liver (2) kidneys (3) skin (4) lungs.

10. The indigestible part of food consists mainly of cartilage and (1) amino acids (2) fatty acids (3) cellulose (4) glucose.

Modified True-False Questions

1. Some wastes are produced in the body as the result of *cell metabolism.*
2. The organs concerned chiefly with excreting carbon dioxide are the *kidneys.*
3. The *sweat glands* help regulate the temperature of the human body.
4. An increase in the amount of body perspiration results from *a decrease* in the rate of oxidation.
5. Urine leaves the body through a tube called the *urethra.*

Essay Questions

1. *a.* State three wastes produced in the body as a result of cellular activity.
   b. Starting with the end product of digestion, describe how each waste in part *a* was formed.

2. *a.* Tell how perspiration helps to regulate body temperature.
   b. Explain why a person cannot survive the loss of both kidneys.

3. *a.* Briefly describe two ways by which small amounts of nitrogenous wastes, produced in muscle cells, may be excreted by the body.
   b. Compare the process of excretion of water vapor in plants with that in man.
   c. Although the kidneys remove certain substances from the blood, they also return useful materials to it. Explain.

Chapter XIV

CHEMICAL COORDINATION IN MAN

Duct Glands. In the chapter on "Nutrition" (pages 120-122), we saw how specialized cells, called *glands*, aid in the process of digestion. For example, the *salivary glands* secrete saliva which contains ptyalin, the enzyme that begins the digestion of starch. Also, the *gastric glands* secrete gastric juice which contains pepsin and rennin, the enzymes that digest proteins. Other glands that play a part in the digestion of foods are the *pancreas*, the *liver* and the *intestinal glands*.

The digestive glands are *duct glands*. Duct glands (1) secrete *enzymes*, and (2) the secretions pass through tubes, or *ducts*, from the glands to the organs where the enzymes are needed for digestion.

Ductless Glands. In addition to the duct glands discussed above, the body contains another type of glands, called the *ductless glands*. They are also known as *endocrine glands*. Ductless glands (1) secrete *hormones*, and (2) the secretions pass from the glands directly into the blood, which circulates the hormones throughout the body.

The hormones are called "chemical messengers" because they (1) *regulate* the activities of organs, (2) *stimulate* the organs into activity, and (3) *coordinate* the activities of all organs. As long as the glands secrete the proper quantities of hormones, the organ systems will function in perfect harmony. But should a gland secrete too little or too much hormone, then one or more organs of the body will be affected, and the harmony among all the organ systems will be disturbed.

DUCT AND DUCTLESS GLANDS COMPARED

Type of Gland	Secretion	Means of Passage	Purpose
duct	enzymes	by tube from gland to organ	digest foods to usable end products
ductless	hormones	by diffusion from gland to blood to organ	regulate, stimulate, coordinate activities of organs

163

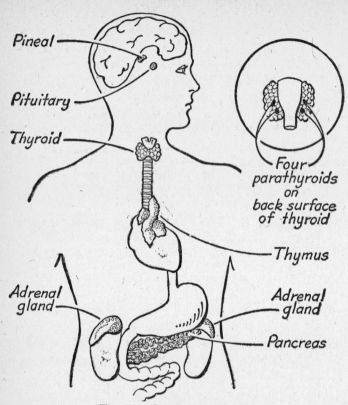

Fig. 64. The Ductless Glands

The Endocrine System. The ductless glands in man are the *thyroid gland, parathyroid glands, adrenal glands, pituitary gland, pancreas, small intestine, sex glands, thymus gland* and *pineal gland.*

The Thyroid Gland. The thyroid gland is located in front of the trachea, at the base of the neck. It consists of two connected lobes. The thyroid gland secretes *thyroxin,* a hormone containing about 65% iodine. Thyroxin (1) regulates the rate at which cells oxidize foods, and (2) influences physical and mental growth.

Thyroid Diseases. If there is a deficiency of iodine in the diet, or if the thyroid gland secretes too much or too little thyroxin, then a number of diseases may result, as follows:

1. *Simple Goiter.* Iodine must be present in the diet in order for the thyroid gland to manufacture thyroxin. An iodine deficiency results in a condition known as simple goiter. This disease is characterized by a swelling of the thyroid gland, sometimes to a very large size. Simple goiter may be prevented by (*a*) the intake of salt-water sea food, (*b*) the use of iodized table salt, or (*c*) the drinking of water to which the city has added iodine. Especially important are the above dietary measures to people living in certain inland areas, such as the Great Lakes region. There, a deficiency of iodine exists in the soil, in the water, and in the fresh-water fish.

2. *Exophthalmic Goiter.* Oversecretion of thyroxin raises the body's rate of metabolism. Restlessness, nervousness and loss of weight are some of the symptoms of an overactive thyroid. Advanced cases develop into a condition known as exophthalmic goiter. This disease is characterized by bulging eyes, an enlarged thyroid, excessive sweating, and tremors of the hands. The disease may be treated by (*a*) destroying some of the cells of the gland by X-rays, (*b*) removing all or part of the gland surgically, or (*c*) using *radioactive iodine.* The latter is a recently developed method for treating overactivity of the thyroid gland, as well as cancer of the gland. As the radioactive iodine disintegrates, rays are given off that destroy some of the thyroid cells.

3. *Cretinism.* A marked undersecretion of thyroxin reduces the body's rate of metabolism. This condition in an infant is called cretinism. A *cretin* is abnormally small in size; he is also called a *dwarf.* The abdomen protrudes, and the skin is rough and scaly. A cretin's intelligence rarely exceeds that of a normal five-year-old child.

If cretinism is recognized and treated in its early stages, the cretin's condition may be greatly improved, possibly even cured. Treatment consists of administering thyroid extract obtained from the thyroid glands of cows and sheep, or synthetic thyroxin prepared in the laboratory. Medication continues as long as the thyroid remains underactive.

4. *Myxedema.* In an adult, mild undersecretion of thyroxin causes obesity. But extreme undersecretion in an adult results in the disease called myxedema. The disease causes a puffing of the eyes, loss of hair on the head, physical weakness, mental dullness, and obesity. Sufferers are treated with thyroid extract.

The Parathyroid Glands. Embedded on the back surface of the thyroid gland are four parathyroid glands. Two parathyroid glands are situated on each thyroid lobe. The parathyroids secrete *parathormone*. This hormone regulates the amount of calcium in the blood. Parathormone affects bones, muscles and nerves, because the growth and function of these structures require calcium.

Underactive parathyroid glands secrete too little parathormone, thus reducing the amount of calcium in the blood. Disease of the parathyroid glands, or the absence of these glands from the body, causes violent muscular spasms. This disease, known as *tetany*, is treated by means of calcium or parathormone.

Overactive parathyroid glands secrete too much parathormone. This condition weakens bones and muscles.

The Adrenal Glands. On top of each kidney is an adrenal gland. The inner region of the two adrenal glands is called the *medulla*. The outer area is called the *cortex*.

1. *The Adrenal Medulla.* The medulla secretes the hormone called *adrenalin* (or *adrenin*). Adrenalin regulates body activity. The quantity of adrenalin produced in the body depends upon the body's need for this hormone. In times of sudden anger or sudden fright, or in any emergency, the medulla increases its secretion of adrenalin. The hormone stimulates the liver to release increased amounts of glucose to the bloodstream. The glucose provides extra energy for the cells. The adrenalin also stimulates the heart to beat faster and stronger. Consequently, the blood carries additional oxygen and glucose to the cells at a faster rate. Furthermore, the adrenalin increases the rate of breathing to facilitate the exchange of gases.

Adrenalin is used by physicians (a) to stop excessive bleeding; (b) in surgical operations to raise the patient's blood pressure; (c) in asthma sufferers, to relieve an attack by opening up the bronchial tubes; and (d) to stimulate a failing heart.

2. *The Adrenal Cortex.* The cortex secretes the hormones *cortin* and *cortisone*. The adrenal cortex is stimulated to secrete its hormones, particularly cortisone, by *ACTH*. This hormone is a secretion of the pituitary gland.

Cortin regulates the amount of sodium and potassium in the blood. Undersecretion of cortin brings on *Addison's disease*. Symptoms are low blood pressure, muscular weakness, and bronzed skin. Extracts of cortin are administered to treat this disease.

Cortisone is necessary for the well-being of the body. Sufferers of rheumatic fever, arthritis and certain allergies are given great relief by the administration of cortisone extracted from the glands of cattle and sheep. Synthetic preparations are also used. ACTH is sometimes used in place of cortisone, especially in the treatment of arthritis and certain allergies.

The Pituitary Gland. Attached to the base of the brain is the *pituitary gland.* It consists of two lobes:

1. *The Anterior Lobe.* The front lobe is called the anterior lobe. It secretes many hormones. One hormone regulates the growth of bones. Another hormone regulates the secretion of milk by the mammary glands. Other hormones produced by the anterior lobe affect the activities of *all* the other ductless glands. For this reason, the pituitary is often referred to as "the master gland."

2. *The Posterior Lobe.* The back lobe of the pituitary gland is called the posterior lobe. This lobe secretes several hormones which control body activities. One hormone regulates the functioning of the kidneys. Thus, the amount of water in the blood is controlled. Another hormone produced by the posterior lobe regulates blood pressure.

Effects of Undersecretion and Oversecretion of the Growth Hormone. Undersecretion of the growth hormone retards the development of the long bones in the body. Undersecretion in a child causes *dwarfism.* This type of dwarf has a well-proportioned body, and possesses average intelligence. In these respects, he is quite different from the dwarf resulting from a thyroxin deficiency. The latter type of dwarf has a misshapen body and very low intelligence.

Oversecretion of the growth hormone causes excessive bone growth. *Gigantism* results if the individual is still in the growing stage. Some pituitary giants reach a height of from eight to nine feet. If oversecretion occurs in an adult, the bones in the hands, feet and face become excessively large. This condition is known as *acromegaly.*

The Pancreas. Lying just behind and beneath the stomach is the pancreas. This gland is *both* a duct and a ductless gland. Some cells of the pancreas secrete pancreatic juice, which flows through a duct to the small intestine. In the small intestine, the enzymes contained in the pancreatic juice act on foods.

The pancreas contains certain cells, called the *Islands of Langerhans,* which secrete the hormone *insulin.* Since the insulin is poured directly into the bloodstream, the pancreas, in this way, functions as a ductless gland. The Canadian scientist, Frederick G. Banting, was the first person to extract insulin from the pancreas.

Insulin. Normally, sugar in the blood is being drawn upon by cells for oxidation. The rest of the sugar is taken from the blood by the liver and stored as glycogen. The hormone insulin regulates both of these functions of oxidation and storage of sugar. If the pancreas secretes a normal amount of insulin, the sugar level in the blood is maintained properly. But if the pancreas secretes too little insulin, then the sugar level of the blood becomes too high. As the blood flows through the kidneys, the excess sugar passes through the filter and appears in the urine. Thus, the energy-giving sugar, instead of being used by the body, is excreted.

This abnormal condition resulting from an undersecretion of insulin is called *diabetes.* One sympton is an excessive thirst.

Diabetes is treated by injections of insulin extracted from the pancreas of animals. The diabetic is thus supplied with the hormone that his own body does not manufacture sufficiently. Insulin injections are not a cure; they must be continued for life. Diabetics carefully follow a diet that regulates the intake of carbohydrates.

The Lining of the Small Intestine. The initial few feet of the small intestine contain cells that secrete the hormone *secretin.* The secretion takes place as food from the stomach enters the small intestine. Secretin is carried by the blood to the pancreas, where the secretin stimulates the pancreas to give off pancreatic juice.

The Sex Glands (Gonads). The sex glands are also known as *gonads.* The gonads secrete a number of hormones which influence a person's *secondary sexual characteristics.* These are the outward physical traits by which we can distinguish between the male and the female sexes of a species. Some of these characteristics in humans are the pitch of the voice, the muscular development of the body, and the distribution of hair on the face and chest. In other animals, some distinguishable characteristics are the bright plumage of the male peacock, the presence of antlers on the male deer (the stag), and the comb and the spurs on the male rooster.

The Thymus and Pineal Glands. The thymus and pineal are considered ductless glands, but little is known about them.

The *thymus* gland lies in the upper part of the chest. The gland is largest at birth, and remains large throughout adolescence. Afterward, the thymus gland becomes smaller, and practically disappears in later life. It is therefore believed that the thymus affects physical growth and sexual development.

The *pineal* gland lies at the base and to the rear of the brain. So far, the function of the pineal gland is unknown.

Completion Questions

1. Enzymes are secreted by (*duct, ductless*) _____ glands.
2. Ductless glands are sometimes called _____ glands.
3. The chemical substances secreted by the ductless glands are called _____.
4. The secretion of a ductless gland is carried throughout the body by the _____.
5. Because they coordinate the activities of all organs, hormones are also known as _____.
6. _____ is the hormone which regulates the metabolism of the body.
7. A deficiency of iodine in water and food may cause a disorder of the _____ gland.
8. An enlargement of the thyroid gland is known as _____.
9. Myxedema is a disease in an adult which results from an under-secretion of _____.
10. Overactivity of the thyroid gland is being treated by the use of the recently discovered chemical called radioactive _____.
11. The proper amount of calcium in the blood is maintained by a hormone secreted by the _____ glands.
12. Excitement causes a sudden increase in secretion of the _____ glands.
13. A physician can cause a person's heart to beat faster by inject-ing a very dilute solution of the hormone _____ into the heart tissue.
14. A hormone secreted by the adrenal glands which is used to treat arthritis is _____.
15. The "master gland" of the body is the _____.
16. ACTH is a hormone secreted by the _____ gland.
17. A gland found below the stomach which secretes enzymes and a hormone is the _____.
18. The hormone _____ regulates the amount of sugar in the blood.
19. The hormone _____ causes the pancreas to secrete pan-creatic juice.
20. The outward traits by which we can distinguish the sexes are known as _____.

Multiple-Choice Questions

1. Endocrine glands produce (1) chyme (2) endoplasm (3) hor-mones (4) serums.

2. Secretions of the ductless glands pass (1) into tubes or ducts (2) directly into the blood (3) directly into the organs where they are used (4) out of the body.
3. Hormones are chemical substances which (1) carry on digestion (2) fight bacteria (3) stimulate the activity of organs (4) prevent deficiency diseases.
4. Thyroxin contains a high percentage of (1) calcium (2) hemoglobin (3) iodine (4) iron.
5. Normal mentality in children depends on a sufficient secretion of (1) adrenalin (2) thyroxin (3) insulin (4) secretin.
6. Inactivity of the thyroid gland from infancy may produce a condition known as (1) diabetes (2) beriberi (3) cretinism (4) Addison's disease.
7. Weakened bones and muscles result from an oversecretion of the (1) thyroid (2) adrenals (3) pancreas (4) parathyroid.
8. The body is stimulated to unusual activity by increased secretion from the (1) pancreas (2) adrenal glands (3) thyroid gland (4) thymus gland.
9. The hormone which causes the liver to release an increased amount of glucose into the blood is (1) thyroxin (2) parathormone (3) adrenalin (4) the growth hormone.
10. The concentration of sodium and potassium in the blood is controlled by (1) adrenin (2) cortin (3) insulin (4) secretin.
11. Growth of the long bones of the body is most directly controlled by secretion from the (1) adrenal (2) pancreatic (3) pituitary (4) thyroid   gland(s).
12. An oversecretion of the pituitary gland in the adult may lead to a condition known as (1) gigantism (2) dwarfism (3) acromegaly (4) goiter.
13. A hormone that enables the body to store and oxidize sugar is (1) thyroxin (2) insulin (3) adrenalin (4) secretin.
14. Diabetes is caused by the improper functioning of the (1) parathyroids (2) thyroid (3) pancreas (4) adrenals.
15. (1) Hooke (2) Brown (3) Schleiden and Schwann (4) Banting   discovered the hormone insulin, which is used in treating diabetes.

Essay Questions

1. Ductless glands produce secretions that aid in coordinating the activities of body organs.
   a. State two ways in which a ductless gland differs from a digestive gland.

    b. Give two differences between an enzyme and a hormone.

    c. The normal functioning of the organ systems of man is said to depend on the activity of the endocrines. Explain the meaning of this statement.

2. *a.* Describe three changes that will take place in a person whose thyroid gland becomes overactive.

    b. Explain why thyroid extract is often prescribed for a person who is excessively overweight.

    c. There are fewer cases of simple goiter in the world today than there were many years ago. Describe three ways being used today to prevent this disease.

    d. Research in atomic energy has added many new chemicals which are being used by physicians to treat diseases. Name one such chemical being used to treat a disorder of the thyroid, and explain how this chemical reduces the activity of the thyroid.

3. *a.* Name a body process that will not go on normally if the parathyroid fails to function properly.

    b. Describe the effect of an injection of adrenalin on the heartbeat and on the distribution of blood in the body.

    c. Cortisone is a recently discovered hormone secreted by the outer region of the adrenal glands. Name two diseases which are treated with cortisone.

4. *a.* The pituitary gland is frequently referred to as "the master gland" of the body. Explain why.

    b. Give two differences between the pancreas as a gland with a duct and the pancreas as a ductless gland.

    c. How would a biologist answer someone who said that injections of insulin into a diabetic patient result in a permanent cure of the disease?

    d. Explain why a chemical analysis of the urine is used to test for the presence of diabetes.

    e. Give two differences between secretin and secretion.

5. Give a biological explanation of each of the following:

    a. A woman became thin although she ate heartily.

    b. A man swam beyond his usual distance to rescue a child.

    c. A boy grew to a height of seven feet.

    d. The amount of sugar in a patient's blood was reduced by injections of an extract taken from the pancreas of sheep.

    e. Although an individual has sufficient calcium in his diet, his bones become weakened.

Chapter XV

BEHAVIOR

BEHAVIOR IN PLANTS
AND ONE-CELLED ANIMALS

Stimulus and Response. The environment contains many factors to which organisms are sensitive. Living things are sensitive to light, water, gravity, heat. A factor in the environment that affects the life activities of an organism is called a *stimulus*. The way that an organism reacts to a stimulus is called a *response*. For example, a plant responds to light by turning its leaves toward it.

Irritability. The ability of organisms to respond to stimuli is due to the property of protoplasm called *irritability*, or *sensitivity*. This life function must be carried on by every living thing. Survival of an organism depends upon its ability to respond to stimuli. For example, in order to carry out photosynthesis, the green plant *must* turn its leaves toward sunlight for energy, and *must* grow its roots toward moisture in the soil. All the responses that an organism makes to the various stimuli in its environment are called its *behavior*.

Tropisms. Plants and one-celled animals do not have a nervous system. They respond to stimuli by tropisms. A *tropism* is the response of an organism not having a nervous system, or having a very simple one. A tropism is the simplest type of response to a stimulus.

Plants and unicellular animals do not learn how to behave. They will always respond in the same way to the same stimulus. This is because a tropism is an *inborn* reaction, not a learned activity.

Kinds of Tropisms. Tropisms have various names, according to the stimuli causing the response.

172

Names of Tropisms	Stimuli	Nature of Tropisms (Responses by plants and one-celled animals)
phototropism	light	Leaves turn toward light. Ameba and paramecium move away from bright light.
hydrotropism	water	Roots grow toward water.
geotropism	gravity	Roots grow downward toward gravity. Stems grow upward away from gravity.
chemotropism	chemicals	Roots grow toward dissolved minerals in the soil, but away from poisonous materials. Ameba and paramecium move toward some chemicals, such as dissolved food, but away from others, such as strong acids.
thigmotropism	touch	Stems of certain plants, such as bean or ivy, grow around other plants or twist around objects for support. Ameba and paramecium swim away from sharp objects in their path.
thermotropism	heat	Ameba and paramecium move away from regions of high temperature and toward regions of moderate temperature.

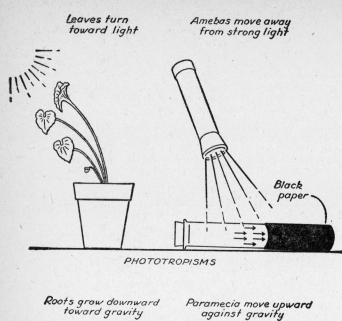

Leaves turn
toward light

Amebas move away
from strong light

Black
paper

PHOTOTROPISMS

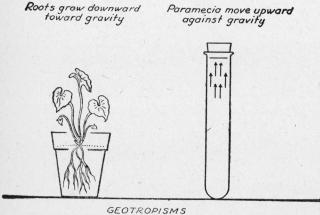

Roots grow downward
toward gravity

Paramecia move upward
against gravity

GEOTROPISMS

Fig. 65. Tropisms

Positive and Negative Tropisms. A *positive* tropism is a response *toward* a stimulus. A *negative* tropism is a response *away from* a stimulus.

Positive Tropisms	Negative Tropisms
Roots grow downward toward gravity. (positive geotropism)	Stems grow upward away from gravity. (negative geotropism)
The euglena moves toward light. (positive phototropism)	The ameba moves away from strong light. (negative phototropism)

How Tropisms Take Place. In one-celled animals, tropisms are *immediate* responses. This is because all animals, even one-celled species, have some means of *locomotion*. The ameba forms pseudopods in its direction of flow. The paramecium propels itself through water by the beating of its cilia. The euglena swims through water by the lashing of its flagellum.

Plants, however, have no means of locomotion. Therefore, plant tropisms are *very slow* responses. In order for leaves to turn toward the sunlight, or for roots to obtain moisture in the soil, the plant must *grow* its structures toward the stimulus.

Plant hormones, called *auxins,* stimulate the growth of those cells in a structure that are reacting to a stimulus. For example, in order for a leaf to turn toward the light, the cells on the dark side of the stem must grow at a more rapid rate than the cells on the light side. The stem bends in the direction of the shorter cells, which face the light. The more rapid growth of the cells on the dark side is believed to be due to the action of the auxins.

BEHAVIOR IN LOWER ANIMALS

What Is a Nervous System? Multicellular animals (with few exceptions) possess special structures for receiving stimuli and making responses. These structures together make up the nervous system of the organism. The functions of the nervous system are (1) to help an animal coordinate its activities, and (2) to permit the animal to respond to stimuli.

Nervous Systems in Lower Animals. As animals rise in classification by phylum, the animals show greater specialization of structure. The better developed the nervous system of an animal, the more varied is its behavior, as illustrated below.

1. *The Sponge.* Scattered over the body of the sponge are some cells which can detect stimuli. These cells transmit *nervous impulses* (or messages) to nearby cells. The response is made, not by the entire body, but by a few neighboring cells that receive the impulse.

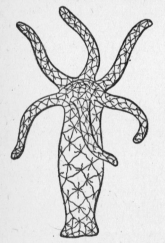

Fig. 66. Nerve Net of the Hydra

2. *The Hydra.* In both body layers of the hydra are special cells for detecting stimuli. These cells are connected by nerve fibers arranged throughout the body in the form of a *nerve net*. The nerve net permits the transfer of nervous impulses throughout the body. Thus, the responses of the hydra are coordinated. For example, if a tentacle of a hydra comes in contact with an object, the hydra rapidly coordinates its entire body by rolling up into a ball.

3. *The Earthworm.* The first phylum of animals having a true nervous system is the annelids. The earthworm has a *simple brain*, a *nerve cord* running the full length of its segmented body, and *nerves* from the nerve cord leading to all parts of the body. (See page 83 for a more complete description of the earthworm's nervous system.)

Sense organs (eyes, ears, nose, etc.) are lacking. However, nerve cells on the entire surface of the body make the earthworm sensitive to such stimuli as light, touch, chemicals, and food. As soon as the nerve cells detect the stimulus, the nervous impulses are carried over the nerve cord to the brain. The earthworm then makes a coordinated response by moving away from bright light, rolling up if touched, and moving toward food.

4. *The Insect.* The nervous system of the insect is similar in plan to that of the earthworm. However, the insect's structures, being more intricate, are capable of more complex activities. Especially significant in the insect are its well developed sense organs.

HUMAN BEHAVIOR

Man's Nervous System. Man has the most highly developed nervous system. Man has special structures, called *receptors,* that receive stimuli. The receptors are the sense organs: the eyes, ears, nose, tongue, skin. When a stimulus is received by a receptor, a reaction, called a *nervous impulse,* is set up. A nervous impulse is believed to be both chemical and electrical in nature. The impulse is carried along a chain of nerves to the brain or to the spinal cord. The brain or spinal cord sends a message to an *effector,* which is either a muscle or a gland, to make the response. All the responses together make up man's behavior.

THE SENSE ORGANS

What Are the Sense Organs? There are five sense organs: the *eye, ear, nose, tongue* and *skin.* The sense organs are the receptors of the nervous system. Nerve cells in the sense organs receive the stimuli and transmit nervous impulses to the brain for interpretation as *sight, sound, odor, taste* and *touch.*

THE EYES

Description of the Eye. The eyes are securely housed in the bony sockets of the skull. Muscles attach the eyes to the sockets, and permit the eyes to be rotated upward, downward and to either side. The *eyeball* is nearly round, its shape being maintained by the presence of fluids. The tear gland secretes a fluid that keeps the surface of the eyeball moist. Dirt and dust are washed from the eyeball by this secretion. The *eyelids,* at the ends of which are the *eyelashes,* move up and down by muscles in the eyelids. The exposed region of the eyeball is protected by the eyelids and eyelashes.

At the front end of the eye, located centrally, is transparent tissue, called the *cornea.* The cornea is the forward bulge of the eyeball. Behind the cornea is the *iris,* in the center of which is a circular opening known as the *pupil.* Immediately behind the pupil is the *lens,* which is a transparent structure held vertically in place by fibers. At the rear of the eyeball is the *retina,* a region of nerve cells sensitive to light. The retina is continuous with the *optic nerve,* which leads to the brain.

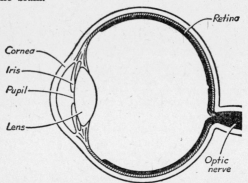

Fig. 67. The Eye

How We See. When we look at an object, the light rays striking the object are reflected to our eyes. The rays pass through the cornea, which is transparent, and through the pupil, which is an opening, and finally through the lens, which is also transparent. The lens bends the rays to form the image on the retina. This sets up nervous impulses that the optic nerve carries to the brain. The brain then interprets the impulses as an image.

How Muscles Adjust the Eye to Light and Distance. As every amateur photographer knows, the amount of light passing through the lens of a camera determines whether or not a picture will be too dark, too light, or just right. The iris of the eye controls the amount of light entering the eyeball. In dim light, the iris relaxes, making the pupil larger to admit more light. In bright light, the iris contracts, making the pupil smaller to admit less light. The muscles that adjust the opening of the pupil work *automatically*, according to the intensity of the light. This human mechanism, therefore, is far more efficient than the most costly camera, which must be adjusted *mechanically* to the conditions of light.

There also are muscles that automatically change the thickness of the lens. To focus distant objects directly on the retina, the lens becomes thinner. To focus nearby objects, the lens becomes thicker. Here, again, the eye is superior to the camera, which must be focused by hand.

Some Common Defects in Vision. Clear vision requires that an image come to a point directly on the retina. This cannot be achieved by a person having a structural defect of the eye. He must wear eyeglasses to correct the defect, as follows:

1. *Nearsightedness.* A person may have an eyeball longer than normal, or a lens too convex. He sees distant objects indistinctly, but near objects clearly. Concave lenses correct the defect.

2. *Farsightedness.* A person may have an eyeball shorter than normal, or a lens not convex enough. He sees near objects indistinctly, but far objects clearly. Convex lenses correct the defect.

3. *Astigmatism.* A person may have an irregular curvature of the lens or of the cornea. He sees certain horizontal and vertical lines indistinctly. The image spreads over the retina. Lenses that offset the faulty curvature correct the defect.

THE EARS

Description of the Ear. The ear is divided into three parts: (1) the *outer ear*, (2) the *middle ear*, and (3) the *inner ear*. The part of the ear that we see is the external flap, which is part of the outer ear. Both the middle ear and the inner ear are protected within the bones of the skull.

1. The *outer ear* includes the fan-shaped external structure and the *auditory canal*. This hollow tube terminates with a membrane, called the *eardrum*. The eardrum separates the outer ear from the middle ear.

2. The *middle ear* contains three tiny bones, known as the *hammer*, *anvil*, and *stirrup*. The hammer is attached to the eardrum, and the stirrup to another membrane that separates the middle ear from the inner ear. Thus, the three bones form a chain linking the two membranes.

3. The *inner ear* contains a snail-shaped tube, called the *cochlea*. Lining the cochlea are ciliated nerve cells sensitive to vibrations. A fluid in the cochlea circulates over the nerve cells. The nerve cells are connected to the *auditory nerve*, which leads to the brain.

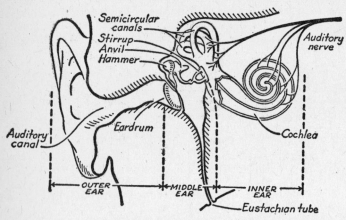

Fig. 68. The Ear

How We Hear. Sound waves picked up by the fan-shaped outer ear pass through the auditory canal and strike the eardrum. The impact causes the tightly-stretched eardrum to vibrate. These vibrations are transmitted across the middle ear by the hammer, anvil and stirrup to the membrane separating the middle ear from the inner ear. The vibrating membrane causes the fluid within the cochlea to vibrate. As the fluid stimulates the cilia of the sensitive nerve cells lining the cochlea, nervous impulses are produced. The impulses are carried by the auditory nerve to the brain. The brain interprets these nervous impulses as sound.

The Eustachian Tube. The external air pressing inward against the eardrum is equalized by air from the middle ear pressing outward against the eardrum. The air is brought into the middle ear from the throat by means of a hollow passageway, called the Eustachian tube.

How We Maintain Our Sense of Balance. Working in conjunction with the brain is an organ of balance called the *semicircular canals*. They are three tubular loops containing a fluid. The loops lie at right angles to each other, and are located in the inner ear. As the body changes its position, the liquid also changes position and stimulates different nerve cells. The nervous impulses are carried by the auditory nerve to the brain for interpretation. In this way, we can keep our balance, or sense of *equilibrium*.

THE SKIN

The Skin as a Sense Organ. Nerve cells in the skin are sensitive to the sensations of *touch, pressure, pain, heat,* and *cold.* When stimulated, the nerve cells send nervous impulses to the brain. The brain interprets the impulses as the sensations we feel.

For each of the sensations there are specialized nerve cells sensitive to that sensation. The various types are present everywhere in the skin. However, they are more concentrated in certain areas where they perform their specialized functions. For example, at the fingertips there is a greater concentration of nerve cells sensitive to touch.

THE NOSE

The Nose as a Sense Organ. An odor is a gas given off by a substance. By a chemical reaction, the gas stimulates specialized nerve cells in the upper part of the nasal passages. These nerve cells are connected to the *olfactory nerve,* which leads to the brain. Stimulation of the nerve cells creates nervous impulses which the olfactory nerve carries to the brain. There the odor is interpreted.

THE TONGUE

The Tongue as a Sense Organ. On the tongue are groups of specialized nerve cells, called *taste buds.* When a substance comes into contact with the taste buds, a chemical reaction takes place. Nervous impulses are thus produced in the taste buds, and are carried by a nerve to the brain. The brain then interprets the impulses as taste.

Taste buds are scattered all over the tongue, but groups of specialized taste buds appear more numerously in certain regions. Specialized taste buds around the tip of the tongue are more sensitive to sweet and salty tastes; taste buds on the sides of the tongue are more sensitive to a sour taste; and taste buds on the back of the tongue are more sensitive to a bitter taste.

The sense of taste works in harmony with the sense of smell. For example, when we have a head cold, the nasal passages have become clogged. In this condition, the odors do not reach all the nerve cells sensitive to smell. The result is that foods do not have their true taste.

THE NEURON: THE BASIC UNIT OF THE NERVOUS SYSTEM

What Is a Neuron? A *neuron* is another name for a nerve cell. Neurons are specialized cells for carrying nervous impulses from one part of the body to another part. Neurons are found everywhere in the body, and together make up the nervous system of man. Since nerve cells cannot reproduce, their number remains constant during the lifetime of an individual.

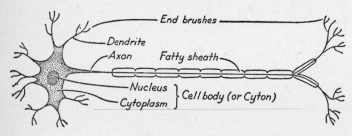

Fig. 69. A Neuron

A neuron, like all other cells, is made up of protoplasm. A neuron consists of: (1) the *cell body* (or *cyton*), which includes the nucleus and surrounding cytoplasm; (2) *dendrites*, which are several short protoplasmic projections from the cyton; and (3) an *axon*, which is a long protoplasmic projection from the cyton. Around the axon is a thin fatty *sheath*, which protects the axon. The dendrites and axon branch out into *end brushes*.

The dendrites carry nervous impulses *to* the cell body. The cell body transmits the impulses to the axon. The axon carries the impulses *away from* the cell body.

The Synapse. A nervous impulse enters a neuron through the dendrites and leaves the neuron through the axon. The end brushes of the axon of one neuron lie near to, but do not touch, the end brushes of the dendrites of the next neuron. The region of near contact between two neurons is called a *synapse*. In order for an impulse to go from one neuron to another neuron, the impulse must cross the synapse.

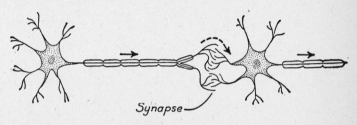

Synapse

Fig. 70. A Synapse

Sensory, Motor and Associative Neurons. The sense organs, or *receptors*, receive stimuli from the environment. Stimulation of nerve cells produces nervous impulses. Nervous impulses are carried by the *sensory* (or afferent) *neurons* to the brain or spinal cord for interpretation. After the interpretation has been made, the *motor* (or efferent) *neurons* carry the impulses to a muscle or to a gland, which makes the response. The muscle or gland that makes the response is called the *effector*. Connecting a motor neuron with a sensory neuron is an *associative neuron*.

The Nerve. The cell bodies of most neurons are located in the brain and the spinal cord. From the cell bodies, nerve fibers extend to all parts of the body. These nerve fibers (mostly axons) are bound together by connective tissue to form cable-like bundles, called *nerves*.

Like neurons, nerves are classified as *sensory* (or afferent) if they conduct impulses from the receptor *to* the brain or spinal cord, and *motor* (efferent) if they conduct impulses *from* the brain or spinal cord to the effector.

THE HUMAN NERVOUS SYSTEM

The Divisions of Man's Nervous System. The nervous system is divided into two main parts: (1) the *central nervous system,* and (2) the *autonomic nervous system.*

THE CENTRAL NERVOUS SYSTEM

The Structures of the Central Nervous System. The central nervous system is the center for the coordination of almost all the nervous activities of the body. The central nervous system consists of (1) the *brain,* (2) the *spinal cord,* and (3) the *nerves* attached to the brain and spinal cord.

1. The Brain. The brain is a mass of neurons housed and protected in the *cranium.* The cranium is a cavity within the bony skull that encloses the entire brain. (See Fig. 46 on page 101.)

There are three divisions of the brain: (*a*) the *cerebrum,* (*b*) the *cerebellum,* and (*c*) the *medulla.*

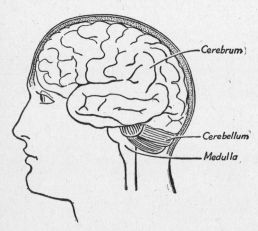

Fig. 71. The Brain

a. The Cerebrum. This is the largest division of the brain. It lies in the upper and forward region of the cranium. The cerebrum consists of two hemispheres, joined together by nerve fibers.

The cerebrum is made up of two layers, an outer layer and an inner layer. The *outer* layer, called the *cortex*, consists mainly of cytons. Since cytons are gray, the cortex is commonly referred to as the "gray matter" of the brain. The cortex is covered with numerous folds, known as *convolutions*, which greatly increase the surface area of gray matter.

The *inner* layer is made up of nerve fibers (mostly axons with some dendrites), projecting from the cytons of the neurons. Because the fatty sheaths protecting the axons are white, the inner layer is referred to as the "white matter" of the brain.

b. The Cerebellum. This division of the brain is much smaller than the cerebrum, and lies below and to the rear of the cerebrum. The cerebellum, like the cerebrum, is made up of two hemispheres and two layers: an outer layer of gray matter, and an inner layer of white matter. The cerebellum cortex is also covered with convolutions, but they are fewer in number and shallower than in the cerebrum.

c. The Medulla. This is the smallest division of the brain, and lies beneath the cerebellum. The lower part of the medulla is the point where the brain and spinal cord meet. In the medulla, there are neuron centers controlling specific functions of the body.

2. **The Spinal Cord.** The spinal cord is a mass of nerve tissue, running lengthwise from the medulla nearly the full length of the spinal column. The vertebrae of the spinal column protect the spinal cord. The outer layer of the spinal cord is white matter, and the

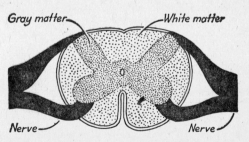

Fig. 72. The Spinal Cord

inner layer is gray matter. This is the reverse of the layers of tissue in the brain. From the spinal cord, nerves lead to all parts of the body.

Functions of the Cerebrum:

1. The cerebrum interprets the nervous impulses received from the sense organs. Thus, the brain "sees," "hears," "tastes," etc.

2. The cerebrum is the center of all our thinking. In this part of the brain we think, reason, judge, remember, etc. All our learning takes place in the cerebrum.

3. The cerebrum controls all our voluntary actions. The things we wish to do, or the things we want to say—indeed, all our conscious activities originate in the cerebrum.

The Activity Centers of the Cerebrum. The functions of the cerebrum are carried out in fairly definite areas of the cortex. *Sensory centers* receive and interpret nervous impulses from the sense organs. *Speech centers* enable us to speak. *Motor centers* are areas of neurons which permit us to carry out voluntary muscular acts.

Functions of the Cerebellum:

1. The cerebellum coordinates all voluntary muscular activity. Motor impulses originating in the cerebrum and traveling downward are relayed by the cerebellum to the proper muscles.

2. The cerebellum functions with the semicircular canals (see page 181) in helping us maintain our balance, or equilibrium. As the cerebellum is informed of changes in body position, it coordinates the muscles to meet the change.

Functions of the Medulla:

1. The medulla controls involuntary muscular activities. It regulates the heartbeat and the breathing rate, as well as the activities of various glands and involuntary muscles.

2. The medulla is the center of many complex reflex actions, such as sneezing, swallowing and blinking.

Functions of the Spinal Cord:

1. The spinal cord is the pathway of nerves that connect the brain with all parts of the body.

2. The spinal cord is the center of numerous simple reflexes, such as pulling the hand away from a hot stove.

THE AUTONOMIC NERVOUS SYSTEM

The Structures of the Autonomic Nervous System. The autonomic nervous system consists of (1) *two chains of nerves* lying alongside the spinal cord, one on each side, (2) *ganglia*, which are clusters of nerve cells that link the chains, and (3) *plexuses*, which are groups of ganglia found in specialized centers of the body. By means of the nerves of the autonomic nervous system, messages are relayed among the glands and internal organs.

The autonomic nervous system is connected to the spinal cord and to the medulla. Consequently, the autonomic nervous system works independently, but in harmony with, the central nervous system.

The functions of the internal organs and glands, and the related activities of all systems in man, are coordinated by the autonomic nervous system. When we take in food, we start a series of chemical and muscular processes that digest the food, that carry the digested food and oxygen to the cells, and that take away the waste products.

That the activities of the autonomic nervous system take

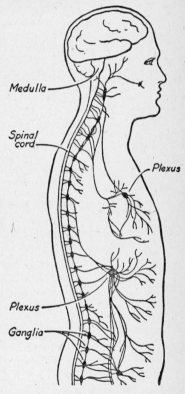

Fig. 73. The Autonomic Nervous System

place automatically, and at all times, is highly significant. For if the vital organs and glands were under our control, we would soon prove unable to carry out all the complicated internal activities that are required to maintain us.

TYPES OF RESPONSES

The Simple Reflex. In man, the simplest type of response to a stimulus is the *simple reflex*. Examples are jumping at the sound of a sudden loud noise, pulling your hand away from a hot object, jerking the knee in response to a slight blow below the kneecap.

1. The simple reflex is *inborn*. Being part of your behavior at birth, the simple reflex does not have to be learned.

2. The simple reflex is *involuntary*. Since the simple reflex is not controlled by the brain, the response is automatic and immediate.

3. The simple reflex is *protective*. Useful simple reflexes protect the body from injury. Examples are coughing to dislodge something from the throat; blinking to keep dust from the eyes; dodging a blow.

How a Simple Reflex Takes Place. A simple reflex takes place over a definite pathway, called a *reflex arc*. When pulling your hand away from a lighted match, a nervous impulse travels from receptor to effector over the following reflex arc:

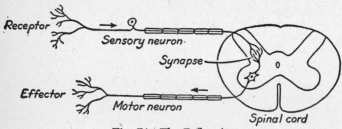

Fig. 74. The Reflex Arc

1. *The Receptor.* When your finger touches a burning match, the skin (the receptor) receives the stimulus of heat and sets up a nervous impulse.

2. *The Sensory Neuron.* The impulse is carried by a sensory neuron to the spinal cord.

3. *The Associative Neuron.* In the spinal cord, the impulse crosses the synapse to the associative neuron, which relays the impulse to the proper motor neuron.

4. *The Motor Neuron.* The motor neuron carries the impulse to the effector.

5. *The Effector*. The effector makes the response. In this illustration, the muscle in your arm is the effector. Contraction of the muscle pulls your hand away from the lighted match.

(A gland may also respond to a stimulus. The tear gland will secrete a fluid to wash away dirt or dust that has blown into the eye.)

Since the action of the simple reflex in withdrawing the hand from the flame was so very rapid, severe pain or injury was avoided. The consequence would have been more severe if the action had involved the use of the brain.

Pavlov's Experiments on the Conditioned Reflex. *Ivan Pavlov,* a Russian scientist, experimented with dogs to determine how he could change their behavior.

1. He started an experiment, now famous, by giving a dog some food and observing the mouth-watering reaction as soon as the dog saw or smelled the food. This response to food is a simple reflex action involving the secretion of saliva by the salivary glands.

2. Pavlov then started the ringing of a bell just before presenting the food to the dog. At first, the ringing bell brought no response from the dog; but the food, when brought into view, caused the dog's mouth to water.

3. After repeating the procedure several times, Pavlov found that as soon as the dog heard the ringing of the bell, the dog's mouth began to water. Apparently, the dog had learned to associate the ringing of the bell with the offering of food.

4. Pavlov then observed the dog's reaction to the sound of the ringing bell without the offering of food. Pavlov found that the dog began to salivate although no food was in sight. In other words, the dog responded to a new stimulus (the ringing of the bell) just as he had responded to the original stimulus (the food).

5. Pavlov continued the procedure of ringing the bell without giving the dog food, and observed that the dog's response gradually lessened until he finally failed to respond at all. That is, the mere sound of the ringing bell would no longer cause the flow of saliva. However, the sight or smell of food always produced the same response of mouth-watering.

Conditioned Reflexes. As we have seen from Pavlov's experiment, a substituted stimulus may produce the same response as the original stimulus. This type of response is called a *conditioned reflex.* Man conditions animals to perform useful and entertaining activities. Dogs are conditioned to herd sheep, and horses to pull plows and wagons. Dogs, seals and bears are conditioned to perform all sorts of entertaining "tricks," such as we commonly see in the circus and on the stage.

Unlike the simple reflex, which is inborn, the conditioned reflex is *learned,* or *acquired.* Also unlike the simple reflex, which remains part of an individual's nervous response for life, the conditioned reflex may be broken, or unlearned. In human behavior, a great deal of learning and habit formation results from conditioned reflexes acquired through experience, or repetition.

Instincts. An instinct is an action consisting of a series of reflexes. Each completed reflex serves as a stimulus for the next reflex, until the final response has been made.

For example, when a bird builds a nest, the bird performs a series of steps, each one a reflex. The completion of one step, or reflex, acts as a stimulus for the next step, or reflex, until the entire action has been completed.

The instinct of building a nest is *inborn, unlearned.* The bird had never been taught to do so by man or by another bird. Nor does the bird build her nest by intelligent planning, because a bird does not possess the mental powers to think, or reason, or plan.

Other examples of animal instincts are the spinning of webs by spiders, and the building of dams by beavers.

Human instincts are confined mainly to the simple responses of infants. For example, when a child grasps an object, he is not performing intelligent behavior, but inborn instinctive behavior. Other stimuli to which infants respond instinctively are: loud noise, loss of support, restriction of movement, and pleasurable sensations such as rocking and patting.

Habits. Habits are *acquired, automatic* acts. A habit is formed by first learning an act and then repeating it over and over again in a fixed order. In first learning how to do something, the cerebrum—which is the seat of learning—is involved. After repeated practice, the act becomes habitual, and thought is not required. Some common habits are writing, speaking, typing, dancing, driving a car, brushing the teeth, and obeying traffic lights.

The Value of Habits:

1. *Man can do more than one thing at a time.* When an act has become automatic, thought is no longer required. Therefore, the cerebrum is free to concentrate on other matters. For example, a be-

ginning typist must think about which finger to use in striking a particular key on the typewriter. But when typing has become habitual, that person no longer has to think about the mechanics (machine part) of typing and can concentrate on the material to be typed.

2. *Man gains greater efficiency and saves time.* When an act has been repeated over and over again, this act can be performed more efficiently and quicker. For example, a typist achieves speed and accuracy with practice. "Practice makes perfect."

Forming Good Habits and Breaking Bad Habits. Man is the product of habits. His behavior is the result of habits—good and bad —that he has acquired over the years. Because habits are voluntary acts, good habits can be formed and bad habits can be broken—if one's will is strong enough.

Forming Good Habits:

1. Resolve to make a particular act a habit.

2. Get a clear idea of the steps involved.

3. Practice the act regularly.

4. Sense a feeling of accomplishment as the activity gradually becomes automatic.

Breaking Bad Habits:

1. Carefully consider all the undesirable aspects of the bad habit. For example, toward breaking the habit of smoking, consider the cost, the annoyance to other people, the effect upon the health, bad breath, and the unsightly appearance of a yellow stain on the fingers.

2. Substitute a good habit for a bad habit. For example, toward breaking the bad habit of "daydreaming" while studying, form the habit of working according to a definitely organized plan.

Intelligence. Intelligence is *voluntary* behavior, originating in the cerebrum. Intelligence is the ability to put into action all the higher thought processes, such as *thinking, reasoning, will, judgment* and *memory.* Man shows intelligence when he remembers, analyzes situations, draws conclusions, applies knowledge, solves problems, and meets new and different situations in his environment.

Only in man is the cerebrum developed enough to permit of thought processes. Animal behavior is either inborn or learned through repetition—but without the process of thinking. For example, fishes in an aquarium can be conditioned to associate their owner's footsteps with food, so that they will rise to the top of the aquarium in response to the owner's approach. Also, rats learn by trial and error to find their way through a maze (an intricate series of pathways with many turns) in order to obtain food.

Hygiene of the Nervous System. Short periods of rest during the day and ample sleep at night are essential to the proper functioning of all the systems of man, including the nervous system. Highly important, too, is the relaxation that comes from hobbies, sports, music, reading, the theatre, and all other worthwhile forms of entertainment and physical activity. Finally, good relationship with people is necessary for the well being of man. We must develop a friendly, kindly, and cooperative attitude toward all people—fellow students, teachers, friends, neighbors, family, etc. All these procedures make for happiness, good health, optimism, enthusiasm and a feeling of security—a feeling of being wanted, of being a part of our environment.

Under the above conditions, man functions best. Any psychological disorder may result in a physical disorder. For example, mental distress over an extended period may cause stomach distress; extreme anger or excitement may result in a rapid or irregular heartbeat. This is because all organ systems work in close harmony with the nervous system. A physical disorder may affect the nervous system. For example, a severe pain, such as a toothache or an earache, interferes with the normal mental processes of thinking, remembering, etc. Of course, these unpleasant effects may be temporary, and cause no injury to the body. But frequent occurrences over a long period of time can become serious. Therefore, we must avoid extended mental agitation. We must seek peace of mind. Toward this end, we must avoid worry, anger, fear, conflict, gloom, dishonesty, laziness, and all other tension-producing situations and mental states.

SUMMARY OF BEHAVIOR

Organism	Response	Characteristics of Response
plants and one-celled animals	tropism	Simplest type of response. Inborn, unlearned. Plant tropisms accomplished by growth; animal tropisms by movement of the entire body.

SUMMARY OF BEHAVIOR (*Continued*)

Organism	Response	Characteristics of Response
lower animals	tropism	Simple behavior in which the entire body responds.
	simple reflex	Simplest type of nervous response. Inborn, unlearned. Never varies and never lost.
complex animals	simple reflex	Same as above.
	conditioned reflex	A substituted stimulus produces the same response as the original stimulus. Learned, acquired. Can be lost.
	instinct	A series of reflexes. Inborn, unlearned.
man	simple reflex	Same as in lower animals.
	conditioned reflex	Same as in complex animals.
	instinct	Same as in complex animals. Confined to infants, not adults.
	habit	Acquired. Formed by first learning an act, and then repeating it over and over. Once acquired, requires no thinking. Can be lost.
	intelligence	Voluntary. The result of higher thought processes. Only man is capable of intelligent behavior.

Completion Questions

1. Organisms respond to conditions in their environment called _____.
2. The property of protoplasm that enables an organism to react to its environment is _____.
3. Responses of plants to external stimuli are called _____.
4. The response shown when ivy attaches itself to a wall is known as _____.
5. The turning of the leaves of a plant towards light is a (*positive, negative*) _____ phototropism.
6. The nervous system of a hydra consists of fibers arranged to form a (an) _____.
7. The first lower organism in which we find a true nervous system is the _____.
8. The structures which are specialized to detect stimuli in the environment are called _____.
9. The _____ is the part of the eye which contracts in very bright light.
10. One condition that may cause a person to be nearsighted is that the _____ of the eye is too convex.
11. The structure which conducts nervous impulses from the ear to the brain for interpretation is the _____.
12. The _____ are the structures found in the ear which aid us in maintaining balance.
13. The _____ is both an organ of excretion and a sense organ of touch.
14. The nerve cells on the tongue, which are responsible for detecting the different sensations of taste, are called _____.
15. The unit of structure of the nervous system is called the _____.
16. The longest part of a neuron is the _____.
17. In traveling from one neuron to another, an impulse crosses an area called the _____.
18. Bundles of axons tied together by connective tissue make up _____.
19. Nerves that carry impulses inward from the surface of the body are called _____.
20. Nerves that carry messages from the brain are called _____.
21. The brain and the _____ are the major parts of the human central nervous system.
22. The largest part of the human brain is the _____.

23. The part of the brain controlling conscious activity is the _____.

24. Muscular coordination and balance are controlled by that part of the brain called the _____.

25. The _____ is the center for the regulation of heartbeat and breathing rate.

26. In the human body, the simplest type of response to a stimulus is the _____.

27. The act of removing the hand from a hot stove is called a (an) _____.

28. The training of an animal consists largely of setting up responses called _____.

29. The spinning of a web by a spider is an example of a type of response called a (an) _____.

30. A set of automatic responses that regularly occur in a fixed order but are not inborn is a (an) _____.

Multiple-Choice Questions

1. When roots grow towards moisture, the action is an example of (1) geotropism (2) chemotropism (3) hydrotropism (4) phototropism.

2. Many plant responses are controlled by the presence of chemical secretions called (1) chlorophyl (2) carbohydrates (3) auxins (4) insulin.

3. A structure, such as a muscle or gland, which makes a response to a stimulus is called (1) a receptor (2) an effector (3) a sense organ (4) a nervous impulse.

4. One of man's sense organs is (1) the solar plexus (2) the cortex of the brain (3) the medulla (4) the eye.

5. The part of a neuron that is covered with a fatty sheath is the (1) axon (2) cyton (3) dendrites (4) end brushes.

6. The part of a neuron that receives the impulses from another neuron is the (1) end brush (2) axon (3) cell body (4) dendrites.

7. The neurons that stimulate glandular secretion are (1) motor (2) sensory (3) afferent (4) associative.

8. The surface layer of the brain is composed largely of (1) cell bodies (2) axons (3) end brushes (4) dendrites.

9. The spinal cord is made up of (1) bone tissue (2) cartilage tissue (3) connective tissue (4) nerve tissue.

10. Nerves from the eyes and ears are connected to the (1) cerebellum (2) cerebrum (3) medulla (4) spinal cord.

11. The solar plexus is (1) part of the autonomic system (2) part of the brain (3) an associative center (4) a receptor.

12. A nervous response in man that is automatic from birth is called (1) a voluntary act (2) a habit (3) a reflex (4) a tropism.

13. The drawing of the finger away from a hot stove (1) causes the pain (2) is the result of the sensation of pain (3) precedes the pain (4) increases the pain.

14. A scientist who experimented with conditioned reflexes was (1) Banting (2) Brown (3) Metchnikoff (4) Pavlov.

15. A type of behavior in which a new stimulus may cause a response similar to the response produced by the original stimulus is called (1) an instinct (2) a conditioned reflex (3) a habit (4) a simple reflex.

16. Habits are (1) acts of will power (2) inborn reflexes (3) autonomic activities (4) acquired reflexes.

17. An example of a habit is a person (1) brushing his teeth (2) thinking of an injured foot (3) wishing for some water (4) breathing rapidly.

18. Habits and conditioned reflexes are alike in that both (1) are inherited (2) are learned responses (3) appear only in dogs (4) appear only in man.

19. Rats may learn to find their way through a maze by (1) instinct (2) trial and error learning (3) conditioned reflex (4) intelligence.

20. Although animals appear to act intelligently, their responses do *not* involve (1) reflexes (2) instincts (3) thought (4) conditioning.

Modified True-False Questions

1. The type of response made by simple organisms to external stimuli is called a *reflex*.

2. All the ways in which a plant or animal responds to factors in its environment make up the organism's *behavior*.

3. If a one-celled organism moves towards a stimulus, the response is called a *negative* tropism.

4. The nervous system of an insect is characterized by its well-developed *sense organs*.

5. The reaction set up when a sense organ is stimulated is called a *nervous impulse*.

6. An image normally falls on the *cornea*.
7. External pressure on the eardrum is equalized by air entering the middle ear through the *Eustachian tube*.
8. Cells specialized to carry stimuli are *muscle* cells.
9. In higher animals, axons always carry impulses *toward* the cell body.
10. In a reflex act, the first kind of neuron to be affected is the *associative* neuron.

Essay Questions

1. *a.* What is a tropism?
   b. State the difference between a tropism and a stimulus.
   c. Describe one advantage to an organism of the property of irritability.
   d. Explain why the responses made by plants are slow.
2. *a.* Give the scientific term that may be used to express each of the following types of responses:
      (1) Roots grow downward.
      (2) Leaves turn toward the light.
      (3) Roots grow toward moisture.
      (4) An ameba moves away from a drop of strong acid.
      (5) A bean plant twists around a stick.
   b. Describe an experiment that illustrates each of the following:
      (1) A tropism of a protozoan.
      (2) Roots responding to water.
      (3) The effect of auxins on plant growth.
      (4) The response of roots to the pull of gravity.
3. *a.* Make a labeled diagram of a neuron. Indicate two structures found in a neuron which are not found in other animal cells.
   b. Give two reasons why the shape of a neuron enables it to do its special work.
   c. Briefly describe each of the following: (1) afferent neuron, (2) synapse, (3) efferent neuron.
4. *a.* State a function of each of the following: (1) the cerebrum, (2) the cerebellum, (3) the medulla, (4) the spinal cord.
   b. Name two organs controlled principally by the autonomic nervous system.
5. The simplest type of response in man is the simple reflex.
   a. Sudden contact with a hot object will cause either a very young baby or an adult to pull his hand away quickly. Explain why both the baby and the adult perform this act equally well.

  b. Make a labeled diagram showing the nerve path involved in a simple reflex action.

  c. Describe the process by which you might develop a conditioned reflex in some animal.

  d. Give two differences between a simple reflex and a conditioned reflex.

6. *a.* Describe three steps that should be taken in order to make some desirable act a habit.

  b. In establishing a habit, certain parts of the brain are involved. List the structures involved and explain what part each plays in the formation of the habit.

  c. State two advantages of habits.

  d. Explain how a shy pupil could overcome the habit of not taking part in class discussions.

  e. Justify the statement "Practice makes perfect."

  f. Show one way in which reflexes and habits are similar, and one way in which they are different.

7. Tell whether each of the following statements is true or false, giving a reason for each answer:

  a. To live effectively, a person must have many habits.

  b. Many voluntary acts are governed by the central nervous system.

  c. If the cerebellum were removed from an animal, the animal would have difficulty in getting its food.

  d. Some voluntary acts are governed by the autonomic nervous system.

  e. If the left arm is paralyzed after a blow on the head, a surgeon can open the skull at the exact place where a clot may be resting on the brain.

  f. Sudden injury to the medulla may result in the inability to move a limb.

8. Give a biological explanation of each of the following:

  a. The brain of a frog is destroyed, but the frog will raise its legs in response to a drop of acid placed on its abdomen.

  b. Heart muscle contracts regularly, though we are usually unaware of the contractions.

  c. After an interval of 20 years, a man finds himself still able to ride a bicycle.

  d. Man sees with his brain.

  e. At birth, a human being has no conditioned reflexes.

  f. Reflex movements are quicker than movements in which the nervous impulses must first go to the brain.

Chapter XVI

ASEXUAL REPRODUCTION

Reproduction. The life process by which organisms give rise to new individuals of their own kind is called *reproduction*.

Asexual reproduction is the method of producing offspring from only *one* parent. Lower plants and animals reproduce asexually. Higher plants and animals—as well as some of the lower forms—reproduce sexually. In *sexual* reproduction, *two* parents are required to produce a new individual. This type of reproduction will be discussed in the next chapter.

The power to reproduce is a property of protoplasm possessed by every mature living thing. Reproduction is essential for the continuance of life from one generation to the next, because every individual must eventually die.

The Theory of Spontaneous Generation. Until scientists proved that "all life comes from life," people believed that offspring arose from nonliving matter. This is the *theory of spontaneous generation.* According to this false belief, maggots and worms arose from decaying meat; rats and mice from old rags; and snakes from horse hairs.

Scientists Disprove the Theory of Spontaneous Generation:

1. *Francesco Redi.* The first experimenter to disprove the theory of spontaneous generation was this Italian physician. In 1668, Redi conducted an experiment to prove that maggots (the larvae of flies) did *not* arise from decaying meat.

Redi first cooked the meat in order to kill all organisms on it. After allowing the meat to decay, Redi put a piece of the decaying meat into each of three jars, as follows:

1. He left the first jar uncovered, exposing the meat to the air and allowing the odor of the decaying meat to issue from the jar. He observed that maggots later appeared on the meat.

2. He covered the second jar with fine gauze, preventing flies from entering the jar and coming in contact with the meat, but allowing the odor of the decaying meat to escape. He observed that maggots appeared on the gauze, but not on the meat.

3. He covered the third jar with heavy parchment, barring the escape of the odor of the decaying meat. He observed that *no* maggots appeared, either on the meat or on the parchment.

199

Redi thus proved that maggots did *not* arise from the decaying meat, but from eggs laid by the flies. The odor of the decaying meat attracted them to jars 1 and 2. But the flies were not attracted to jar 3, because the odor had not reached the flies.

2. *The Work of Other Scientists.* Redi's experiment inspired a host of scientists to perform independent experiments, with the result that the theory of spontaneous generation was completely discarded. Among the most important contributors were: *Lazzaro Spallanzani* (18th century), *Louis Pasteur* (19th century), and *John Tyndall* (19th century).

Methods of Asexual Reproduction. Asexual reproduction can be carried out in five different ways: *binary fission, budding, spore formation, vegetative propagation* and *regeneration.*

1. Binary Fission. Binary fission is a method of asexual reproduction in which the nucleus divides equally by mitosis, and the cytoplasm also divides equally. Binary fission is the simplest method of reproduction, occurring mainly in the unicellular forms of life. Examples are the *spirogyra* and *bacteria* (plants), and the *ameba* and *paramecium* (animals).

Binary Fission in the Ameba. By the process of binary fission, an ameba becomes two amebas as follows:

a. When an ameba reaches full size, the nucleus divides into two equal parts. The nuclei move away from the center, both going to opposite ends of the cell.

b. The cytoplasm also divides equally, each half enclosing a newly-formed nucleus.

c. The division of the parent cell forms two new individuals, called *daughter cells.*

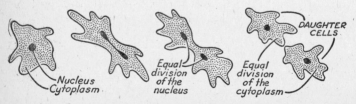

Fig. 75. Binary Fission in the Ameba

Note that the parent cell passes out of existence after binary fission has taken place. Half of the nucleus and half of the cytoplasm of the parent cell have been given to each of the daughter cells. When the daughter cells reach maturity, they then undergo binary fission, each cell becoming two.

2. Budding. Budding is another simple method of asexual reproduction. In budding, the nucleus divides equally, but the cytoplasm divides unequally. Examples of organisms that reproduce by budding are the *yeast* (one-celled plant), and the *sponge* and *hydra* (simple multicellular animals).

Budding in the Yeast. Budding takes place in the yeast as follows:

a. Part of the cytoplasm pushes out of the parent cell, forming a knoblike growth, called a *bud*.

b. The nucleus of the parent cell moves towards the bud, where it divides equally.

c. One nucleus enters the bud, the other nucleus remaining in the parent.

d. A cell wall forms between the bud and the parent cell.

e. The bud grows, and then may break away from the parent, thus giving rise to two individual plants.

The bud may not break away from the parent cell, and may give rise to a bud of its own. After a few such divisions, there is formed a chain of attached yeast cells, called a colony.

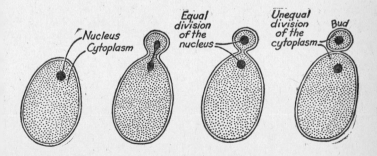

Fig. 76. Budding in the Yeast

Budding in the Hydra. The hydra is a simple multicellular animal which reproduces by budding. A small outgrowth, the bud, appears on one side of the body of the parent hydra. As the bud grows larger, tentacles appear. When the bud is fully developed, it breaks away from the parent and continues life as a completely new individual.

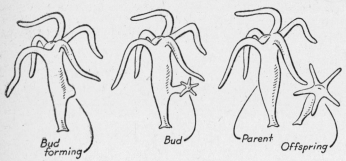

Fig. 77. Budding in the Hydra

3. Spore Formation. This is an asexual method of reproduction by which a number of small cells, called *spores*, are produced by an organism, each spore capable of giving rise to a new individual. Spores are formed in a *spore case*, or *sporangium*. Fungi, such as *mushrooms, molds, rusts* and *mildews*, are plants that produce spores.

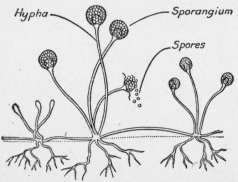

Fig. 78. Spore Formation in the Bread Mold

4. Vegetative Reproduction. The rise of a new plant from a part of a plant is an asexual process called *vegetative propagation*, or *vegetative reproduction*.

a. Bulbs. A bulb is a short underground stem with fleshy leaves that contain stored food. A bulb taken from the parent plant and placed in the soil will develop into a new individual plant. Plants that reproduce from bulbs are the lily, tulip and onion.

b. Tubers. A tuber is an enlarged underground stem containing stored food. The white potato is a tuber. Scattered over the white potato are numerous buds, called "eyes." The white potato can be propagated by planting a whole tuber or part of a tuber containing a few eyes.

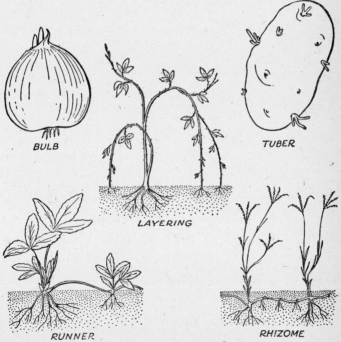

BULB

LAYERING

TUBER

RUNNER

RHIZOME

Fig. 79. Vegetative Reproduction

c. Runners (Stolons). A runner, or stolon, is a stem that grows along the ground. Several inches away from the parent, it takes root and gives rise to an individual plant. The strawberry plant and some grasses reproduce vegetatively from runners.

d. Rhizomes. A rhizome is a long stem that grows horizontally underground. From buds which form at intervals on the rhizome, new leaves and roots are produced, thus forming a new plant. The iris, fern and several grasses propagate in this manner.

e. Layering. This process of reproduction is common among the plants having long slender stems, such as the raspberry, blackberry, gooseberry and certain grapes. When the stem bends over, and its growing tip touches the ground, roots form in the ground and give rise to a new plant.

f. Slips (Cuttings). A slip, or cutting, is a piece of a stem detached from a growing plant. When planted in moist soil, a slip forms roots and grows into a new plant. Common household plants, such as the geranium, begonia and ivy, are propagated by this method.

g. Fleshy Roots. A fleshy root is the storage area of the plant's food. The sweet potato, beet and turnip are examples of fleshy roots. The planting of a fleshy root produces a new plant.

h. Grafting. Grafting is a type of vegetative reproduction performed artificially by man. A new organism is *not* produced by the process. Grafting is employed for the following reasons: (1) to maintain a desired type of fruit or flower where there is a possibility that seeds will not give rise to the same plant, and (2) to propagate desirable varieties of seedless fruits which cannot be continued any other way.

In the process of grafting, man inserts a part of one tree into another tree. The rooted tree that receives the graft is called the *stock*. The part of the original tree that had been removed and is being grafted is the *scion*. To be successful, the scion and the stock must be of the same or of closely related species. For example, a branch may be removed from a Bartlett pear tree (scion) and grafted onto a crab-apple tree (stock). The scion will continue to bear the same type of fruit it bore before it was grafted, namely, Bartlett pears.

Frequently, grafts are made onto stocks which are strong and healthy, but which are not bearing desirable fruits or flowers. For example, commercial rose growers graft branches of valuable roses onto stocks that are healthy but flowering poorly.

A scion may be either a branch or a bud.

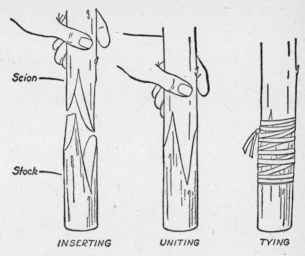

INSERTING   UNITING   TYING

Fig. 80. Grafting

Grafting a Branch. A branch is cut from a young tree of a desired variety and inserted into a branch of a mature tree. Such a graft is used to produce varieties of apples, plums, pears and walnuts.

Grafting a Bud (Budding). The growing tip of a stem containing a bud is cut from a desired variety of tree or bush and inserted into a slit under the bark of a young tree or bush. Budding produces varieties of peaches, cherries, plums and roses.

For a successful graft, the cambium, or growing tissue (see page 66), of the scion and of the stock must make contact with each other. In this way, minerals and water can pass from the stock into the grafted scion. After growth has taken place, the scion becomes a permanent part of the stock.

5. **Regeneration.** Regeneration is the reproduction of a lost part of an organism. Lower animals, such as the hydra, planaria (flatworm), and starfish, have the ability to regenerate (or regrow) a part of its body that has been injured or cut off.

Regeneration is a process closely related to vegetative reproduction, because a new individual can be formed from a part of the organism. For example, if a hydra, planaria or starfish is cut into two or more pieces, each piece may give rise to a complete organism.

Animals, such as the lobster and crab, are not able to produce a completely new organism by regeneration, but can replace certain parts lost through injury. Man has the ability to heal wounds by regeneration, but cannot reproduce a lost part. That is, a finger, arm or leg cut from the body will not grow back.

Economic Importance of Regeneration:

a. Fishermen cultivate sponges by cutting living sponges into a few small pieces and planting the parts in sponge beds in shallow water. When the pieces develop into complete organisms, they are harvested.

b. An enemy of oyster fishermen is the starfish, for this animal feeds on oysters. Until quite recently, angry fishermen, upon catching a starfish, would cut it up into several pieces and throw them back into the water, believing that they had thus destroyed the animal. They did not know then that each of the pieces could regenerate into a complete starfish. Today, fishermen simply keep the starfishes out of the water and under strong sun until they die.

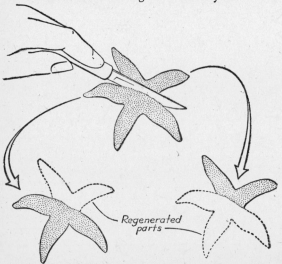

Regenerated parts

Fig. 81. Regeneration in the Starfish

Advantages of Asexual Reproduction. The offspring that arise by asexual reproduction (1) are all alike in characteristics, (2) are produced in great numbers, (3) are generated in a comparatively short period of time, and (4) as a result of grafting—are of a desired variety and may be of a seedless type which cannot be propagated by any other means.

Completion Questions

1. The life process necessary for the continuation of a species is _____.

2. The belief that life arose from dead matter is known as the theory of _____.

3. The simplest way in which a protozoan may reproduce is by _____.

4. In binary fission, the nucleus divides into two equal parts by the process of _____.

5. A small outgrowth from a parent that develops into a new individual is called a (an) _____.

6. A group of cells, such as yeast cells, live independently but attached to each other in the form of a (an) _____.

7. In binary fission, both the nucleus and the cytoplasm divide equally; in budding, however, the _____ divides equally and the _____ divides unequally.

8. A multicellular animal that may reproduce by budding is the _____.

9. When an organism produces a number of similar cells by asexual reproduction, and each cell is capable of developing into the same form as the parent, the process is called _____.

10. The asexual reproductive bodies in a mold plant are called _____.

11. When a higher plant asexually reproduces a new plant from one of its structures, the process is called _____.

12. An underground stem from which a new plant may develop is known as a (an) _____.

13. Potatoes are usually propagated by means of underground structures known as _____.

14. A strawberry plant reproduces vegetatively by means of structures called _____.

15. The part of a geranium that is used to propagate a new geranium plant asexually is called a (an) _____.

16. The _____ is an example of a fleshy root.

17. Seedless fruits can be propagated by _____.
18. The branch which is grafted onto a rooted plant is the _____.
19. The power of an animal to replace parts lost as a result of injury is called _____.
20. An advantage of asexual reproduction is _____.

Multiple-Choice Questions

1. The man who first questioned the theory that decayed meat turns into maggots was (1) Pasteur (2) Redi (3) Schwann (4) Spallanzani.
2. Spirogyra reproduces by the simple process of (1) binary fission (2) budding (3) fertilization (4) spore formation.
3. When the nucleus is removed from a protozoan, it can no longer (1) excrete wastes (2) move (3) reproduce (4) respond to stimuli.
4. Unless conditions are unfavorable, the yeast reproduces by (1) budding (2) spore formation (3) cutting (4) binary fission.
5. The sporangium of the bread mold contains (1) seeds (2) spores (3) zygotes (4) fruit.
6. The parts of a higher green plant not normally used for reproduction which may sometimes be used for reproducing the plant are called (1) hypha (2) sporangia (3) vegetative structures (4) fibrovascular bundles.
7. Tulips are usually propagated by (1) runners (2) bulbs (3) cuttings (4) slips.
8. The small structures found on the potato and frequently called "eyes" are (1) spores (2) buds (3) rhizomes (4) slips.
9. The part of the seedless grape plant that is used in producing more plants is the (1) stem (2) leaf (3) flower (4) seed.
10. Asexual reproduction is sure to result in (1) large numbers of offspring (2) improved offspring (3) offspring that differ in appearance (4) offspring that have the same genetic (hereditary) make-up.

Modified True-False Questions

1. The simplest way in which animals reproduce is by *conjugation*.
2. The new organisms formed as a result of binary fission are known as *daughter cells*.

3. The bread mold reproduces asexually by *budding*.
4. The *scion* is the rooted part of a graft.
5. When two related plants are grafted, the *cambium* layers must be brought into contact.

Essay Questions

1. *a.* For many centuries it was believed that life arose from non-living matter. Describe an experiment that was performed in an attempt to disprove this theory.
   b. What is the modern belief concerning the origin of life?

2. *a.* Make labeled diagrams showing fission, budding, and asexual spore formation in organisms. Name the organism in each case.
   b. Compare two of these types of reproduction giving a similarity and a difference.
   c. Tell what special advantage the process has for each species of organism named in *a*.

3. Name an animal or a plant that illustrates each of the following statements:
   a. The reproductive cells have hard protective coats.
   b. A piece of the stem is used to reproduce the plant.
   c. The plant sends out runners that take root to form new plants.
   d. An enlarged underground stem may be used to reproduce the plant.
   e. A desired type of fruit is maintained by grafting.

4. Give the biological explanation of each of the following statements:
   a. Vegetative propagation in plants produces offspring that are much alike.
   b. Reproduction in the bread mold enables it to survive unfavorable conditions.
   c. There is little or no variation in one-celled animals which reproduce by fission.
   d. Several days after students had thrown away the bread on which they grew molds, the same kind of mold plants appeared on food left in an animal cage.
   e. Grafting is not actually a method by which plants reproduce.
   f. Farmers usually do not propagate potatoes from seeds.

5. Define the following terms: runner, binary fission, vegetative propagation, budding, spore formation.

Chapter XVII

Sexual Reproduction

What Is Sexual Reproduction? As we learned in the previous chapter, simple organisms reproduce *asexually,* a method in which a new individual arises from *one* parent. However, most higher organisms reproduce *sexually,* a method in which *two* parents are involved in giving rise to offspring. Sexual reproduction is carried on by all the complex plants and animals. Some of the lower forms which reproduce asexually, also reproduce sexually at times.

The Nature of Sexual Reproduction. In sexual reproduction, each of the two parents produces a sex cell, called a *gamete.* The union of two gametes forms a single cell, called a *zygote.* The zygote undergoes repeated cell divisions and thus develops into a new individual.

SEXUAL REPRODUCTION IN SIMPLE PLANTS AND ANIMALS

Conjugation. In simple plants and animals, the gametes are similar in size and structure. Such sex cells are called *isogametes.* The formation of a zygote by the union of two similar gametes is known as *conjugation.*

Examples of Conjugation:

Paramecium. The paramecium is a one-celled animal that usually reproduces asexually by binary fission. After several fissions, the nuclear material becomes weakened. The paramecium then reproduces sexually by conjugation. In this process, two paramecia adhere together and exchange nuclear material, thus revitalizing their nuclear material. The two paramecia then separate, each capable of starting a new series of fissions.

In paramecium, conjugation does *not* result in the formation of a zygote and the subsequent development of a new individual. Conjugation is considered a method of reproduction because it rejuvenates the organism so that it can reproduce by binary fission.

Spirogyra. The spirogyra is an alga (one-celled **green plant**) that lives in a colony of cells. The cells are attached end to end in a *filament* several inches long. (See page 40.) Like the paramecium, the spirogyra reproduces both by binary fission and conjugation. The spirogyra conjugates as follows:

Two filaments lie parallel to each other, with the cells side by side in pairs. Paired cells become joined when projections growing from each of the two cells finally meet, forming a connecting tube, called the *conjugation tube.* The two paired cells act as gametes, as the protoplasm of one cell moves through the tube into the other cell. The union of the two gametes forms the zygote, which then secretes a hard protective coat around itself. This cell is called a *zygospore.* Because of its hard coat, the zygospore is able to withstand the unfavorable winter conditions. In the spring, the zygospore develops into a new spirogyra cell, which, by repeated cell divisions, forms into a new filament of spirogyra.

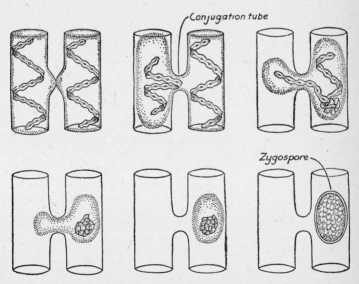

Fig. 82. Conjugation in the Spirogyra

Fertilization. In higher plants and higher animals, and in some lower forms of life, the gametes are dissimilar. One gamete is the male sex cell, while the other gamete is the female sex cell. The formation of a zygote by the union of a male and a female gamete is called *fertilization*.

An Example of Fertilization. Like the spirogyra, the oedogonium is an alga consisting of a filament of independent cells. However, the oedogonium produces a zygote by the union of a male and a female gamete. One cell of the oedogonium is specialized to produce a large female gamete, called an *egg*. Another cell is specialized to produce several small male gametes, called *sperms*. Sperms are released from the cell, but the egg remains stationary. Sperms of the oedogonium are equipped with cilia. These structures enable a sperm to swim to an egg for the formation of a zygote.

A Zygote Is Formed. Sperm cells are usually liberated in great numbers in the vicinity of the egg cells. Due to some chemical attraction, the sperm cells swim to the eggs. The first sperm to touch the plasma membrane of an egg cell enters the egg cell. The tail of this sperm, being no longer of any use, is left outside the egg cell. Immediately after the entrance of the sperm, a *fertilization membrane* quickly forms around the egg cell. This membrane prevents the entrance of another sperm. Then the nucleus of the sperm which entered the egg cell unites with the nucleus of the egg cell, thereby forming a single nucleus. The single cell formed by the union of the sperm cell and the egg cell is called the *fertilized egg*, or *zygote*.

ALTERNATION OF GENERATIONS

What Is Alternation of Generations? Reproduction that involves a sexual generation alternating with an asexual generation is called *alternation of generations*. Some plants and a few animals reproduce in this manner, as described below.

Life Cycle of the Moss:

The Sexual Generation. The familiar leafy moss plant reproduces by gametes, and therefore is called the sexual generation, or *gametophyte*.

On the top of some moss plants, both male and female reproductive organs are present. Within a female organ, a single egg cell is produced. Within a male organ, many sperms, each with two flagella, are produced. In wet weather, the sperms are liberated. The sperms swim through drops of rain or dew and enter the female organ. Here a sperm fuses with the egg and produces a fertilized egg. This ends the sexual generation and starts the asexual generation.

The Asexual Generation. The fertilized egg develops into a stalk-like plant attached to the top of the leafy plant. The stalk-like plant bears a capsule in which asexual spores are formed. These spores are released and spread by air currents. Since the stalk-like plant reproduces by spores, it is called the asexual generation, or *sporophyte.* A spore develops into an alga-like growth, eventually forming another leafy plant which reproduces sexually.

Life Cycle of the Fern. As we have seen, in mosses, the familiar moss plant is the gametophyte, or sexual generation. However, in ferns, the familiar leafy plant is the sporophyte, or asexual generation.

The Asexual Generation (Sporophyte). At certain times, brown dots, or *sori,* form on the under side of the fern leaves. Inside each sorus are several spore cases, *sporangia,* in which the spores are produced. When the spores are ripe, the sporangia open and liberate the spores.

The Sexual Generation (Gametophyte). A spore develops into a small heart-shaped gametophyte, which bears both sperm-forming and egg-forming organs. A sperm swims from the male organ through drops of water to reach the egg cell in the female organ. The fertilized egg cell, or zygote, then develops into a leafy *sporophyte,* and the cycle is complete.

Life Cycle of the Jellyfish. An animal whose life cycle consists of a sexual and an asexual generation is the jellyfish. The free-swimming jellyfish is the sexual generation, which forms eggs and sperms. A fertilized egg gives rise to a hydra-like growth which attaches itself to some object for support. This hydra-like growth is the asexual generation. It reproduces by budding and gives rise to the free-swimming jellyfish, thus completing the cycle.

SEXUAL REPRODUCTION IN FLOWERING PLANTS

Flowers Are Reproductive Structures. The highest form of plant is the seed-forming plant. The seed-bearing plants that have flowers are known as *angiosperms* (see page 46). The flower is specialized to carry on the reproductive process of the plant as follows: (1) Male and female gametes are formed in the flower. (2) Fertilization occurs within the flower. (3) The zygote is enclosed within a seed formed by the flower. (4) The seed germinates to produce a new plant.

The Structure of a Flower. A typical flower has four main structures: the *calyx*, the *corolla*, the *stamens* and the *pistil*.

1. *The Calyx.* Starting at the bottom of the typical flower, there is a circle of tiny green leaves, called *sepals*. The sepals enclose and protect the flower when in the bud. The entire circle of sepals is called the *calyx*.

2. *The Corolla.* Within the calyx is a circle of modified leaves, called *petals*. Generally, the petals are brightly colored and scented, probably to attract insects. The entire circle of petals is called the *corolla*.

3. *The Stamens.* Within the corolla is a circle of *stamens*. The stamens are the male reproductive organs. Each stamen is composed of two parts. (*a*) The *anther* is the top-most structure in which the pollen is produced. (*b*) The *filament* is the stalk which supports the anther.

4. *The Pistil.* In the center of the flower is the *pistil*. The pistil is the female reproductive organ. The pistil is composed of three parts: (*a*) The *stigma*, the top-most part of the pistil, is sticky for the purpose of catching and holding pollen grains. (*b*) The *style*, a slender stalk, supports the stigma and connects it with the ovary. (*c*) The *ovary* is the enlarged structure at the lower end of the pistil. Inside the ovary, several egg-shaped *ovules* may be found.

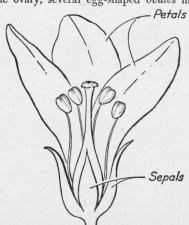

Fig. 83. The Accessory Organs of a Flower

The Essential and Accessory Organs. Since the stamens and the pistil are the only structures that are absolutely necessary for reproduction, they are called the *essential organs*. The calyx and the corolla are not directly involved in reproduction, and so are called the *accessory organs*.

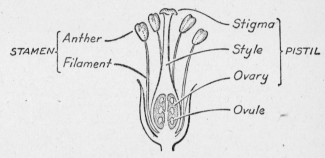

Fig. 84. The Essential Organs of a Flower

Formation of the Gametes:

1. *Male Gamete.* In the anther, pollen grains are formed. Each pollen grain contains two nuclei: (*a*) a tube nucleus, and (*b*) a sperm nucleus, or male gamete.

2. *Female Gamete.* Inside the ovary are ovules. Each ovule contains a structure called the *embryo sac*, from which will develop a true egg cell, or female gamete, and a double nucleated cell.

Pollination. Pollination is the process of removing a pollen grain from an anther and placing it on a stigma. By pollination, a male plant gamete is brought close enough to a female plant gamete so that fertilization can occur. There are two types of pollination, as follows:

1. *Self-pollination.* When a pollen grain is transferred from the anther of a flower to the stigma of the same flower (or to the stigma of another flower on the same plant), the process is called *self-pollination*.

2. *Cross-pollination.* When a pollen grain is transferred from the anther of one flower to the stigma of a flower on another plant, the process is called *cross-pollination*.

Agents of Pollination.   Pollination is often accomplished by the following agents: bees, other insects, wind, water, and some birds. When pollen is transferred by man, as in breeding experiments, the process is called *artificial pollination.* Often, cellophane bags are placed over experimental flowers to keep unwanted pollen out.

Double Fertilization.   After a pollen grain has been deposited on the stigma, the pollen grain grows, thereby producing a *pollen tube.* Under the influence of the tube nucleus, the pollen tube grows downward through the style and into the ovary. Finally, the pollen tube finds its way through a tiny opening in the ovule.

Meanwhile, the sperm nucleus of the pollen grain has divided into two sperm nuclei, which are carried by the pollen tube into the ovule. Within the ovule, one sperm nucleus fertilizes the true egg cell, forming the zygote, which later becomes the embryo plant. The other sperm nucleus unites with the double nucleated cell of the embryo sac, thereby forming the *endosperm nucleus,* which later becomes the food supply of the embryo plant. These two cell unions are called *double fertilization.*

Formation of the Seed.   The seed is a ripened ovule. Within the ovule, the zygote undergoes a number of divisions until the embryo plant consists of the following structures: (1) the *plumule,* which is to form the stem and leaves of the new plant,   (2) the *hypocotyl,* which is to form the root, and   (3) one or more *cotyledons,* which contain stored food for the embryo plant. Monocots, such as the corn, are so called because their seeds have *one* cotyledon; dicots, such as the bean, have *two* cotyledons.

When the above three structures are formed, the embryo enters a resting stage. The walls of the ovule form a *seed coat.* Within this

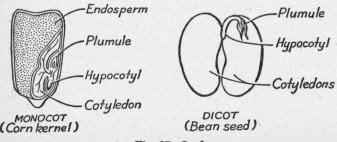

MONOCOT
(Corn kernel)

DICOT
(Bean seed)

Fig. 85. Seeds

covering are (1) the embryo, and (2) a food supply sufficient for the young plant until the plant has leaves and can carry on photosynthesis.

In the moncot, the *endosperm* (which develops from the endosperm nucleus) is large and contains most of the stored food. In the dicot, the stored food is in the cotyledons, and the endosperm is small or may be completely lacking.

The Fruit. The fruit is a ripened ovary. While seed formation is taking place, the ovary is forming into a structure to enclose the seeds. This structure is called the *fruit*. All seed plants produce a fruit.

Seeds Are Scattered. A plant does not drop its numerous offspring, the seeds, near to itself. This is because the many seeds and the parent plant would compete with each other for the necessities of life, namely, water, sunshine and minerals. Therefore, plant seeds are scattered over a wide area in order that some will reach places favorable for growth. The greater the distribution of many seeds, the better the chance of survival for a few seeds. The process of scattering seeds over a wide area is called *seed dispersal*.

Adaptations for Seed Dispersal. Seeds have adaptations for dispersal by wind, water and animals. Each plant has a particular method, as explained below.

1. *The Wind Disperses Seeds.* This is the most common method by which plants accomplish seed dispersal. Adaptations are the following:

The maple produces seeds which bear structures like *wings*. They whirl like a propeller as the seed flies. This wing action enables the seed to travel a considerable distance from the tree.

The seeds of the milkweed, thistle and dandelion have silky structures, shaped like a *parachute*. The seeds are thus able to float in air for considerable distances.

The touch-me-not and the squirting cucumber have an *explosive* fruit. When touched, the fruit snaps open and explodes its seeds several feet into the air.

2. *Water Disperses Seeds.* Some seeds, such as those of the coconut and of many weeds, are adapted for floating. These seeds are carried by currents of water for considerable distances.

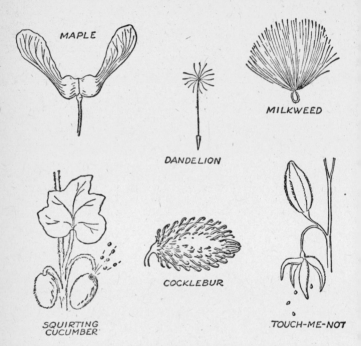

Fig. 86. Adaptations for Seed Dispersal

3. *Animals Disperse Seeds.* The burdock and cocklebur produce seeds equipped with barbs, or hooks. These structures attach themselves to the coats of passing animals. The animals carry the seeds away, often dropping them some distance from the plant.

When fruits are eaten by animals, especially by birds, the undigested seeds are eliminated as wastes. The seeds are thus carried far from the plant which originally produced them.

Seeds Grow into New Plants. After separation from the parent plant (dispersal), seeds of most species remain dormant for a period of time. After this dormant period, a seed normally germinates, or begins to grow, if the environmental conditions are suitable. The conditions necessary for the germination of seeds are: (1) suitable warmth, (2) a proper supply of moisture, and (3) a supply of oxygen. Fig. 87 below shows the steps in the development of a monocot (corn) and Fig. 88 on the next page shows the development of a dicot (bean).

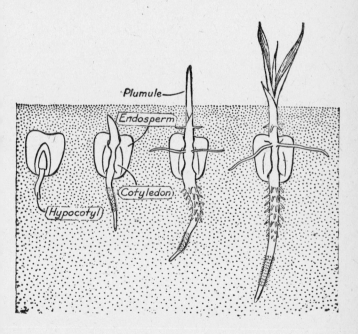

Fig. 87. Germination of a Monocot (Corn)

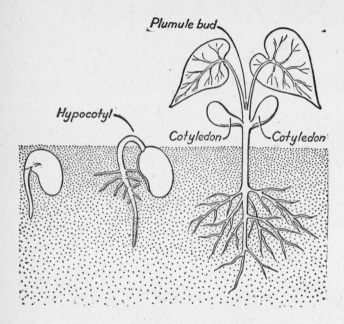

Fig. 88. Germination of a Dicot (Bean)

SEXUAL REPRODUCTION IN COMPLEX ANIMALS

How Complex Animals Reproduce. Almost all multicellular animals reproduce sexually, although a few also reproduce asexually. However, all vertebrates, including man, produce offspring only sexually. The sexual process is by fertilization, which involves the union of a male and a female gamete to form a zygote, or a single fertilized egg.

Gametes Produced in Gonads. Complex animals have specialized reproductive organs for the production of gametes. The *testis* is the male organ which produces the sperm cells. The *ovary* is the female organ which produces the egg cells. Both the male and female reproductive organs are called *gonads*.

Animal Sperm and Egg Cells Compared. Fertilization takes place upon the fusion of a sperm and an egg. These reproductive cells are quite different in appearance and structure, as follows:

The *sperm* is small and pointed. It has very little cytoplasm. It has a head composed largely of chromatin. It has a tail-like flagellum for swimming. A male animal produces many more sperms than a female produces eggs.

The *egg* is large and round. It contains a great amount of cytoplasm and stored food, called yolk. The egg does not swim about (that is, it is non-motile).

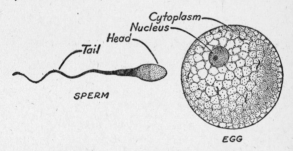

Fig. 89. Reproductive Cells of Animals

Internal and External Fertilization. An egg may be fertilized either outside or inside the body of the female.

1. *External Fertilization.* In some species, the eggs are laid and then fertilized outside the body of the female. This is called *external fertilization.* For example, in most fishes, the female lays the eggs in a suitable place. The male immediately discharges the sperms among the eggs. The sperms swim to the eggs and fertilization occurs. External fertilization is found also in frogs and toads.

2. *Internal Fertilization.* In some species, the sperms are discharged into the body of the female, where fertilization occurs. This is known as *internal fertilization.* Internal fertilization is found in insects, spiders, reptiles, birds and mammals.

Where the Young Develop. In some animals, the eggs are laid and the young develop *outside* the body of the female. Such species are called *oviparous*. All animals having external fertilization are oviparous. In some animals, such as birds, fertilization is internal, but the eggs are laid and develop *outside* the body of the female, thereby making the species oviparous.

In other animals, for example the mammals, the eggs are fertilized internally and development occurs *within* the body of the female. The young are eventually born. Species in which the young are born are called *viviparous*.

How an Egg Becomes an Animal. All life starts from a single cell, the zygote. By a series of mitotic divisions, called *cleavage*, the single fertilized cell develops into a complex animal having different types of tissues and various organs. Development from egg to animal takes place as follows:

The zygote divides by mitosis into two cells attached to each other. The two cells then divide, forming four cells. The four divide, forming eight. Eight divide, becoming sixteen. Division continues until the cells form a bunch resembling the parts of a blackberry. This is called the *morula* stage.

As more cells form, they take the shape of a hollow ball. This is the *blastula* stage.

Gradually, one side of the blastula pushes inwards and forms two layers of cells. This is the *gastrula* stage.

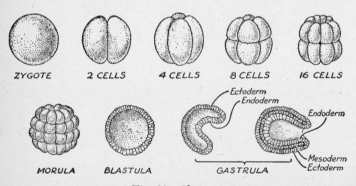

Fig. 90. Cleavage

In the gastrula, the outer layer of cells is called the *ectoderm*. The inner layer of cells is the *endoderm*. Between the ectoderm and the endoderm is eventually formed a third layer of cells, the *mesoderm*.

The ectoderm, mesoderm and endoderm are known as the *primary germ layers*. It is from these layers that all of the organs of the new individual are formed. The structures formed from each layer are shown in the table below. The process by which the primary germ layers become the organs is called *differentiation*. Differentiation takes place early in the development of the embryo.

STRUCTURES FORMED FROM THE PRIMARY GERM LAYERS

Ectoderm	Mesoderm	Endoderm
Outer skin.	Muscles.	Mucous linings of digestive and respiratory tracts.
Nervous system.	Blood.	
Parts of sense organs.	Blood vessels.	
	Connective tissue.	Parts of digestive glands (liver and pancreas).
	Skeleton.	
	Excretory system.	
	Reproductive system.	

Reproduction in Insects. The sexes are separate in insects; that is, some insects are males, while other insects are females. Sperms, produced in the testes of the male, are stored in the *seminal vesicles*. During mating, the sperms are passed to the *seminal receptacles* of the female. Eggs produced in the ovaries, are covered with a shell bearing a small pore through which the sperm can enter. The eggs, when mature, pass through the oviducts into the vagina, where they are fertilized by the sperms from the seminal receptacles. Later, the eggs are laid near the type of food on which the young insect feeds.

The Life History of Insects. It is commonly known that every butterfly was once a caterpillar, and every fly was once a maggot. The changes of form encountered in the life history of an insect are called *metamorphosis*. There are two types of insect metamorphoses, as follows.

1. *Incomplete Metamorphosis* (egg, nymph, adult). This type is found in the grasshopper. After mating, the adult female deposits the fertilized eggs. The young, upon hatching from the eggs, resemble the adult in form and structure, except that they are smaller and lack wings. The young gradually assume adulthood by passing through the stages as shown in Fig. 91 below.

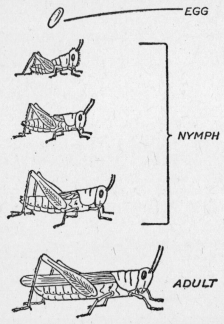

Fig. 91. Development of the Grasshopper by Incomplete Metamorphosis

The young of an insect having incomplete metamorphosis is known as a *nymph*. During the development from a nymph to an adult, the insect must occasionally cast off its hard chitinous skin. Since the hard skin does not grow, the insect sheds it and grows new skin. Being soft and elastic, the new skin adjusts to the size of the growing body and then hardens. An insect may undergo several sheddings, or *molts*, before reaching adulthood.

2. *Complete Metamorphosis* (egg, larva, pupa, adult). This type is found in the change of a caterpillar into a butterfly or moth. The egg hatches into a worm-like *larva*, which bears no structural relation or resemblance to the adult. At this stage, the insect is the familiar caterpillar. After much eating, the larva enters a helpless resting stage, the *pupa*. Some insects, notably the moths, weave a silken covering, called a *cocoon*, about themselves for protection during the pupa stage. The pupa of a butterfly is called a *chrysalis*. The pupa stage lasts for a definite length of time, depending on the species and the climate. During this time, the amazing transformation to the adult form takes place. When the cocoon finally opens, the winged adult emerges. It is completely grown and sexually mature.

An insect does *not* grow after reaching the winged adult stage. Hence, small flies do not grow into large flies. Large flies are of one species, and small flies are of another species.

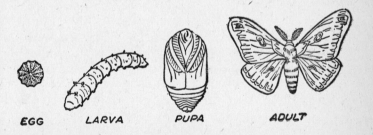

EGG   LARVA   PUPA   ADULT

Fig. 92. Development of the Moth by Complete Metamorphosis

The Metamorphosis of the Frog. Fig. 93 below shows the successive stages in the development of the frog. As the tadpole transforms into a frog, the following changes occur: (1) External gills for breathing and respiration are replaced by internal gills. (2) Hind legs appear and later the forelegs develop. (3) The tail is absorbed (not shed). (4) Lungs develop and take over the work of the gills. (5) The form changes to that of the adult frog, which is able to live both on land and in the water.

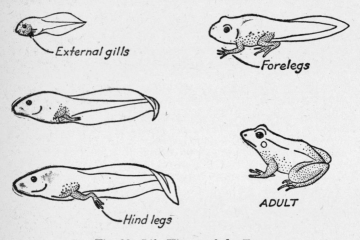

Fig. 93. Life History of the Frog

Reproduction in Mammals. Reproduction in all mammals is similar. The sperm cells are produced in the testes of the male, and the egg cells are produced in the ovaries of the female. A zygote is formed in the body of the female as follows: The egg leaves the ovary and enters the upper portion of the tubelike *oviduct*. At the same time, the sperm, which had been introduced through the *vagina* (the external opening of the female reproductive organs), ascends. The sperm swims to the upper portion of the oviduct, where fertilization takes place. The embryo then slowly moves downward to an enlarged portion of the oviduct, called the *uterus*. Here, the embryo attaches itself to the wall of the uterus by means of a membrane called the *placenta*. The placenta develops as the tissues of the uterus and of the embryo join together. The placenta contains numerous capillaries of the embryo closely intertwined with capillaries of the mother. By osmosis, food and oxygen pass from the capillaries of the mother to the capillaries of the embryo in the placenta. Also by osmosis, wastes leave the capillaries of the embryo in the placenta and enter the capillaries of the mother. The food and oxygen of the mother are delivered from the placenta to the embryo by means of the *umbilical cord.* In reverse, wastes are carried through the umbilical cord from the embryo to the placenta, and then to the mother. Since the embryo of the mammal obtains its nourishment from the bloodstream of the mother, the mammalian egg contains little or no stored food. The egg of the mammal is microscopic in size.

The embryo remains in the uterus until fully formed. Then the walls of the uterus undergo a series of contractions which force the new individual and the placenta out of the body. The time required for complete development is called *gestation.* The gestation period varies among the mammals.

Parental Care of the Young. The amount of care parents give their young varies widely among animals. Many fishes and amphibians deposit their eggs in the water and provide the young with no care whatever. Exceptions are (1) the seahorse, the male of which carries the eggs in a pouch, and (2) the sunfish, which builds a nest and guards the eggs until they hatch. Parental care is greatest in birds and mammals. In man, parental care is most extensive and prolonged.

Obviously, if the young of a species are left to make their way alone, they are subject to a lack of food, the attacks of enemies, and other perils. As a result, many do not survive. On the other hand, if given much parental care, most young develop into adults. Thus, a species exercising little or no parental care must produce many eggs; a species which cares for its young can maintain its numbers by producing comparatively few offspring.

Parthenogenesis. In all the animals we have studied thus far, an organism was formed from an egg that had been fertilized. In some species of animals, however, a new individual is able to develop naturally from an egg that has *not* been fertilized. This process of the development of a new individual from an unfertilized egg cell is known as *parthenogenesis.* Parthenogenesis is a normal occurrence in such insects as aphids, bees, ants and wasps. Although most of these insects reproduce sexually, parthenogenesis also takes place. In some insects, parthenogenesis produces male organisms, while the fertilized eggs give rise to females. In the bee, for example, the drones (males) come from the unfertilized eggs, while the workers and queens (females) develop from the fertilized eggs.

Scientists have been able to cause the unfertilized eggs of starfish, sea urchins, some worms and mollusks to develop into new individuals. This is accomplished by placing the unfertilized eggs in sea water to which chemicals are added, and then returning the eggs to normal sea water. The chemicals seem to replace the sperm in causing the unfertilized egg to divide and form a new individual.

Advantages of Sexual Reproduction. Sexual reproduction has two important biological advantages over asexual reproduction as follows:

1. *Greater Variation.* In sexual reproduction, hereditary characteristics from the male parent are carried by the chromatin in the nucleus of the sperm cell. Hereditary characteristics from the female parent are carried by the chromatin in the nucleus of the egg cell. Thus, in sexual reproduction, the offspring inherit characteristics from *two* parents. This results in greater variation among the offspring than would be possible in asexual species, where there is only one parent. We shall see that variation is highly desirable.

2. *Increased Vigor.* Scientists have proved that the mixing of chromatin when two gametes unite, often results in a new organism having greater vigor than either of its parents. Frequently, the desirable features of both parents are passed along to the new individual.

Completion Questions

1. The process requiring two parents to produce offspring is called _____.

2. A (an) _____ is the general name for a cell that unites with another cell to form a new organism.

3. The one cell resulting from the union of two sex cells is called a (an) _____.

4. The process in which similar cells unite in reproduction is called _____.

5. The cells that reproduce sexually in spirogyra are called _____.

6. Conjugation in spirogyra results in the formation of _____.

7. The union of two dissimilar gametes is called _____.

8. The most important event in fertilization is the fusion of the _____ and the egg.

9. The cell resulting from the union of the male and female gametes is called the _____.

10. In alternation of generations, the fern plant that develops from a spore is the _____.
11. The reproductive organs of flowering plants are found in structures called _____.
12. Pollen grains are produced in the _____.
13. Within the ovary of a flower is the _____, in which the egg cell is located.
14. The essential organs of a flower are the stamens and the _____.
15. A pollen grain contains a sperm nucleus and a (an) _____ nucleus.
16. Seeds develop from the structures in the ovary known as _____.
17. The part of the flower that develops into the fruit is called the _____.
18. The _____ is the reproductive cell which has a flagellum.
19. The egg-producing organ of a backboned animal is the _____.
20. Stored food in an animal egg is called the _____.
21. _____ is the process in which a sperm unites with an egg outside the body of the female.
22. The hollow-ball stage in the development of an embryo is called the _____.
23. The layers from which all the organs and tissues of a complex animal develop are known as the _____.
24. The changes in form that an organism goes through in developing from an egg to an adult is called _____.
25. In the metamorphosis of a frog, the gills are replaced by _____.

Multiple-Choice Questions

1. Conjugation is a simple form of (1) fission (2) grafting (3) nutrition (4) sexual reproduction.
2. Sexual reproduction in spirogyra produces (1) a seed (2) an embryo (3) a zygote (4) a gamete.
3. The type of reproduction in which one generation of an organism reproduces sexually and another generation asexually is (1) binary fission (2) conjugation (3) alternation of generations (4) mitosis.
4. The part of the flower that produces the pollen is the (1) pistil (2) ovule (3) stamen (4) petal.

5. The egg nucleus of the flowering plant develops from (1) the seed (2) the embryo sac (3) the stigma (4) the pollen grain.

6. Transfer of pollen from the anther to the stigma of a flower is called (1) fertilization (2) oogenesis (3) pollination (4) maturation.

7. Pollen from a plant may be used to bring about fertilization in (1) any other plant (2) closely related plants (3) any plant of about the same size (4) any plant in its environment.

8. A growing pollen grain becomes (1) a pollen tube (2) an embryo sac (3) a seed (4) an ovary.

9. The sperm nuclei of the flowering plant develop from (1) the seed (2) the ovary wall (3) the stigma (4) the pollen grain.

10. The part of a flower that forms the seed is the (1) ovule (2) ovary (3) receptacle (4) stigma.

11. The young plantlet in a seed is called (1) the placenta (2) the endosperm (3) the embryo (4) the embryo sac.

12. The process of scattering seeds is known as (1) seed formation (2) seed germination (3) seed dispersal (4) pollination.

13. A condition *not* necessary for seed germination is (1) a supply of oxygen (2) a proper temperature (3) moisture (4) sunshine.

14. The male gametes of the fish are produced in the (1) ovary (2) oviduct (3) spermiduct (4) testes.

15. The head of an animal sperm is composed largely of (1) chromatin (2) cytoplasm (3) nuclear sap (4) cell sap.

16. The egg of a fish is larger than the sperm because it contains (1) a cell membrane (2) centrosomes (3) food (4) more chromosomes.

17. When a zygote undergoes cell division, the process is known as (1) fertilization (2) maturation (3) conjugation (4) cleavage.

18. In the developing embryo, the nervous system arises from the primary germ layer called the (1) ectoderm (2) endoderm (3) morula (4) mesoderm.

19. Fertilization in insects takes place in the structure of the female called the (1) seminal receptacle (2) ovary (3) oviduct (4) vagina.

20. The process in which the young of an insect goes through a series of great structural changes to become an adult is (1) mitosis (2) cleavage (3) metamorphosis (4) reduction division.

21. In mammals, the embryo develops in the (1) ovary (2) uterus (3) intestines (4) oviduct.

22. During development, the rabbit embryo obtains its food through the (1) albumen (2) placenta (3) ovaries (4) ova.
23. The developing embryo of a mammal lives on food supplied by (1) both parents (2) the female parent (3) the male parent (4) sometimes the male and sometimes the female parent.
24. The greatest amount of parental care is given by organisms (1) producing many offspring (2) producing few offspring (3) reproducing asexually (4) having external fertilization.
25. The greatest amount of parental care is given by birds and (1) fish (2) protozoa (3) insects (4) mammals.

Modified True-False Questions

1. The cell produced by the fusion of gametes is called the *zygote*.
2. Paramecia reproduce sexually by *binary fission*.
3. Sexual reproduction in the moss plant gives rise to the *sporophyte* generation.
4. The brightly colored leaf-like parts of most flowers are called *sepals*.
5. The pollen grain contains the *female* gamete.
6. In flowering plants, pollination takes place *after* fertilization.
7. The bee is valuable for its work in *fertilizing* apple blossoms.
8. Fertilization in flowers occurs within the *anther*.
9. Cleavage *increases* the number of cells.
10. Parthenogenesis is the development of a new organism from a (an) *fertilized* egg.

Essay Questions

1. *a.* State one difference between asexual and sexual reproduction.
   b. Make a series of labeled diagrams to illustrate conjugation in a plant.
   c. Explain why the process of conjugation is considered necessary for the continuation of paramecia.
2. *a.* Draw a diagram of the essential parts of a flower and label the following: anther, petals, ovary, stigma, style, ovule.
   b. What is the function of each of the parts labeled in *a?*
   c. In what way does pollination differ from fertilization in flowering plants?
   d. Tell why flowers that have stamens but no other reproductive organs do not bear fruit.
   e. Describe three ways by which seed dispersal may take place.

3. *a.* Give one way in which the sperm cells and the egg cells of mammals are alike and two ways in which they are different.
   b. Illustrate each of the following kinds of reproduction by giving a specific example: (1) sexual reproduction with external fertilization, (2) sexual reproduction with internal fertilization.
   c. Describe the process that a zygote undergoes in becoming a new individual.
   d. Describe: (1) incomplete metamorphosis, (2) complete metamorphosis.
   e. State two structural changes that occur when a tadpole develops into a frog.

4. *a.* State two ways in which the process of reproduction is similar in all vertebrates.
   b. State one way in which reproduction in the chicken is different from reproduction in the rabbit.
   c. Give two ways in which a bean seed and a fertile chicken egg are similar.
   d. Name and briefly describe two processes which take place in the reproduction of both higher plants and higher animals.

5. *a.* State fully the difference between (1) gamete and zygote, (2) spore and seed, (3) ovule and plant embryo, (4) conjugation and fertilization.
   b. Give two factors on which the successful reproduction of a higher species depends and show how these factors tend to insure success.

6. Give a biological explanation for each of the following:
   a. Heavy rains at the time fruit trees blossom may reduce the amount of fruit that will develop.
   b. The yolk (egg cell) of a sparrow's egg is about one hundred times larger than the egg cell of an elephant.
   c. Mammals produce fewer eggs than do frogs.
   d. Sexually produced offspring show greater variation than do those produced asexually.
   e. The codfish produces millions of eggs each year.
   f. Many weeds produce seeds equipped with hooks or barbs.
   g. Parental care is more essential in higher animals than in lower animals.

Chapter XVIII

THE PHYSICAL BASIS OF INHERITANCE

Chromatin, the Carrier of Hereditary Traits. *Heredity* (or *inheritance*) is the passing of characteristics (traits or characters) from parents to offspring. Traits are carried by the chromatin material present in the nucleus of every cell. During the resting stage, chromatin is scattered in the entire nucleus; but during cell division, the chromatin arranges itself in definite pairs of rod-like structures called *chromosomes*. The chromosomes of a pair are the same in size and shape, but differ from all other chromosome pairs. Chromosomes are composed of many units, called *genes,* chained together like strands of beads. Each pair of genes is the determiner of a specific trait, such as color of eyes, color of hair, size of body, shape of nose, etc. Genes are even smaller than the microscopic chromosomes; they are not visible under the ordinary compound microscope. Because genes control heritable traits, the science of heredity is known as *genetics.*

The Work of T. H. Morgan. The gene theory states that the pairs of genes are the carriers of individual traits from parents to offspring. This theory was proposed by the American biologist, *Thomas H. Morgan.* He reached this conclusion as the result of long experimentation with the fruit fly.

Morgan selected the fruit fly, *Drosophila melanogaster,* for his experiments because:

1. Drosophila has many distinct and recognizable unit characters.
2. Drosophila is small, easy to care for and requires little food.
3. Drosophila mates readily and produces a new generation in ten to twenty days.
4. Drosophila produces a large number of offspring, sometimes several hundred from one mating.
5. In the salivary glands of the larva, Drosophila has "giant chromosomes" which aid in microscopic studies.

Morgan made *chromosome maps* (drawings of chromosomes) locating pairs of genes according to the specific traits that they determine.

Chromosome Number. The number of chromosomes in the nuclei of body cells varies with each species, but is constant within a species. For example, all fruit flies have 8 chromosomes (or 4 pairs); all pea plants have 14 chromosomes (or 7 pairs); all humans have 48 chromosomes (or 24 pairs). The number of chromosomes in the body cells of an organism is known as the *chromosome number* of that species.

Diploid and Haploid Numbers. Each body cell of an organism has its full number of choromosomes. A body cell is said to have the *diploid number* of chromosomes. But the reproductive cells (or gametes) contain just one-half the number of chromosomes of that species. A reproductive cell is said to have the *haploid number* of chromosomes.

For example, the diploid number of chromosomes in the human body cell is 48, or 24 pairs of chromosomes, each pair of which carries the genes for specific traits. The haploid number of chromosomes in the human reproductive cell is 24, or one chromosome from each of the original 24 pairs. When a male gamete unites with a female gamete, the zygote (fertilized egg) receives the haploid number of chromosomes from each of the gametes and then possesses the diploid number. The gametes must be haploid in order to prevent the continual increase in chromosome number each time that fertilization occurs.

How Gametes Are Formed. In the testes of the male and in the ovaries of the female are the diploid *primary sex cells*. These cells produce the haploid gametes: sperms in the male and eggs in the female. The entire process of gamete formation is called *maturation,* or *gametogenesis,* and involves two divisions—mitotic division and reduction division. As a result of these divisions, a primary sex cell gives rise to four sperm cells in the male but only one egg cell in the female.

Maturation in the Male:

1. *Reduction Division.* A primary sex cell is diploid. By reduction division it becomes two daughter cells. Each daughter cell is haploid, since it receives only one chromosome from each chromosome pair present in the primary sex cell.

2. *Mitotic Division.* Each of the haploid daughter cells then divides by mitosis (see page 26). In this division, the chromosomes of each daughter cell split lengthwise, thus assuring an equal number of chromosomes to the two cells formed.

Thus, the two daughter cells become four cells. Each of these cells changes in shape, develops a tail and becomes a sperm cell. Each sperm has the same number of chromosomes as the haploid daughter cells, but only one-half the number of chromosomes as the original primary sex cell.

Maturation in the Female:

1. *Reduction Division.* A diploid primary sex cell becomes two haploid daughter cells by reduction division. One daughter cell is small, while the other is large.

2. *Mitotic Division.* The small daughter cell divides by mitosis into two small cells. The large daughter cell divides into one large cell and a small cell.

Thus, the two daughter cells become four cells, three small and one large. The large cell is the true egg cell. The three small cells, called *polar bodies,* do not enter into reproduction, but disintegrate.

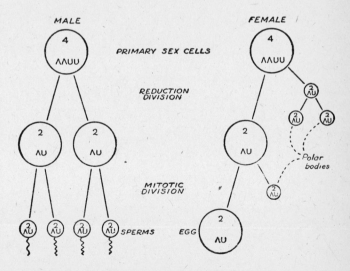

Fig. 94. Gametogenesis (Maturation) in a Species
Having Four Chromosomes

Fertilization Restores the Diploid Number. Fertilization takes place when the nuclei of the sperm and the egg fuse together, forming the zygote. The chromosome number, which was reduced during reduction division, is now restored. The chromosomes are again in pairs. One chromosome of every pair came from the male reproductive cell and the other chromosome of every pair came from the female reproductive cell. Therefore, the genes carrying the heritable traits are contributed equally by each of the parents to the new individual.

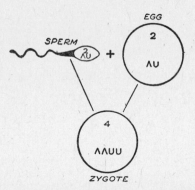

Fig. 95. Fertilization Restores the Diploid Number
(in a Species Having Four Chromosomes)

Completion Questions

1. The transmitting of traits from one generation to the next is known as _____.
2. Rod-like structures composed of chromatin are _____.
3. Hereditary characters are carried by invisible structures called _____.
4. The _____ is the organism with which Morgan conducted his experiments in heredity.
5. One reason for using this organism in the study of genetics is that it has _____ in the salivary glands.
6. The _____ of the human species is 48, or 24 pairs.
7. In the sperms and eggs of all species, the number of chromosomes is _____ that of the body cells.

8. The process by which the gametes of an organism are formed is called _____.

9. The diploid number of chromosomes is reduced to the haploid number by a type of division called _____.

10. The normal number of chromosomes is restored by the process of _____.

Multiple-Choice Questions

1. The tiny structures making up the chromosomes are the (1) nuclei (2) chromatin (3) genes (4) beads.

2. The number of chromosomes found in the body cells of every member of a species is known as the (1) haploid number (2) chromosome number (3) reduced number (4) chromosome pairs.

3. In an organism that produces gametes having 20 chromosomes, the number of chromosomes in the body cells is (1) one half as many (2) one quarter as many (3) one eighth as many (4) twice as many   as that of the reproductive cells.

4. If the number of chromosomes in a root cell is twelve, the number of chromosomes in the sperm cell of the same organism will be (1) three (2) six (3) nine (4) twenty-four.

5. The primary sex cell of man contains (1) the haploid number of chromosomes (2) the diploid number of chromosomes (3) 24 chromosomes (4) one gene for each character.

6. The chromosomes of a cell split lengthwise during the process of (1) reduction division (2) mitosis (3) fertilization (4) chromosome mapping.

7. Polar bodies are formed during (1) binary fission (2) maturation of the egg (3) maturation of the sperm (4) spore formation.

8. The two processes that occur during gamete formation are reduction division and (1) maturation (2) gametogenesis (3) mitotic division (4) fertilization.

9. The process of sperm formation results in the formation of (1) one functional sperm (2) an egg cell (3) a polar body (4) four functional sperms.

10. The process in which there is a fusion of egg and sperm nuclei is (1) maturation (2) gametogenesis (3) reduction division (4) fertilization.

Essay Questions

1. Maturation, mitosis and fertilization are processes of great importance in the lives of all higher organisms.
   a. Tell why each process is important.
   b. Show by labeled diagrams the essential steps in the formation of sperms in an organism having three pairs of chromosomes.

2. *a*. By making diagrams of each of the following, show that fertilization restores the normal species number of chromosomes: (1) a sperm cell (2) an unfertilized egg cell (3) a fertilized egg.
   b. Explain how the study of giant salivary chromosomes in the fruit fly has furnished evidence that supports the theory of the gene.

3. Explain each of the following statements:
   a. Gametes carry only one gene for each character.
   b. An organism that develops from a fertilized egg receives genes contributed by each parent.

Chapter XIX

THE MENDELIAN LAWS

Gregor Mendel, the Father of Genetics. *Gregor Mendel,* an Austrian monk, was the first scientist to apply the scientific method to the study of heredity. Experimenting with garden peas, Mendel discovered how characters are transmitted from parents to offspring. He published his laws in 1865, but his work was ignored by biologists of the day. Mendel died without recognition. In 1900, however, three scientists, DeVries, Correns and Tschermak, independently discovered Mendel's laws and referred to them in their original writings. Mendel was then given full credit for his discoveries, and was proclaimed the "founder of the science of genetics."

Mendel's Experiments. For his experiments, Mendel chose garden peas because this plant is self-pollinating and possesses many different traits which are easily distinguishable. Some heritable traits that Mendel noticed in pea plants were length of stem, color of pod, color of flower, type of seed and color of seed.

Mendel observed that contrasting characters existed in all the traits. *Contrasting characters* are opposite traits. For example, some stems were tall, others dwarfed. Some pods were green, others yellow. Some flowers were purple, others white. Some seeds were smooth, others wrinkled. Some seeds were yellow, others green.

Mendel cross-pollinated for all the heritable traits through several generations, but each crossing was for the study of one trait only.

Obtaining a Pure Strain. Mendel took seeds from a long-stemmed variety and planted them. All the offspring had long stems. He then took seeds from the offspring and planted them. Again, all the offspring gave rise to long-stemmed plants. He was now sure that he had a pure strain of long-stemmed plants. A *pure strain* is a variety in which a particular trait will appear in successive generations.

In the manner described above, Mendel obtained a pure strain of short-stemmed plants. He now had pure strains of both long and short-stemmed varieties.

Crossing Organisms with Contrasting Characters. Mendel cross-pollinated tall-stemmed plants with short-stemmed plants, and also short-stemmed plants with long-stemmed plants. He did this by transferring pollen from the stamen of one plant to the pistil of the other. At the same time, he removed the stamens from the pollinated plant and covered the plant with a paper bag. This prevented self-pollination and cross-pollination (such as by insects or wind) from occurring. After fertilization took place in the pollinated plant, Mendel removed the seeds and planted them. All the offspring of the crossings appeared with long stems.

The character that appeared in the offspring as the result of crossing contrasting characters, Mendel called the *dominant character*. The character that the offspring inherited, but which was overshadowed by the dominant character, Mendel called the *recessive character*.

In the above crossing of a tall-stemmed parent with a short-stemmed parent, the offspring inherited both characters. However, the dominant character (long stem) appeared, while the recessive character (short stem) remained hidden. Such an organism that inherits both the dominant and the recessive character, but in which only the dominant appears, Mendel called a *hybrid*. A hybrid resembles only one parent.

In the same manner that Mendel investigated the trait of stem inheritance, he studied the other traits by obtaining pure strains and crossing them. All the offspring resulting from these crossings resembled only one of the parents. For example, the crossing of plants having green pods with plants having yellow pods, always produced offspring having green pods as the dominant character. In crossings of plants having purple flowers with plants having white flowers, purple flowers were dominant. Similarly, he found that smooth seeds were dominant over wrinkled seeds, and yellow seeds were dominant over green seeds.

From these observations, Mendel stated the *Law of Dominance:* When two organisms pure for contrasting characters are crossed, one of these characters appears in the hybrid while the other character remains hidden.

Crossing Hybrids. Up to this point in Mendel's experiments, he had crossed pure strains of opposite characters and obtained hybrid offspring. The pure strains he designated with the letter P, meaning *parent* generation. The offspring of the P generation he labeled F_1, denoting the *first filial* generation. He then crossed thousands of F_1 hybrid plants for a study of each of the traits. The offspring of these crossings he called F_2, or the *second filial* generation.

Mendel noticed that some of the F₂ plants possessed the dominant characters and some possessed the recessive characters. That is, the crossings of hybrid tall with hybrid tall produced some offspring having tall stems and some having short stems. The number having the dominant characters greatly exceeded those having the recessive characters. Mendel found that the ratio of dominant characters to recessive characters actually was 3 to 1. This is known as the *Mendelian ratio*.

From these observations, Mendel formulated his second law, the *Law of Segregation:* When two hybrid organisms are crossed, the recessive character, which had been hidden in the F₁ generation, is separated (or *segregated*) from the dominant character and appears in some of the F₂ generation.

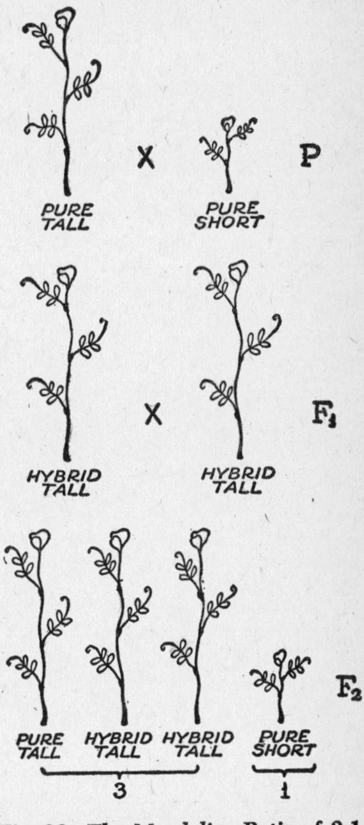

Geneticists express in ratios the average results of the mating of organisms. They (1) cross thousands of organisms, (2) tabulate the results, and (3) arrive at a mathematical ratio of the appearance of traits. For example, out of one experiment crossing hybrid tall plants, 3,100 offspring may be tall and 900 short. This illustrates Mendel's ratio of 3:1. However, another experiment crossing hybrid plants may result in 2,900 tall and 1,100 short. Although the result of one experiment varies slightly from the result of the other, the average of both experiments is 3:1.

Fig. 96. The Mendelian Ratio of 3:1

A ratio cannot be constant because there is no positive way of determining in advance which sperm will unite with an egg. In all crossings involving a single trait, there are four possible combinations. For example, in the crossing of two hybrids:

1. The sperm carrying the dominant trait may fuse with the egg carrying the dominant trait. Result: pure tall.

2. The sperm carrying the dominant trait may fuse with the egg carrying the recessive trait. Result: hybrid tall.

3. The sperm carrying the recessive trait may fuse with the egg carrying the dominant trait. Result: hybrid tall.

4. The sperm carrying the recessive trait may fuse with the egg carrying the recessive trait. Result: short.

Thus, there are three chances that an offspring will be tall to one chance of its being short.

Crossing Dihybrids. In the previous experiments crossing hybrids, all the pea plants were hybrid for a single trait. Such organisms hybrid for only one trait are called *monohybrids*.

Mendel then investigated the inheritance of two traits in a single crossing of peas. An organism hybrid for two traits is known as a *dihybrid*. He crossed plants that were pure tall and had pure yellow seeds with plants that were pure short and had pure green seeds. He obtained dihybrid plants all of which were hybrid tall and had hybrid yellow seeds.

He then crossed thousands of dihybrid plants and obtained offspring possessing different combinations of length of stem and color of seeds. Mendel found that the combinations of characters appeared in a ratio of 9:3:3:1. This means that per 16 plants:

9 had long stems and yellow seeds

3 had long stems and green seeds

3 had short stems and yellow seeds

1 had a short stem and green seeds

After crossing dihybrids for all the other traits in combinations of two, Mendel stated his third law, the *Law of Independent Assortment:* Each character is inherited independently of any other character that may be present in the parent generation.

Mendel's Laws Explained by Modern Genetics. Mendel's laws were based on conclusions he reached merely by counting the appearance of traits resulting from crossings. He could not explain the results, not knowing about chromosomes and genes.

Since the development of the gene theory and recent genetic findings, the results of crossings can be predicted and explained. It should be noted that Mendel's principles have been found correct, barring a few exceptions. His laws still serve as the basis of heredity.

Genes are the determiners of the traits inherited by organisms. Our present-day knowledge of genetics enables us to symbolize the genetic make up of organisms and to predict the probable genetic make up of their offspring.

Genes are represented by letters. The first letter of the word for the dominant trait is chosen to represent both genes for that trait. For example, in the garden pea, tall stem is the dominant trait. Therefore, capital T represents the gene for tall stems, while small t represents the gene for short stems. Also, since yellow seeds are dominant, the gene for the trait with respect to color of seeds is written Y for yellow seeds and y for green seeds.

Since genes for a trait exist in pairs (one gene from each of the parents), two letters are used to represent the genetic make up of each individual. For example, a pure tall pea plant is represented genetically by TT. A pure short pea plant is represented by tt. An organism having two like genes for a trait is pure for that trait.

On the other hand, an organism having two unlike genes for a trait is hybrid for that trait. A hybrid is represented by a capital letter followed by a small letter. For example, a hybrid tall pea plant is Tt.

Summary of Genetic Make up
in the Pea Plant for Length of
Stem and Color of Seeds

TT = pure tall	YY = pure yellow seeds
Tt = hybrid tall	Yy = hybrid yellow seeds
tt = pure short	yy = pure green seeds

Note: When a dominant trait appears in an organism, that organism may be pure or hybrid for the trait. But when a recessive trait appears, the organism can be pure only.

THE GENE THEORY APPLIED TO MENDEL'S LAWS

The Law of Dominance. Mendel's Law of Dominance states that: When two organisms pure for contrasting characters are crossed, one of these characters appears in the hybrid while the other character remains hidden.

We can genetically represent this law as follows: (In a crossing, it is customary to indicate the female organism first.)

Female		Male		Offspring
TT	×	tt	=	Tt
(pure tall)		(short)		(hybrid tall)

We know from our previous study of maturation that the body cells of an organism have a pair of genes for every trait, but the gametes have only one gene for a trait. Therefore, the eggs of the female organism illustrated above carry only the T gene, whereas the sperms of the male carry only the t gene. When these gametes unite, the only possible combination of genes in the offspring is Tt—a hybrid tall organism.

Genetic crossings can also be shown by a "checkerboard" device called a *Punnett square*. The Punnett square below shows that only a hybrid tall (Tt) organism can result from crossing a pure tall (TT) organism with a short (tt) organism.

Key: T = tall, t = short

TT × tt

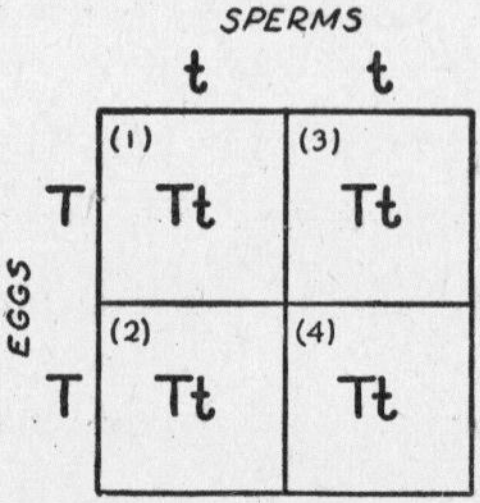

Result: 100% hybrid tall (Tt).

Fig. 97. Crossing a Pure Tall With a Pure Short
(Illustrating the Law of Dominance)

How to Represent a Crossing by a Punnett Square:

1. First prepare a key to indicate what each letter represents.

2. Then write the genetic make up of the organisms being crossed.

3. On top of the square, place the genes carried by the sperms; on the side, place the genes carried by the eggs.

4. In each of the boxes, write the combination of genes that would result if that particular sperm fertilizes that particular egg.

For example, in the Punnett square on the previous page:

Box 1 represents the genetic make up of the offspring if egg T is fertilized by sperm t. (The capital letter of a pair is always written first.)

Box 2 represents the genetic make up of the offspring if egg T is fertilized by sperm t.

Box 3 represents the genetic make up of the offspring if egg T is fertilized by sperm t.

Box 4 represents the genetic make up of the offspring if egg T is fertilized by sperm t.

Thus, we can see that when a pure tall (TT) organism is crossed with a short (tt) organism, all four possible gene combinations in the offspring are Tt.

The Law of Segregation. Mendel's Law of Segregation states: When two hybrid organisms are crossed, the recessive character, which had been hidden in the F_1 generation, is segregated from the dominant character and appears in some of the F_2 generation.

This law is represented genetically as follows:

$$\text{Tt} \times \text{Tt} = \begin{cases} \text{one TT (pure tall)} \\ \text{two Tt (hybrid tall)} \\ \text{one tt (short)} \end{cases}$$

According to the Mendelian ratio of 3:1, there are four possible combinations of genes. If a great number of hybrids were crossed, the average would show 3 offspring with the dominant trait to every 1 offspring having the recessive trait. In the above crossings, three plants have long stems and one has a short stem. However, since one tall plant is a pure tall organism, and two tall plants are hybrid organisms, and the short plant is pure, the Mendelian ratio of 3:1

becomes a genetic ratio of 1:2:1. This ratio can be seen by the following genetic crossing in the Punnett square:

Tt × Tt

	T	t
T	TT	Tt
t	Tt	tt

Result: 25% pure tall, 50% hybrid tall, 25% pure short or a genetic ratio of 1:2:1.

Fig. 98. Crossing a Hybrid Tall With Another Hybrid Tall (Illustrating the Law of Segregation)

As said before, the recessive character had been transmitted from one of the parents to the F_1 generation, but was overshadowed by the dominant character. In the F_2 generation, the recessive character reappeared, as follows:

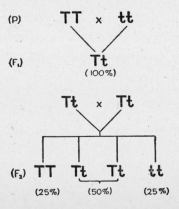

The Law of Independent Assortment. Mendel's Law of Independent Assortment states: Each character is inherited independently of any other character that may be present in the parent generation.

To illustrate this law, we perform two crossings. We first cross two organisms that are pure for two contrasting characters. In the crossing below, one plant is pure tall and has pure yellow seeds while the other plant is short and has green seeds.

Key: T = tall, t = short

Y = yellow seeds, y = green seeds

TTYY × ttyy

	ty	ty
TY	TtYy	TtYy
TY	TtYy	TtYy

Result: 100% dihybrid tall with yellow seeds.

Fig. 99. Crossing Organisms Pure for Two Contrasting Characters

This crossing produces 100% dihybrid organisms, that is, organisms hybrid for two traits. All the plants are genetically TtYy.

We then cross two dihybrids, as follows:

$$TtYy \times TtYy$$

	TY	Ty	tY	ty
TY	TTYY	TTYy	TtYY	TtYy
Ty	TTYy	TTyy	TtYy	Ttyy
tY	TtYY	TtYy	ttYY	ttYy
ty	TtYy	Ttyy	ttYy	ttyy

Fig. 100. Crossing a Dihybrid With Another Dihybrid
(Illustrating the Law of Independent Assortment)

This crossing produces an F_2 generation in which the traits appear in a 9:3:3:1 ratio.

9 plants are tall and have yellow seeds

3 plants are tall and have green seeds

3 plants are short and have yellow seeds

1 plant is short and has green seeds

Thus, the inheritance of any one character does not depend upon the inheritance of any other character. For example, the length of stem has no effect upon the color of seeds.

Other Possible Crossings. The following crossings do not illustrate any Mendelian law. In nature, however, these crosses occur:

A recessive organism may mate with a recessive:

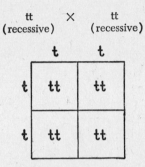

tt (recessive) × tt (recessive)

	t	t
t	tt	tt
t	tt	tt

Result: 100% short.

Fig. 101. Crossing a Short With Another Short

A hybrid organism may mate with a pure dominant:

Tt (hybrid) × TT (pure dominant)

	T	T
T	TT	TT
t	Tt	Tt

Result: 50% pure tall, 50% hybrid tall
or a genetic ratio of 1:1.

Fig. 102. Crossing a Hybrid Tall With a Pure Tall

A hybrid organism may mate with a recessive:

Tt   ×   tt
(hybrid)   (recessive)

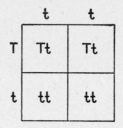

Result: 50% hybrid tall, 50% short
or a genetic ratio of 1:1.

Fig. 103. Crossing a Hybrid Tall With a Short

Incomplete Dominance, an Exception to Mendel's Law of Dominance. The crossing of certain organisms produces offspring having traits intermediate between the traits of the parents. The traits of the parents become blended in the offspring. For example, the crossing of a red-flowered four o'clock plant with a white-flowered four o'clock plant gives rise to pink-flowered offspring. A crossing of two organisms in which neither of the two contrasting characters dominates the other, but the offspring is a blend of both characters, is called *incomplete dominance,* or *blended inheritance,* or *blending inheritance.*

In incomplete dominance, the offspring do not resemble either parent. Thus, incomplete dominance is an exception to the Law of Dominance. According to Mendel, the dominant character overshadows the recessive character and therefore the offspring resemble one parent.

Examples of Incomplete Dominance. A pure red four o'clock crossed with a pure white four o'clock produces pink hybrids. Although the red and white colors blend to produce a pink offspring, the genes for red and white do not lose their identities.

Key: R = red, W = white

RR   ×   WW

(red)   (white)

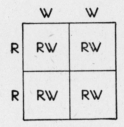

F₁ Result: 100% hybrid pink.

Fig. 104. Crossing a Red Four O'clock With a White Four O'clock

(Illustrating Incomplete Dominance)

When crossing a hybrid pink with another hybrid pink, the contrasting characters of red and white reappear in the F_2 generation. 25% of the offspring are red, 50% are pink, and 25% are white. The genetic crossing is shown below. Since there are no dominant or recessive characters in incomplete dominance, (1) the genes for a trait are written with capital letters only, and (2) the contrasting characters are represented by different letters.

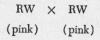

RW × RW

(pink)   (pink)

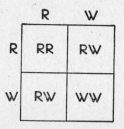

F_2 Result: 25% red, 50% hybrid pink, 25% white

or a genetic ratio of 1:2:1.

Fig. 105. Crossing a Pink Four O'clock With Another Pink Four O'clock

(Illustrating the Law of Segregation)

Another example of incomplete dominance is found in the Andalusian fowl. When a black and a white Andalusian fowl are mated, all the offspring are blue.

Key: B = black, W = white

BB	×	WW	=	BW
(black)		(white)		(blue)

	W	W
B	BW	BW
B	BW	BW

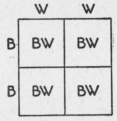

Result: 100% blue (hybrid).

Fig. 106. Crossing a Black Andalusian Fowl With a White Andalusian Fowl (Illustrating Incomplete Dominance)

$$BW \times BW = \left\{\begin{array}{l}1\ BB\\ 2\ BW\\ 1\ WW\end{array}\right.$$

	B	W
B	BB	BW
W	BW	WW

Result: 25% black, 50% hybrid blue, 25% white or a genetic ratio of 1:2:1.

Fig. 107. Crossing a Blue Andalusian Fowl With Another Blue Andalusian Fowl (Illustrating the Law of Segregation)

Linkage. *Linkage* is the inheritance of certain traits together. For example, a fruit fly that inherits short wings also inherits black body. These traits are inherited together because the genes controlling these traits lie on the same chromosome in the parent and are transmitted to the offspring together.

Backcross, to Determine Whether an Organism is Pure Dominant or Hybrid. It is sometimes necessary to know whether an organism is pure dominant or hybrid for one of a pair of characters. Since we cannot distinguish between a pure dominant and a hybrid by external appearance, we must determine the genetic make up of the unknown. This is accomplished by a *backcross,* which is a crossing of an unknown with a recessive. A recessive is used because whenever a recessive trait appears in an organism, that organism is known to be pure.

For example, a red-eyed fruit fly unknown as to RR or Rr is mated with a white-eyed fruit fly, rr. If all the offspring are red-eyed, the unknown is a pure red, RR. If, however, some white-eyed offspring appear, the unknown is a hybrid, Rr.

If unknown is *pure dominant:*
Parents: RR × rr
     (red) (white)

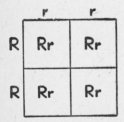

Result: 100% red.

If unknown is *hybrid:*
Parents: Rr × rr
     (red) (white)

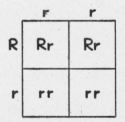

Result: 50% red, 50% white or a genetic ratio of 1:1.

Fig. 108. Crossing a Red-Eyed Fruit Fly With a White-Eyed Fruit Fly
(Illustrating a Backcross)

Completion Questions

1. The scientist who began the study of heredity through his experiments on the garden pea was _____.
2. Such opposites as tall and short stems are known as _____.
3. If all the offspring of a tall-stemmed plant appear with tall stems for many generations, the variety is called a (an) _____.
4. The parental characteristic that appears in all the offspring of a cross involving contrasting characters is said to be _____.
5. A pure dominant crossed with a recessive will produce _____.
6. The F_1 generation of pure-breeding parents differing in traits illustrates Mendel's law of _____.
7. When two hybrid tall pea plants are crossed, the ratio of tall to short offspring is _____.
8. The appearance of the recessive character in the F_2 generation of a cross illustrates the law of _____.
9. The percentage of hybrid offspring resulting from a cross of hybrid parents is _____.
10. An individual which is hybrid for two characters is called a (an) _____.
11. If an organism has two like genes for a character, it is said to be _____ for that character.
12. The results of crossing a red with a white four o'clock illustrate the principle of _____.
13. The crossing of blue Andalusian fowls results in _____% blue fowls.
14. One parent of a short pea plant was short and the other was tall. The genetic make up of the tall parent was _____.
15. The method used to determine whether an organism is pure or hybrid for a trait is known as _____.

Multiple-Choice Questions

1. The character which is inherited as the result of crossing organisms with contrasting characters but which remains hidden is the (1) dominant (2) recessive (3) blended trait (4) hybrid.
2. As a result of crossing pure purple-flowered plants with white-flowered plants, all the offspring appeared with (1) white flowers (2) purple flowers (3) pink flowers (4) none of these.

3. The height of the offspring produced when purebred tall pea plants are crossed with purebred short pea plants illustrates (1) dominance (2) independent assortment (3) chance (4) blending.

4. If three-quarters of the offspring of many experimental crosses showed the dominant character, the parents were (1) both pure dominant (2) both hybrid (3) one pure dominant, one recessive (4) one hybrid, one pure dominant.

5. The 3:1 Mendelian ratio results from the crossing of the following organisms: (1) a pure dominant with a pure dominant (2) a pure dominant with a recessive (3) two hybrids (4) a recessive with a recessive.

6. The crossing of dihybrid organisms results in the appearance of traits in the ratio of (1) 1:2:1 (2) 3:1 (3) 9:3:3:1 (4) 1:1.

7. Mendel's Law of Independent Assortment is best illustrated by crossing (1) monohybrids (2) a hybrid tall with a hybrid tall (3) dihybrids (4) a red-flowered with a white-flowered plant.

8. If an organism shows the recessive trait, the organism must be (1) hybrid (2) blended (3) pure (4) dominant for that trait.

9. Gametes are pure for each character because they have (1) no chromosomes (2) four chromosomes (3) double the number of chromosomes (4) one chromosome of each pair.

10. If all of a large number of offspring of a garden pea cross are Tt in genetic make up, the parents were (1) Tt and Tt (2) TT and tt (3) TT and Tt (4) Tt and tt.

11. The ratio of 1:2:1 in the offspring of hybrids best illustrates the law of (1) dominance (2) independent assortment (3) linkage (4) segregation.

12. The law that states that traits are inherited individually is Mendel's law of (1) dominance (2) independent assortment (3) segregation (4) blending.

13. When a red and a white four o'clock flower are crossed, the color of the offspring will be (1) 100% red (2) 100% white (3) 100% pink (4) 50% red and 50% pink.

14. 100% blue Andalusian fowls are produced by the crossing of (1) black and white (2) black and blue (3) blue and blue (4) blue and white parents.

15. A backcross in garden peas could be represented by (1) TT × TT (2) Tt × Tt (3) tt × tt (4) Tt × tt.

Modified True-False Questions

1. If pure tall pea plants are crossed with pure short pea plants, *one half* the offspring will be tall.

2. The offspring of a cross between two recessives are *50% recessive.*

3. The law of independent assortment applies to crosses involving *many* genes lying in different chromosome pairs.

4. A hybrid tall garden pea plant will produce some sperm cells containing genes for *shortness.*

5. To obtain 25% green peas, hybrid yellow peas must be crossed with *pure* yellow peas.

6. A *large* number of offspring is needed to determine the Mendelian ratio.

7. If a hybrid is crossed with a pure dominant, *half* of the offspring will look like the pure dominant parent.

8. When a hybrid and a recessive are crossed, *three-fourths* of the offspring will be recessive.

9. Genes that have their positions in the same chromosome usually remain together because they are *linked.*

10. To determine whether a black guinea pig is pure black (BB) or hybrid (Bb), the usual procedure is to cross it with a *white* (*bb*) guinea pig.

Essay Questions

1. In pea plants, purple flowers are dominant over white flowers.
   a. Give the results of crossing (1) a pure purple flower with a white flower, (2) a hybrid purple flower with a white flower, (3) two hybrid purple flowers.
   b. In what generation is the law of segregation first illustrated?
   c. What is meant by a recessive character?

2. Explain either in words or by diagram the following results obtained in breeding rabbits: (Short hair in rabbits is dominant.)
   a. In a large litter of rabbits, one-fourth are long-haired.
   b. When long-haired rabbits are bred with long-haired rabbits, short-haired rabbits are never produced.
   c. A short-haired rabbit is bred with a long-haired rabbit. In a large litter, 50 per cent are short-haired and 50 per cent are long-haired.
   d. A short-haired rabbit is bred with a long-haired rabbit. In a litter of eight, all are short-haired.

3. There are more gray rats in nature than white rats.
   a. What conclusion can be drawn with regard to the heredity of color in these organisms?

  b. How can it be determined whether a gray rat is pure or hybrid?

  c. Show the results of crossing (1) a hybrid gray rat with a pure gray rat, (2) a hybrid gray rat with a hybrid gray rat, (3) a hybrid gray rat with a white rat, (4) a pure gray rat with a white rat, (5) a white rat with a white rat.

4. *a.* The cross between red-flowered and white-flowered snapdragon plants produces pink-flowered plants. Make a diagram that shows why pink-flowered plants, when crossed, do not produce 100% pink-flowered offspring and explain the diagram.

  b. A spotted rabbit, when crossed with a solid-colored rabbit, produced all spotted offspring. When these F_1 rabbits were crossed among themselves, they produced 32 spotted rabbits and 10 solid-colored rabbits.

   (1) Make a keyed and labeled diagram showing how this result was obtained.

   (2) Tell why your answer explains the actual result described.

5. State whether each of the following statements is true or false and give the reason for your decision. (You may use diagrams to illustrate your reasons.)

  a. The result of crossing pure black mice with white mice is 100% hybrid black offspring.

  b. The result of crossing hybrid black mice with white mice is an excellent example of dominance.

  c. The result of crossing two hybrid blacks illustrates the law of segregation.

  d. If two organisms showing dominant characters are crossed, the result is always pure dominant.

  e. The result of crossing hybrid black guinea pigs with hybrid black guinea pigs will be 50% pure blacks and 50% pure whites.

  f. When hybrids are crossed, all the offspring will show the dominant character.

  g. It is now known that Mendel's results in pea breeding were caused by the behavior of certain nuclear structures.

  h. One-half of the offspring of a cross between a pure tall pea plant and a short pea plant will be tall.

  i. Gametes carry only one gene for each character.

  j. Recessives always breed true.

  k. The genes for some characteristics are linked.

  l. There are instances when neither of the contrasting traits dominates.

Chapter XX

APPLIED HEREDITY

VARIATIONS AND MUTATIONS

Variations. The pea plant, as we learned previously, has such traits as length of stem, color of flowers, type of seed, etc. In each trait, differences exist. For example, not all long-stemmed plants are of the same height. Not all purple-flowered plants have the same shade of purple. And not all wrinkled seeds have the same number of wrinkles. The differences among the members of a species are known as *variations*.

Types of Variations:

1. *Environmental Variations.* Different environments cause variations among members of the same species. For example, plants receiving an abundant supply of raw materials (sunlight, water, minerals) grow better than do plants of the same species receiving a limited supply.

2. *Acquired Characteristics.* Life activities cause variations among members of the same species. For example, a work horse develops muscles different from those of a race horse.

Acquired characteristics as well as environmental variations do not affect the genes, and are therefore not transmitted to the offspring. This biologic fact was proved by the German scientist, *August Weismann.* He cut the tails off mice and crossed the tailless mice for many generations. Each new generation was born with tails. This occurred because the genes controlling the appearance of tails were not affected by the removal of the parents' tails.

3. *Inherited Variations.* Genes cause variations among members of the same species. Inherited variations are transmitted from generation to generation. With each new generation, the offspring may show greater variations in certain traits.

How Genes Cause Variations:

1. *Recombination of Genes.* In a crossing of organisms, the off-spring receive certain traits from one parent and certain traits from the other parent. For example, a fruit fly may inherit red eyes and black body from one parent, and vestigial wings and forked bristles from the other parent. Therefore, this organism will not resemble either of its parents with respect to the combination of these traits.

2. *Crossing Over.* During maturation, the two members of a chromosome pair sometimes twist around each other. Then, when the chromosomes separate, they break apart in such a way that parts of two of the original chromosomes make up each of the new chromosomes. Consequently, new combinations of characters become linked together and variations result in the offspring.

The figure below shows a chromosome pair with genes for brown eyes and brunette hair in one chromosome, and genes for blue eyes and blond hair in the other chromosome. After crossing over occurs, one chromosome contains genes for blue eyes and brunette hair, while the other chromosome contains genes for brown eyes and blond hair.

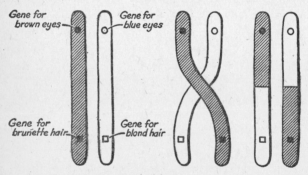

Fig. 109. Crossing Over

3. *Mutations.* A mutation is a new characteristic which appears suddenly in an organism due to a change in a gene. The individual possessing this new trait is called a *mutant.* Usually, the mutant is harmed by the new characteristic. For example, an animal of a horned species is sometimes born without horns. This mutant, lacking a means of defense, falls easy prey to an enemy.

Mutations in Nature. Other mutations found in nature are the seedless orange, albino organisms (individuals lacking normal pigmentation), short-legged sheep, tailless dogs, and many others.

The study of mutations was begun by the Dutch botanist, *Hugo de Vries*. While working with primrose plants, he discovered that occasionally plants would appear with new traits. He called these traits *mutations*. He crossed mutant primroses with normal primroses and always obtained mutant offspring. He therefore concluded that a mutation occurred as a result of a change in the hereditary material. This was the basis for his mutation theory of evolution (see pages 285-286).

Some years later, *Thomas Morgan* explained mutations genetically. While performing his historic experiments with fruit flies, he discovered the sudden appearance of a white-eyed fruit fly in a pure strain of red-eyed flies. Crossing the mutant with a normal red-eyed fly, he found that the new trait was passed on to the offspring. He reasoned that, since the mutation was inherited, the new characteristic must have resulted from a change in a gene.

Changes in genes not only have occurred in nature, but also have been caused in the laboratory. Geneticists have created many mutations by exposing organisms to high temperatures, radium, atomic radiation and X-rays.

The geneticist, *Herman J. Muller*, received the Nobel prize for his work of creating mutations in fruit flies. After exposing fruit flies to X-rays, he mated them. The offspring showed many mutations.

Scientists have found that certain chemicals also cause mutations. One such drug is *colchicine*, which causes a change in the chromosome number of certain plants. As a result, new varieties of tomatoes and cotton have been developed.

IMPROVING PLANTS AND ANIMALS

Plant and Animal Breeding. By applying the principles of heredity, man has developed improved varieties of plants and animals. The production of offspring having desired traits is called *breeding*. Breeding is accomplished by crossing two organisms, each having a desired trait, and obtaining a new individual that combines both of the desired traits.

Let us assume that a breeder wishes to develop a strain of fowl which will combine two desirable heritable characters: high egg production and large size of bird.

1. *Selection* (*or Selective Breeding*). The breeder first selects hens from a strain of fowl having a high egg production and roosters from a strain of unusually large fowl.

2. *Hybridization.* The breeder then hybridizes the hens and roosters. *Hybridizing* is another term for crossing organisms. Since there are many possible combinations of sperm and egg in a crossing, the first few offspring may not possess the desired combination of traits. Therefore, the breeder may have to make many crossings before obtaining two or more new individuals of the desired variety. This type of hybridization is called *outbreeding*. Outbreeding involves the crossing of two organisms derived from different parents. The resulting offspring are superior to the parents, since the offspring received a desirable trait from each of the parents.

3. *Maintaining the Strain.* Having established an improved variety, the breeder then seeks to maintain the strain. This is done by crossing a hen and a rooster of the new strain, both of which arose from the same parents. This type of mating is called *inbreeding*. Inbreeding results in offspring having the same traits as the parents.

Sometimes a recessive trait that had been hidden in the parents is transmitted to the inbred offspring. The recessive trait may improve or weaken the individual. Organisms showing an undesirable recessive trait are not used to continue a strain.

A strain of plants can more easily be maintained than a strain of animals, because a breeder can employ any one of the methods of vegetative propagation (see pages 203-205).

4. *Propagation of Mutants.* If a desirable mutation appears, the breeder continues the type. An animal mutant is maintained by selective breeding, a plant mutant by some form of asexual reproduction, as grafting. The Ancon sheep is a short-legged mutant which is desirable because of its inability to jump fences. The seedless orange is a desirable mutant because of its taste, ease of segmenting, and reduced number of seeds.

Species Improved by Man. By scientific breeding, man has developed the following new varieties having one or more desirable traits: (1) A type of rye combines both winter hardiness and early ripening. (2) Hybrid corn combines increased yield and greater vigor. (3) Marquis wheat combines early ripening and resistance to rust. (4) Strains of cattle, such as the Guernsey and Jersey cows, produce milk with high butterfat. (5) Holstein cows hold the record for large milk production. (6) Rhode Island Reds (fowls) yield high egg production. (7) Texas-Brahman cattle are immune to Texas fever and have a high quality beef.

Luther Burbank, American Plant Breeder. *Luther Burbank* of California was probably the greatest of all plant breeders. Some of the new types of plants which Burbank developed were (1) the spineless cactus, which is used for animal feed; (2) the Burbank potato, which is rot resistant; (3) the Shasta daisy, which is large and beautiful; (4) the plumcot, which is a cross between a plum and an apricot, with an improved taste; (5) the thin-shelled walnut, which is meaty and easy to crack open.

In addition to producing new varieties of economic value, Burbank originated many plant curiosities, such as the white blackberry.

Completion Questions

1. Differences among similar organisms are called _____.
2. Variations which develop during the lifetime of an organism are known as _____.
3. A recombination of genes may result in _____ variations.
4. Mutations are inherited because they are due to changes in _____.
5. The Ancon sheep originated as a (an) _____.
6. Muller produced mutations in fruit flies with the aid of _____.
7. _____ is a chemical which has been used in producing mutations in plants.
8. For rapid improvement of their stock, plant breeders should always be on the lookout for _____.
9. Plant mutants may be multiplied more easily than animal mutants because they are capable of _____.
10. _____ was a famous plant breeder.

Multiple-Choice Questions

1. New traits may appear in the offspring of organisms as the result of (1) environmental variations (2) acquired variations (3) crossing over of chromosomes (4) mitosis.
2. The frequency with which mutations occur can be increased by (1) atomic radiation (2) inbreeding (3) natural selection (4) pasteurization.

3. The desirable characters of two wheat plants may be united in the offspring by (1) selection (2) hybridization (3) grafting (4) inbreeding.

4. Crossing unrelated organisms for the purpose of improving a species is called (1) inbreeding (2) propagating mutants (3) outbreeding (4) maturation.

5. In the breeding of race horses, the practice of crossing closely related animals is known as (1) crossbreeding (2) hybridization (3) inbreeding (4) outbreeding.

6. Crossing carefully selected pea plants of the same strain produces (1) greater variation (2) similarity of type (3) new characters (4) mutations.

7. A plant which originated as a mutant and which has continued is the (1) Shasta daisy (2) plumcot (3) seedless orange (4) spineless cactus.

8. A desirable strain of plants can more easily be continued than a strain of animals because the breeder can use (1) sexual reproduction (2) hybridization (3) vegetative propagation (4) selection.

9. The scientist who disproved the inheritance of acquired characteristics with his tailless mice experiment was (1) Mendel (2) Morgan (3) Weismann (4) Burbank.

10. Of the following, the process which does not produce mutations is (1) mitosis (2) chromosome cross-over (3) atomic radiations (4) X-rays.

Modified True-False Questions

1. The differences which some animals may show as the result of obtaining more food are known as *inherited* variations.

2. In most instances, a mutation is *beneficial* to the organism in which it occurs.

3. The choosing of organisms with desirable traits for the purpose of hybridizing them is *selective breeding*.

4. Although inbreeding is used by breeders, undesirable *recessive* traits frequently appear in the offspring.

5. Disease-resistant plants may be produced by *hybridization*.

Essay Questions

1. Mutations are constantly taking place in nature and are being caused by scientists in laboratories.
   a. What is a mutation?
   b. Name one desirable plant that had its origin as a mutant.
   c. Describe two artificial methods that have been used to bring about mutations.
   d. Why are mutations important to breeders?
   e. Discuss two ways by which genes may cause variations.
2. Man has improved plants and animals to serve his purposes. For example, he wanted more butterfat in milk and so he developed the Jersey cow.
   a. Mention five other examples in which plants and animals have been improved and state man's specific purpose in each case.
   b. Select one of these examples and tell in detail how the improvement was brought about.
3. a. The young men in our armed forces may some day become fathers. Will the exercise that is part of their training result in physically superior children? Give reasons for your answer.
   b. State two reasons why we may expect more rapid progress in plant breeding than in animal breeding.
   c. Explain why inbreeding may produce offspring that are either undesirable or exceptionally desirable.
4. a. Tell why it is more difficult for a breeder to obtain a pure stock with a dominant mutation than one with a recessive mutation.
   b. Refer to some physical trait in cattle and tell how both heredity and environment help to determine this characteristic.
   c. How is a knowledge of the laws of inheritance of value to plant and animal breeders?
5. Give a biologic reason for each of the following:
   a. Wheat is being grown successfully in regions where the wheat-rust fungus flourishes.
   b. Plant mutants may be propagated more easily than animal mutants.
   c. During a breeding experiment, the flowers of the plants should be closely covered.
   d. Hybridization increases the number of variations.
   e. Environmental variations are not inherited.

Chapter XXI

HEREDITY IN MAN

Human Heredity is Difficult to Study. The pea plant and the fruit fly are ideal subjects for the study of inheritance because these organisms (1) can be crossed in the laboratory at will, (2) have a short life span, (3) produce many offspring and many generations, and (4) have only a few chromosomes and therefore possess only a few heritable traits.

On the other hand, man is a very poor subject for the study of heredity because:

1. Experimental crossings cannot be made

2. Since the life span of man is long, an investigator usually cannot study more than two or three generations that lived during the lifetime of the investigator.

3. Because man produces few offspring, ratios of trait inheritance cannot be established conclusively.

4. Man has 48 chromosomes, each composed of thousands of genes. Therefore, the possible combinations of genes in the offspring ma run into the millions.

5. Certain traits are controlled by several pairs of genes.

6. In only very few instances have records been kept of ancestral traits. Hence, the traits of most individuals cannot be traced back t, their origin.

7. Very few pure strains of humans exist today, due to the intermarriage of ancestors who had varied genetic materials.

8. Man has many important mental traits as well as physical traits.

Human Traits Inherited According to Mendel's Laws. Despite the difficulties in studying human inheritance, geneticists have been able to trace some traits from parents to offspring. On the next page is a list of some of the traits which are known to be inherited according to the Mendelian laws.

| | CONTRASTING CHARACTERS | |
TRAITS	*Dominant*	*Recessive*
eye color:	brown	blue
shape of head:	round	long
number of fingers:	six	five
hair texture:	curly	straight
quantity of hair:	baldness (in male)	normal
skin pigment:	dark	fair
nose size:	large	small

Heritable Body Defects and Diseases. There are organic defects and diseases which are known to be handed down from parents to offspring. Some common examples are feeble-mindedness, color blindness, hemophilia, allergies, deaf-mutism. On the other hand, most human diseases (cancer, tuberculosis, diabetes, etc.) are not inherited.

Inheritance of Desirable and Undesirable Traits. From a study of family histories, called *family trees*, investigators have concluded that desirable and undesirable traits are inherited.

The *Edwards family* is a notable example of *good* inheritance. The family tree started with Jonathan Edwards, a clergyman of colonial New England. Among his more than one thousand descendants are found eminent college presidents, doctors, clergymen, professors, judges, lawyers, statesmen and writers.

The *Jukes family* is an outstanding example of *poor* inheritance. Jukes is a fictitious name for a New York State family, about two thousand of whom were paupers, criminals, thieves, and feeble-minded and immoral persons.

The *Kallikak family* shows both *good and bad* inheritance. Martin Kallikak is the fictitious name of a colonial soldier who fought in the Revolutionary War. He, of normal mind, mated with a feeble-minded woman. Born out of this union was a feeble-minded son. Later on, Martin married a normal woman and had several children.

The family tree started by the mating of Martin with the feeble-minded woman includes hundreds of descendants who were feeble-minded, immoral and alcoholic. On the contrary, the family tree started by Martin and the normal woman includes no descendants having the undesirable traits characteristic of the other family tree.

The Environment and Heredity. The environment is closely linked with heredity in determining a person's qualities, abilities and personality. The environment may bring out traits that would otherwise remain dormant. A favorable environment will bring out good traits more readily than will a poor environment. Thus, good inheritance and good environment usually—but not always—assure superior qualities.

Improving the Human Race. Scientists believe that the human race can be improved by applying the laws of heredity. Toward this end, two sciences have evolved: eugenics and euthenics.

1. *Eugenics.* Eugenics is the science of improving the human race by *better breeding*. Eugenics was founded in 1883 by the English biologist, Sir Francis Galton. The eugenics program is aimed at permitting only those who are physically and mentally fit in every way to become parents. This may be accomplished as follows:

a. Study human heredity to determine what traits are inherited.

b. Educate the public to make people aware of the danger of poor inheritance.

c. Set up a program of legislation to (1) require physical examinations before marriage, (2) segregate defectives, (3) sterilize the unfit, and (4) prevent immigration of undesirables.

2. *Euthenics.* Euthenics is the science of improving the human race by *improving the environment*. The euthenics program is aimed at creating a favorable environment in order to foster superior traits. This may be accomplished as follows:

a. Clear slums and build better housing.

b. Construct more schools and provide more recreational and cultural facilities.

c. Extend social security coverage and increase benefits.

d. Improve public health through institutional and governmental assistance.

Twins and Heredity:

1. *Identical Twins.* During the two-cell stage of the cleavage of a fertilized egg, the two daughter cells sometimes separate, instead of remaining attached to each other. The two cells undergo cleavage and develop into two new individuals, called *identical twins*. Since identical twins arise from the same egg and sperm, the two individuals (*a*) have exactly the same hereditary traits, (*b*) look alike, and (*c*) are of the same sex.

Sometimes identical twins are separated at a young age. They grow up differently, and at maturity show variations in personality, ability, character and physical appearance. These variations in a pair of identical twins are studied to determine the role played by the environment in influencing mental qualities and physical traits.

2. *Fraternal Twins.* Occasionally, the human female produces two egg cells at the same time. If fertilization and development of both eggs take place, two individuals, called *fraternal twins*, are born. Since fraternal twins arise from the fusion of two different sperms and eggs, the individuals (*a*) do not have the same hereditary traits, (*b*) do not look alike, and (*c*) may be of different sexes.

Fraternal twins cannot be studied as identical twins are, because fraternal twins have unlike genes. They can be investigated merely as two individuals of the same age, raised in the same environment.

Sex Inheritance. Sex is an inherited trait. Each parent has a pair of chromosomes, called the *sex chromosomes*, differing in shape from all other chromosomes. In the female, the sex chromosomes are alike, and are designated as XX. In the male, the sex chromosomes are unlike, and are designated as XY.

The sex of a new individual is determined when fertilization takes place. The zygote can receive only an X chromosome from the female parent, but may receive either an X or a Y from the male parent. If the zygote receives an XX pair, the child will be a female. If the zygote receives an XY pair, the child will be a male. Thus, the sperm is the sex determiner.

The chance of a child's being male or female is equal, as follows:

XX × XY

SPERMS

	X	Y
X	XX	XY
X	XX	XY

EGGS

Result: 50% male, 50% female

Fig. 110. Sex Inheritance

Sex Linked Traits.   The female sex chromosome (X) carries genes
that control traits other than sex. One such trait is color blindness.
Color blindness is recessive; normal color vision is the dominant contrasting character. If an X chromosome carrying the recessive gene
combines with the Y chromosome, a color-blind son will be born.

Key:

$\underline{X}$ = sex chromosome with recessive gene

X = sex chromosome with gene for normal color vision

Y = male chromosome

$$\frac{X\underline{X}}{(\text{carrier female})} \times \frac{XY}{(\text{normal male})}$$

SPERMS

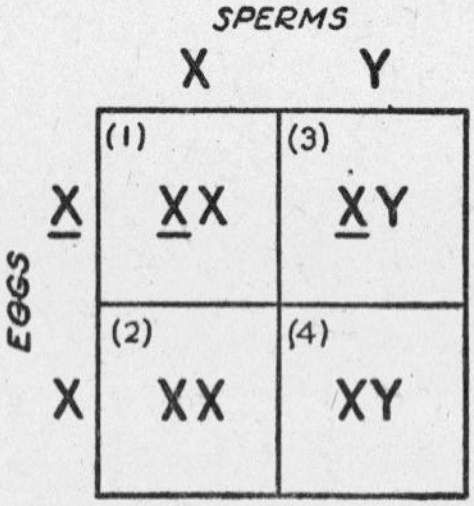

Result: Box 1 = female carrier

Box 2 = normal female

Box 3 = color-blind male

Box 4 = normal male

Fig. 111. Crossing a Female Carrier With a Normal Male

If an X chromosome carrying the recessive gene combines with another X that possesses the recessive gene, then a color-blind daughter will be born. Thus, color blindness in females is rare. In order for a girl to inherit color blindness, she must receive the recessive gene from her mother (in whom the trait is hidden) and the recessive gene from her father (who is color-blind).

$$\underline{XX} \qquad \times \qquad X\underline{Y}$$
(carrier female)   (color-blind male)

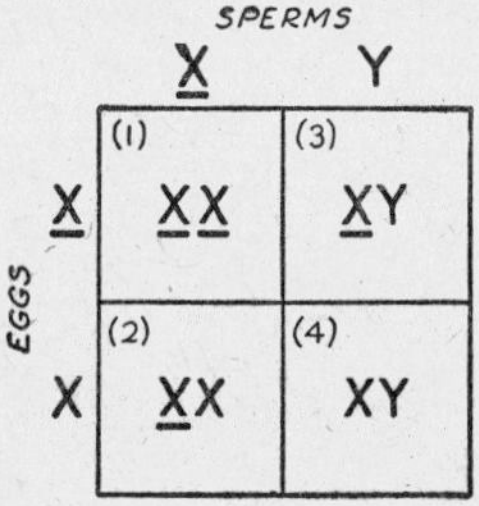

SPERMS

Result: Box 1 = color-blind female   Box 3 = color-blind male
        Box 2 = female carrier   Box 4 = normal male

Fig. 112. Crossing a Female Carrier With a Color-Blind Male

Hemophilia (see page 150) is another sex linked trait which is carried by the mother and is inherited chiefly by the male offspring. This occurs in the same manner as color blindness.

Completion Questions

1. In humans, the appearance of some traits is controlled by more than one pair of _____.
2. Human heredity is investigated by the study of records called _____.
3. The _____ family shows the inheritance of desirable traits.
4. The Jukes family was noted for its _____.
5. The science devoted to the improvement of the human race through heredity is known as _____.
6. The founder of this scientific movement was _____.
7. Twins which develop from the same fertilized egg are called _____ twins.

8. If the sex chromosomes of an organism are XY, the organism is a _____.
9. The sex of an individual is determined at the time of _____.
10. A sex-linked disease of the blood which is inherited is _____.

Multiple-Choice Questions

1. One of the difficulties in the study of human heredity is (1) the short life span of the human (2) too many records of human inheritance (3) there are few pure strains of humans (4) man has few heritable traits.
2. A non-heritable disease in man is (1) hemophilia (2) rickets (3) color blindness (4) deaf-mutism.
3. The character of a person is determined by (1) what he inherits (2) his environment (3) his education (4) the combined effect of inheritance and environment.
4. A eugenic measure suggested for the improvement of the race is (1) better housing (2) sterilization of the unfit (3) old-age pensions (4) child labor laws.
5. The science which attempts to improve the human race by improving man's environment is (1) eugenics (2) genetics (3) euthenics (4) heredity.
6. The chromosome number of the body cells of identical human twins is (1) 12 (2) 24 (3) 48 (4) 96.
7. Fraternal twins develop from (1) one egg fertilized by two sperms (2) one egg fertilized by one sperm (3) two eggs fertilized by two sperms (4) two eggs fertilized by one sperm.
8. In higher animals, the sex of the offspring is determined by the (1) male gametes (2) female gametes (3) age of the parents (4) time of fertilization.
9. The possibility of an organism being a male is (1) 3:1 (2) 9:3:3:1 (3) 1:1 (4) 100%.
10. Red-green color-blindness is most common in (1) men (2) women (3) Caucasians (4) Mongolians.

Modified True-False Questions

1. In the human, *brown* eye color is dominant.
2. The family which illustrates the inheritance of good and bad traits is the *Jukes.*

3. A better housing program is one of the aims of the science known as *eugenics.*
4. Identical twins are studied in heredity to determine the part played by the *genes* in heritable traits.
5. The *Y* chromosome carries the recessive gene for hemophilia.

Essay Questions

1. *a.* State two reasons why it is difficult to gain information about human inheritance.
   b. State two characteristics you inherited and two characteristics you did not inherit.
   c. How is human heredity studied?
   d. Name five human characteristics that are inheritable.
   e. Name three euthenic measures that would tend to improve the race.

2. *a.* State two methods that have been proposed to reduce the number of feeble-minded people.
   b. State one objection to each method and one advantage of each method.
   c. Give one way in which our knowledge of the principles of inheritance may be applied to the improvement of the human race.

3. Identical twins were separated soon after birth and were placed in two homes that were different in many ways.
   a. Name a physical characteristic in which the twins would resemble each other after a period of years.
   b. Name a physical characteristic in which the twins might exhibit a decided difference and give a probable reason for this difference.
   c. It has been said that man's traits are shaped by heredity and environment. Explain.

4. *a.* Explain, or show by keyed diagrams, how maleness or femaleness is inherited in human beings.
   b. Explain, or show by a keyed diagram, how a female may inherit color blindness.

5. Give one good biologic objection to each of the following:
   a. An individual claims that tuberculosis is inherited.
   b. Unrestricted immigration into this country should be permitted.
   c. We should do away with all social security programs.

Chapter XXII

EVOLUTION

Formation of the Earth. It is commonly believed that the earth was formed out of a hot liquid (molten) material that cooled and solidified into *igneous* rocks. The forces of nature, such as rain, wind and freezing temperatures, began to decompose the igneous rocks into smaller particles. Rapid streams carried away these particles and deposited them in quiet bodies of water. The sediments became compressed and hardened into layers, or strata, of rock, called *sedimentary rock*. This rock is so called because it was formed in water from sediments. As pressure and heat acted on the igneous and sedimentary rocks, they were changed into another form, called *metamorphic rock*.

The surface of the earth underwent many changes. Even today the earth is undergoing change—floods, earthquakes, volcanic eruptions, soil erosion, etc. All these changes that altered the earth's surface prepared the way for life.

The Meaning of Evolution. Life did not appear on the earth at the time of its formation. Millions of years elapsed before the first bit of life appeared. It is supposed that the first organism was a small, simple, water-dwelling plant. This species reproduced until the shallow waters became crowded. Then the water plants developed structures for life on land. This plant life was followed by simple animal life. As time passed, the simple plants and animals died out, being replaced by new organisms a little different and a little more advanced in structure. By gradual change over a billion or so years, the simple forms of the past gave rise to the complex species of the present. This progression of living things from the simple to the complex is called *evolution*.

THE PROOFS OF EVOLUTION

Evidences of Evolution. Various branches of biology provide evidence that present-day life descends from past life with changes. The evidences which we shall study in the following pages are (1) fossils, (2) homologous structures, (3) embryology, (4) vestigial structures, (5) taxonomy, (6) geographic distribution, and (7) breeding domestic species.

THE STUDY OF FOSSILS

What is a Fossil? A fossil is a preserved evidence of past life. A fossil may be the actual remains of an organism, such as a shell, or a bone or a tooth. Or a fossil may be the footprint of an animal, or the impression of a leaf, shell or even an entire organism in clay, mud or sand that turned into rock. Most fossils are found in the strata of sedimentary rocks. Few fossils are found in metamorphic rocks. Igneous rocks have no fossils, since this type of rock results from the cooling of heated materials. The heat would destroy the bodies of the organisms.

The Formation of Fossils:

1. *By Sedimentation.* Some of the plants and animals that lived in ponds, lakes or oceans fell to the bottom when they died. Their bodies became covered with a layer of mud or sand when tiny particles of sediment suspended in the water also settled to the bottom. In time, the layer hardened into rock and preserved the hard parts of the organism, such as the bones and teeth. The softer parts were slowly decomposed. On top of this stratum, one or more additional layers of rock later formed and fossilized other plants and animals.

The rock layers reveal the evolution of living things. An examination of certain sedimentary rock shows fossils in each layer to be of increasing complexity. The simple forms are in the bottom-most layer, which is the oldest. And the most complex forms are in the top-most layer, which is the youngest.

Rock layers can be seen at the Grand Canyon, Wyoming, and at the Genesee Gorge, New York. At these places, rivers cut through the rock, exposing many strata that reveal fossils of increasing complexity.

2. *By Refrigeration.* Siberia, an intensely cold region covered with ice, was once the habitat of the *woolly mammoth*. These elephant-like animals became extinct about 25,000 years ago. Recently, however, fossil mammoths, complete with flesh and hair, were discovered in Siberia. Apparently, the animals had fallen into large cracks in the ice, which then completely surrounded the bodies and prevented decay.

3. *By Amber.* Insects that crawled on ancient pine trees were caught and embedded in the sticky resin secreted by the trees. The resin hardened into a yellow plastic-like material, called *amber*, and preserved the insects.

4. *By Tar Pits.* In many regions where oil is found, a thick asphalt-like substance seeps to the surface and forms a tar pit. Large animals that stepped upon the surface of these ancient tar pits were trapped. The animals sank in the soft tar, somewhat as in quicksand. Tar pits containing bones of the extinct *saber-toothed tiger* have been discovered in California.

5. *By Petrification.* Floods of the ancient past submerged whole forests. The water, containing dissolved minerals, prevented the trees from decaying rapidly. In fact, decay was so slow that the millions of cells of a tree decayed only a few at a time. As a cell decayed, its space was filled with minerals from the water. Finally, there remained in place of the original tree a fossil of stone, known as *petrified wood.* The original cell structure can still be seen, but in a solidified state. Excellent examples of petrified wood can be seen at the *Petrified Forest* of Arizona (see also page 279).

6. *By Coal Formation.* North America was once covered with tropical forests. When the giant ferns and other plants fell, some were buried in the swamps. As the plants slowly decomposed, many impurities, such as oxygen and hydrogen, were driven off. Carbon, or *coal,* remained. Excellent impressions of fern leaves and even tree trunks are found in coal beds.

The Five Eras of Life. The billion and a half years that life has existed on earth are divided into five broad *eras.* Each era lasted millions of years. During that time, many layers of sedimentary rock were formed and organisms were fossilized. By studying the layers of rock, scientists can determine: (1) the approximate number of years the era lasted, (2) the types of animals and plants that lived on the earth during a particular era, and (3) the succession of living things. In addition, scientists can determine from the sedimentary rock layers what natural happenings (such as climatic changes, mountain building, sinkings or upliftings of the land) may have caused the organisms to become extinct and the era to come to a close.

From a study of the fossils, we can reconstruct the story of life, era-by-era, and see how life evolved from the simple to the more complex.

1. *Age of Ancient Life (also called the Archeozoic Era).* Life is thought to have originated in the sea about 2 billion years ago during the Archeozoic Era. Early forms of life probably were algae, bacteria and unicellular animals. Because these simple organisms were small and lacked hard parts, they could not be preserved as ac-

tual fossils. The belief that life existed during this era is attributed to the presence of *graphite* in the deepest layers of rock formed during the Archeozoic Era. Graphite is a type of carbon that forms only when living material, protoplasm, partially decays.

2. *Age of First Complex Life (Proterozoic Era)*. About one billion years ago, during the Proterozoic Era, multicellular plants and animals first appeared on the earth. In the layers of rock formed during this era, are the fossils of a few types of invertebrate water inhabitants, such as sponges and worms. Adaptations for land dwelling by animals probably had not yet been developed.

3. *Age of Invertebrates (Paleozoic Era)*. Beginning with the Paleozoic Era, we have an abundance of well-preserved fossils. We know much more of the types of life that existed on the earth from this era onward.

The Paleozoic Era started about 500 million years ago. In the beginning of this era, countless millions of crab-like shellfish, called *trilobites*, crowded the ocean shores. Trilobites are believed to be the ancestors of the present-day crayfish and horseshoe crab.

By the middle of the Paleozoic Era, the trilobites declined in number and gave way to fishes, the first vertebrates. One type of fish, the *crossopterygii*, possessed crude adaptations for land dwelling. They had simple lungs for breathing air, and muscular fins not only for locomotion in water but also for short walks on land. This animal is believed to be the forerunner of the land-dwelling animals that followed.

Toward the end of the Paleozoic Era, amphibians, insects and the first primitive reptiles spread out over the land areas of the earth.

Plants appeared on the land during this era. At first, only simple plants were present. Later, these were replaced by mosses and horsetails. Ferns were the dominant plants. Whole forests, closely packed with many varieties of ferns, covered more than 250,000 square miles of North America. The fossil remains of these plants formed our great deposits of coal.

4. *Age of Reptiles (Mesozoic Era)*. The dominant form of life 200 million years ago was the reptile. Reptiles were everywhere: in the water, on the land, in the air.

In the water there were swimming reptiles, 30 to 40 feet long, that dominated all marine life.

On the land there were the *dinosaurs*, reptiles distinguished by their large size. *Diplodocus* was the largest dinosaur. Although 90 feet long, he had a brain no larger than a man's fist. *Tyrannosaurus rex* was the "king of the dinosaurs." His powerful legs and long sharp teeth enabled him to capture and feast upon other dinosaurs. *Trachodon* was possibly the oddest dinosaur, 25 feet long with a head and bill resembling those of a duck.

In the air there were flying reptiles. The *archaeopteryx,* about the size of a crow, is of special significance because it is believed to represent the evolutionary link between the ancient reptiles and the modern birds. Like other flying reptiles of Mesozoic time, the archaeopteryx had reptile-like characteristics: a set of teeth, scales covering most of the body, and two pairs of claws. Unlike a reptile, the archaeopteryx had feathers. Feathers are a characteristic of birds exclusively.

Modern birds still retain a conspicuous feature inherited from their reptilian ancestors: their feet are covered with scales.

At the end of the Mesozoic Era, primitive mammals appeared and the dinosaurs became extinct. The first mammals were possibly responsible for the extinction of the dinosaurs (see page 279).

5. *Age of Mammals (Cenozoic Era).* In the Cenozoic Era, which has been in progress for the past 60 million years, the dominant plants have been the *flowering plants,* and the dominant animals have been the *mammals.*

In the oldest rock layers of the Cenozoic Era, fossils of many primitive mammals have been discovered. Higher in the strata are more complex descendants of these mammals. One fossil series shows the evolution of the modern horse, *Equus,* from its ancient ancestor, the *Eohippus.*

At the bottom of the Cenozoic rock layers, are fossils of the Eohippus, also called the "dawn horse." Eohippus was only about 15 inches in height, had *four* toes on each of its front feet, and walked on the four toes in the same manner as the modern dog. Higher in the rock layers of this era is another fossil of a horse-like animal. This animal was larger than Eohippus and walked on *three* toes. In the higher rock layers, we find a third fossil of a horse-like animal. This animal was still larger in size and walked on *two* toes.

The modern horse evolved from the fossil ancestors described above. It is slightly larger than its closest ancestor and walks on only *one* toe. This single toe is apparently an adaptation for fast running. Attached to the main bone in the foot of the modern horse are two slender bones, called *splints.* These bones are believed to be the remains (vestiges) of the toes lost through evolution.

The Coming of Man. Man made his appearance about 25,000 years ago. Since man has been able to control his environment to a greater extent than any other species, he has been able to dominate the earth. Some authorities refer to these 25,000 years of man's dominance as the beginning of a new era, the *Psychozoic*.

How Did Former Life Become Extinct? Many plants and animals which once flourished on the earth have disappeared completely. Extinction has been explained as follows:

1. *The Earth Changed.* A living forest was once destroyed when part of Arizona sank beneath the ocean. The forest was submerged for a very long time, during which period petrification occurred (see page 276). Then the land rose to its present level, exposing the petrified remains of the trees. These can be seen in the *Petrified Forest* of Arizona.

There is further proof that the crust of the earth underwent several adjustments, with each change causing the extinction of many organisms in the process. Fossils of water-dwelling shellfish have been found on mountain peaks high above sea level. Apparently, this land was at one time submerged beneath the sea.

2. *The Climate Changed.* *Corals* are small marine animals that are able to live only in very warm tropical waters. The coral animals absorb the lime dissolved in the water, and convert the lime into their mineral skeletons. When the organisms die, their lime skeletons become compressed into large masses, called *coral reefs*. Fossilized coral reefs have been found as far north as New York, Ohio and Michigan. Thus, when the northern climate was warm, corals lived abundantly; but when the climate cooled, corals and other forms of tropical life became extinct in the north.

Coal deposits found in the Arctic regions also indicate that at one time a tropical climate existed to permit the luxuriant growth of vegetation necessary for coal formation.

3. *Some Organisms were Destroyed by Other Organisms.* It is believed that dinosaurs laid large eggs on top of the sand and then walked away, leaving the eggs to hatch in the sun. The eggs may have been eaten by the rat-like mammals that lived on the earth at the time. Thus, reproduction of the dinosaurs was curtailed.

Some species probably were greatly reduced in number, and others may have been wiped out completely, by widespread disease.

The *dodo* and the *passenger pigeon* were once plentiful. But these birds are now extinct, due to the excessive capture and shooting by man.

HOMOLOGOUS STRUCTURES

The forelimbs of different vertebrates show striking similarities in structure, bone for bone, as illustrated in the figure below. Such corresponding parts of different organisms are called *homologous structures.*

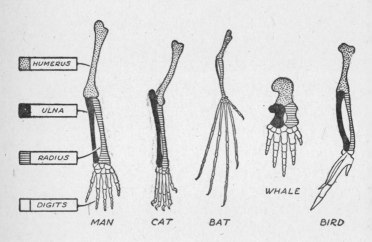

| HUMERUS |
| ULNA |
| RADIUS |
| DIGITS |

MAN   CAT   BAT   WHALE   BIRD

Fig. 113. Similarities in the Forelimbs of Vertebrates

A comparison of the anatomy of the various members of any phylum of animals always reveals basic similarities of structure. For example, all the vertebrates are of the same body plan, having a similar skeleton, similar nervous system, similar digestive system, and many other similarities. Similarities indicate relationship. It is therefore believed that all the vertebrates are related, and all derived (evolved) from one common ancestor. This ancestor probably was a fish-like, water-dwelling animal.

EMBRYOLOGY

Related species resemble each other most closely in the early embryonic stages. As illustrated in the figure below, the young embryos of several vertebrates all look very much alike. Differences do not appear until later stages. This indicates descent from a common ancestor, with changes.

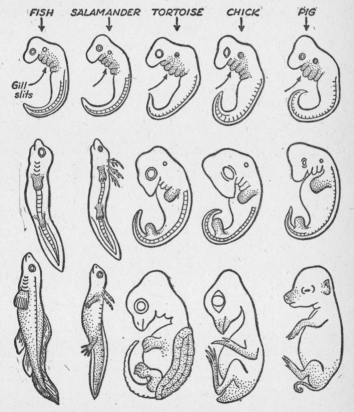

Fig. 114. Similarities in the Embryos of Vertebrates

Slit-like openings, called *gill slits,* are found in the neck region of all vertebrate embryos. The gill slits are used in the fish to pass water from the mouth to the gills in the process of breathing. Mammals have lungs for breathing and therefore have no use for gill slits. However, gill slits are present in the early stages of mammalian embryos. The gills gradually disappear and are gone before the birth of the organism. In the human, one pair of gill slits becomes the openings of the ears. This seems to indicate that mammals were derived from fish-like aquatic vertebrates.

VESTIGIAL STRUCTURES

Many modern species have structures that do not appear to serve any function. It is believed that these structures were once useful organs in the ancestors of present-day organisms. Through many generations of descent with change, these organs gradually lost their function and exist today in a useless rudimentary form, called *vestiges.*

Over 100 vestigial structures have been identified in the human body. For example, the *appendix,* now an apparently useless organ in man, is thought to be the vestige of a useful digestive structure in one of man's ancestors. The appendix still serves as a useful organ in many lower organisms, as, for example, in the rabbit. Man's weak *ear muscles* are believed to be vestiges of powerful muscles that ancestors used in moving their ears to help locate sounds. The *fused vertebrae* (called the coccyx) at the bottom of the human spine are said to be the vestiges of the tail that ancestors used to keep their balance.

In lower animals, the python has vestigial leg bones. The porpoise and the whale have vestigial hip bones. These structures indicate that the snake, the porpoise and the whale probably evolved from an animal having legs.

TAXONOMY

The original Linnean system of classification grouped together all organisms that had similar structures. Modern scientists, using electron microscopes, blood-testing apparatus and other precise laboratory tools, have discovered many additional similarities among organisms in each group. The conclusion is that organisms in each group are similar because they were derived from a common ancestor. Separate paths of evolution, taken by the offspring of the common ancestor, explain the differences in structure from group to group.

GEOGRAPHIC DISTRIBUTION

Closely related species are found living near each other but separated by some natural barrier, such as water, desert or mountain. It is believed that they originally were one species. But when the barrier was formed, the one species was split into two or more groups. Through the years, the separate groups evolved a bit differently in response to the needs of their own environment.

Australia was once connected to the mainland of Asia. At that time, primitive mammals were widely distributed in both Australia and Asia. Then the ocean flooded the area between Australia and Asia, forming a barrier impossible for the mammals to cross. Isolated in Australia, the animals remained primitive, while elsewhere they developed into higher types or became extinct. In Australia alone are found the egg-laying mammal, the duckbill (platypus); and a pouched mammal, the kangaroo.

BREEDING DOMESTIC SPECIES

Direct evidence of descent with change is afforded by numerous domesticated species. For example, from the wild cabbage as the common ancestor, man has produced cauliflower, garden cabbage, brussels sprouts, kale and broccoli. From the wild horse, man has developed many desirable types. Man's success in breeding plants and animals has given him a clue as to how, in nature, new species may have evolved from a single common ancestor with change.

THE THEORIES OF EVOLUTION

Scientists Explain Evolution. So far in this chapter we have studied the evidences that all living things descended from a single ancestor, that complex species developed from simple species, that organisms changed according to the needs of their environment.

How can the rise in complexity of life on earth be explained? How did one species develop from another species, with change? How did plants and animals develop the adaptations they possess in order to succeed in life?

In answer to the aforesaid questions, scientists proposed certain *theories of evolution*. All existing explanations of evolution are called *theories* because they are merely guesses. The major theories are those advanced by Lamarck, Darwin and DeVries.

Lamarck's Theory of Inheritance of Acquired Characteristics (1809). According to the Frenchman, *Jean Lamarck* (1744-1829), the environment compels an organism to develop its structures. An organ in continual *use* becomes larger and stronger. On the other hand, an organ under constant *disuse* becomes weaker and smaller, and finally disappears. These changes, or *acquired characters,* are inherited by the offspring. Through several generations of similar *use and disuse,* the changes result in the development of a new or a modified species.

Evolution of the Giraffe's Neck—According to Lamarck. The giraffe once had a short neck. In the process of eating leaves from the branches of trees, the giraffe began to stretch its neck in order to reach leaves higher up. The acquired character of a longer neck was passed on to the next generation. Likewise, the new generation stretched its neck and passed the acquired character to the next generation. And so, with each generation, the giraffe's neck became longer and longer until the modern-day long-necked giraffe appeared.

Lamarck's Theory Disproved. The modern long-necked giraffe could *not* have evolved from an ancient short-necked giraffe in the manner explained by Lamarck. This is because *acquired characters are not inherited.*

For example, if a soldier loses an arm in combat, his children are *not* born with one arm. The strong muscles of a laborer are *not* inherited by his offspring. Cutting off a dog's tail does *not* result in puppies with short tails.

That acquired characters are not inherited was proved by the German, *August Weismann* (1834-1914), in his "tailless mice" experiments described on page 259. Weismann showed that acquired characteristics affect only the *somatoplasm* (body cells), but not the *germplasm* (genes). These changes can therefore not be inherited.

Darwin's Theory of Natural Selection (1859). The English naturalist, *Charles Darwin* (1809-1882), spent more than five years visiting many isolated areas of the earth where he studied the various forms of plant and animal life. Then, after spending over twenty years in arranging his material and collecting related data, Darwin presented his *Theory of Natural Selection* in a book called "The Origin of Species." Darwin emphasized "survival of the fittest."

Darwin's theory includes the following five main points:

1. *Overproduction.* All species tend toward producing far more offspring than can survive and reach maturity.

2. *Struggle for Existence.* There is not enough food and other life necessities for all offspring. Therefore, the young of a species must compete with each other in order to survive. The continuous competition and battle for life's needs are known as the *struggle for existence.*

3. *Variation.* In any species, no two individuals are exactly alike. Individuals may differ in size, shape, strength, health, etc. These differences between the members of a species are called *variations.*

4. *Survival of the Fittest (Natural Selection).* In some individuals, the variations are useful and assist them in obtaining food, escaping enemies, and in other factors of survival. Individuals lacking these useful variations die. Individuals having these useful variations survive and pass all the useful characteristics to their offspring. In each generation, then, nature selects the fittest organisms to be the parents of the next generation, and eliminates those organisms which are not fitted to survive.

5. *Evolution.* Since variations are inherited, each generation, in turn, shows some advance over the preceding generation.

Evolution of the Giraffe's Neck—According to Darwin:

1. *Overproduction.* The early giraffe, which originally had a short neck, produced more offspring than could survive.

2. *Struggle for Existence.* The young giraffes had to compete for food.

3. *Variation.* Some of the giraffes had longer necks than others.

4. *Survival of the Fittest.* The giraffes with the longer necks were better able to reach the high leaves on which to feed. Consequently, the long-necked individuals survived, while the others died. The characteristic "long neck" was passed on to the next generation.

5. *Evolution.* The natural selection of longer-necked individuals in each generation gradually developed the present long-necked species.

DeVries' Theory of Mutation (1901). *Hugo DeVries* (1848-1935) was a Dutch scientist who experimented with evening primrose plants. He noticed that occasionally an offspring arose having different structures, and that these plants were able to breed pure. Such offspring are called *mutants* (see pages 260-261). Since mutations breed true and might explain the variations appearing suddenly in organisms, DeVries reasoned that evolution had occurred as a result of *chance mutations* in the past.

Evolution of the Giraffe's Neck—According to DeVries. A mutant with an abnormally long neck was born in a litter of normal-necked giraffes. The mutant giraffe reproduced offspring with long necks. The very long neck of the modern giraffe was inherited directly from the original mutant.

How Modern Science Explains Evolution. As we have seen, Lamarck's theory is of historical interest only, since it has been proved false. Darwin's theory does not explain variations satisfactorily. DeVries' theory does not explain all known examples of evolution.

Today's scientists explain evolution by combining Darwin's theory with DeVries', and adding some additional knowledge gained through recent studies in evolution and heredity.

Completion Questions

1. The advance of living things from simple to more complex forms is known as _____.
2. Rocks which formed from the molten state are called _____.
3. The meaning of evolution can be expressed by the term _____.
4. Traces of plants and animals that lived long ago are called _____.
5. Some prehistoric _____ were preserved in hardened resin called amber.
6. The type of fossil formation in which dissolved minerals replace the cells of an organism is called _____.
7. The existence of life on the earth is divided into long intervals of time called _____.
8. The _____ were prehistoric reptiles that sometimes reached gigantic size.
9. There are several kinds of evidence to show that birds are direct descendants of _____.
10. The four-toed Eohippus was a prehistoric ancestor of the modern _____.
11. Evidence that the climate changed on the earth is provided by the discovery of deposits of _____ in the polar regions.
12. An animal that has become extinct within the last 100 years is the _____.

13. Structural similarities between two different organisms show _____

14. A vestigial organ found in man is the _____.

15. Vertebrates resemble each other very closely during their _____ stage.

16. Obstacles which prevent the spread of species are known as _____

17. Lamarck explained evolution by his theory of _____.

18. The man who proved that acquired characteristics are not inherited is _____.

19. The author of the theory of the origin of species by natural selection was _____.

20. DeVries explained evolution by his theory of _____.

Multiple-Choice Questions

1. The most conclusive line of evidence that evolution has occurred is (1) fossil records (2) geographic isolation (3) sinking of land (4) uplifting of mountains.

2. Fossils are most frequently found in rocks that are (1) sedimentary (2) metamorphic (3) volcanic.

3. Fossils found in the early rocks are those of animals (1) the same as (2) more complex than (3) more simple than most animals of today.

4. A mammal that has become extinct is the (1) passenger pigeon (2) bison (3) dodo (4) saber-toothed tiger.

5. The giant reptiles of the past were the (1) dinosaurs (2) giant sloths (3) mammals (4) mastodons.

6. The organism whose fossil indicates a link between reptiles and birds was the (1) Tyrannosaurus (2) Archaeopteryx (3) Diplodocus (4) Eohippus.

7. The ancestor of the horse was about the size of a (1) rat (2) fox (3) present-day horse (4) dinosaur.

8. The splints in the skeleton of the horse's leg are examples of (1) homologous structures (2) fractures (3) vestigial structures (4) adaptations.

9. A vestigial structure in man is the (1) appendix (2) tooth (3) toe (4) fingernail.

10. The finding of gill slits in the embryo of the pig supports the theory of (1) regeneration (2) common ancestry of the vertebrates (3) analogy (4) survival of the fittest.

11. The plants of New Zealand differ from those of southern Asia on account of (1) nearness to the ocean (2) high mountains (3) type of soil (4) long separation from the mainland.

12. Lamarck thought the important factor in evolution was (1) mutation (2) hormones (3) inheritance of acquired characteristics (4) chromosomes.

13. Weismann thought that environmental changes do not affect the (1) somatoplasm (2) germplasm (3) cytoplasm (4) body plasm.

14. Darwin's explanation of evolution is called (1) use and disuse (2) natural selection (3) mutation (4) continuity of germplasm.

15. The mutation theory of evolution was first presented by (1) Lamarck (2) Müller (3) Darwin (4) DeVries.

Modified True-False Questions

1. In evolutionary history, land forms appeared *later* than water forms.

2. The wood of petrified trees has been replaced by *carbon.*

3. The life history of the amphibians indicates that their remote ancestors were *land* animals.

4. The general arrangement of the bones in the forelimbs of birds is *similar to* that of mammals.

5. The lungs and the bony structures of the flipper show that the whale descended from an earlier *sea* animal.

6. A structure useless in man but similar to one that is useful in a lower animal is called a *fossil.*

7. Gill slits are present in an early stage of all *vertebrate* embryos.

8. More closely related species of animals show a *greater* similarity in the chemical make-up of their blood.

9. A pouched mammal found only in Australia is the *platypus.*

10. Survival of the fittest is associated with the theory of evolution proposed by *Lamarck.*

Essay Questions

1. *a.* Describe two methods by which fossils are formed.
   b. Why are few fossil remains of the lowest forms of life found in rock layers?
   c. How do you account for the fact that fossils of fish are not present in the older layers of rock?

 d. Fossils of the following animals have been found in the various strata of the earth's crust: reptiles, amphibians, early man, fish, mammals, invertebrates.

  Write the names of these fossil organisms in the order in which they would be found in the rock strata, beginning with the organism found in the deepest layer.

 e. Explain, with examples, how fossils indicate that climates have changed over long periods of time.

2. *a.* Biologists call one period in the earth's history "The Age of Reptiles." Explain the meaning of the term and give examples to illustrate your answer.

 b. Describe two ways in which the Eohippus differed from the modern horse.

 c. Present evidence to show that each of the following statements is false:

  (1) The newspaper cartoon that shows a dinosaur used by man as a domestic animal is based on fact.

  (2) Trilobites were the first organisms to appear on the earth.

  (3) Fossils may be found embedded in the lava on the slopes of Mt. Vesuvius.

 d. How do scientists explain the fact that the brain of birds and mammals are similar?

 e. Explain why the native animals of northern Canada and Siberia are similar.

3. Explain briefly how each of the following is an evidence of organic evolution: fossils, similarity in structure of organisms, comparative structures of embryos, geographic distribution, vestigial structures.

4. *a.* Biologists believe that modern birds are descendants of reptile-like ancestors. Tell how Darwin's theory of evolution explains this change.

 b. How would DeVries' explanation of the evolution of birds differ from Darwin's?

 c. Explain Lamarck's theory of evolution.

 d. Upon what basis did Weismann criticize Lamarck's theory of evolution?

5. Give a reason for or an explanation of each of the following statements:

 a. During part of their embryo stage, certain birds have teeth.

 b. Only a few of the many organisms of past ages have left fossils.

   c. Fossils are found only in sedimentary rock.
   d. It is common to find new groups of animals appearing in the fossil history of the earth near the end of a geological era when great climatic changes were occurring.
   e. In parts of New York State, fossil shells are found many feet above the present level of rivers and lakes in these regions.
   f. Very few existing land animals will become fossils.
   g. When organisms are said to be the "fittest," it does not always mean that they are the strongest.

6. State the significance of each of the following facts:
   a. In the Gobi desert many fossils are found in what are apparently the former sites of ancient bogs.
   b. The fossil forms of life found in the lower layers of rocks are simpler than those found in the upper layers.
   c. Traces of limb bones are present in some snakes.
   d. The animals in South America are very different from those in Africa.
   e. Living specimens of organisms resemble fossil forms.
   f. The bones of the skull of a fish are similar to those of a cat.
   g. Fossils are being formed today.

Chapter XXIII

BACTERIA

What Are Bacteria? Bacteria are one-celled non-green plants (fungi) of extremely small size, some hardly visible under the microscope. Bacteria are present everywhere in nature. A single bacterium is a small mass of granular protoplasm surrounded by a thin membrane around which is a cell wall. A bacterium does not have a definite nucleus; the nuclear material is scattered throughout the cell.

Shapes of Bacteria. Bacteria are of three types, according to their shapes: (1) *coccus* is round, (2) *bacillus* is rod shaped, and (3) *spirillum* is spiral shaped. (See figure on page 41.) Some bacteria live by themselves, and others live in pairs, chains or clusters.

Conditions for Growth of Bacteria:

1. *Food.* Since bacteria lack chlorophyll, they cannot make their own food. Some bacteria live on dead organic matter (*saprophytes,* see page 41). Others live on the tissues of living organisms (*parasites,* page 41). Still others live in partnership with some other living organisms (*symbionts,* page 43).

2. *Oxygen.* Some bacteria, called *aerobic* bacteria, use oxygen from the air. Others, called *anaerobic* bacteria, obtain oxygen by decomposing certain compounds containing oxygen.

3. *Proper Temperature.* Some bacteria thrive at low temperatures, others at high temperatures. Most varieties prefer a moderate temperature, about that of the human body. Extreme heat will kill most bacteria. Man destroys harmful bacteria present in foods, on surgical instruments, containers, etc., by subjecting the bacteria to extreme heat. This process is known as *sterilization.*

4. *Moisture.* All bacteria need moisture for their life activities.

5. *Darkness.* Most bacteria grow best in darkness. Some will die when exposed to sunlight. One reason for aerating drinking water is to destroy the harmful bacteria present in the water. Virtually all bacteria are destroyed when subjected to the rays of ultra-violet light.

Spore Formation in Bacteria. At times, a bacterium may find environmental conditions unfavorable for its growth. For example, it may temporarily lack moisture, or be subjected to a temperature

291

too high or too low, or it may be exposed to sunlight. Under these unfavorable conditions, the bacterium secretes a thick wall, known as a *spore,* around itself. In this form of a spore, the bacterium remains dormant until favorable conditions are restored, at which time the protective wall breaks open and releases the bacterial cell.

Culturing Bacteria. In the laboratory, careful studies of bacteria are made by *bacteriologists.* The growing of bacteria in the laboratory is known as *culturing* bacteria. All the conditions necessary for bacterial growth are created. The bacteria are given food, moisture, oxygen, warmth, darkness, and a place to live.

The material from which the bacteria will derive their nutrition is called the *culture medium.* Some bacteria grow best in a solid medium, others in a liquid medium. The most commonly used solid medium consists of nutrient agar-agar (obtained from a type of sea weed), meat extract, salt, water and peptones. Common liquid media are beef broth, sugar solution, milk and blood.

The culture medium is heated. Thus, the medium is liquefied and sterilized, any bacteria present being destroyed.

The medium is poured into a sterilized *Petri dish.* This consists of two glass plates that fit securely, one over the other, so as to prevent the outside air from contaminating the culture. For some studies, the medium is poured into a test tube and the tube closed with a cotton plug.

The bacteria to be cultured are transferred from a source to the medium. For example, a drop of water or a drop of milk may be placed on the medium; or the dish may be exposed to the air; or the finger may be touched lightly on the medium.

The Petri dish is then covered and placed in a warm, dark environment. This allows *incubation* (bacterial growth) to take place.

Studying Bacteria. Bacteria reproduce asexually by binary fission (pages 200-201). By this process, the bacterial cells divide into two daughter cells. When conditions are favorable, bacteria reproduce about every twenty minutes. However, when the supply of food has been depleted, or when bacterial wastes have accumulated, or when some other condition for growth has been withdrawn, reproduction ceases. Thus, the growth of bacteria cannot continue indefinitely.

A single bacterium, or a small number of bacteria, soon results in a *colony.* This is due to the rapid and continuous division of the cells. Whereas a bacterium is microscopic, a colony is visible to the naked eye. A colony consisting of only one type of bacterium is called a *pure culture.*

For the study of bacteria, a specimen is taken from the colony, placed on a slide, and then *stained*. Stain is a dye that brings out the structural characteristics of the organism. One of the ways by which bacteria are identified is the manner in which they react to different types of dyes.

Useful Bacteria. Most bacteria known to man are harmless. Many varieties are even essential for man's well being. Some of the useful contributions by bacteria are: They help give flavor to cheese and butter. They aid in the making of sauerkraut, vinegar, linen and leather. The bacteria of decay work towards restoring the fertility of the soil (see nitrogen cycle, pages 53-54).

Louis Pasteur, Father of Bacteriology. The French scientist, Louis Pasteur (1822-1895), founded the science of bacteriology. He proved the existence of bacteria and demonstrated that bacteria cause fermentation. His work disproved the theory of spontaneous generation, a false belief that life can rise from non-living matter. (See page 199.) Pasteur demonstrated that certain bacteria are the cause of disease. This concept, called the *germ theory of disease,* is one of the great medical discoveries of all time.

Pasteur is also noted for his development of vaccination for the sheep disease anthrax, and for his method of preventing hydrophobia (rabies), a disease spread by the bite of a mad dog. He developed *pasteurization,* a process of heating milk (or other products) for the purpose of killing the harmful bacteria present. Pasteur's work was the foundation on which many scientists built our present knowledge of germ diseases.

Robert Koch, Founder of Bacteriological Techniques. Following in the steps of Pasteur, Robert Koch (1843-1910), a German scientist, made important discoveries about germs. Koch developed the method for culturing bacteria on agar-agar, a solid medium (see page 292). This method was a vast improvement over the earlier method of growing bacteria in a broth. On agar-agar, the bacteria are easily located, since they cannot move about as in a broth. Koch discovered the bacterium, *tubercle bacillus,* which is the cause of tuberculosis. He laid down the rules, still followed today, for proving that a particular bacterium causes a specific disease. (See *Koch's Postulates,* page 299.)

Joseph Lister, Founder of Aseptic Surgery. Until the middle of the 19th century, surgical operations were very often followed by wound infection and frequently death. Basing his work on that of Pasteur, Joseph Lister (1827-1912), an English physician, reasoned that wound infection, like fermentation, must be due to bacteria. He believed that if germs could be kept away from a surgical wound, infection would be prevented and many lives saved. Lister's techniques in attaining extreme cleanliness in the operating room include the sterilization of surgical instruments, the use of antiseptics (preparations which retard the growth of germs), and the use of sterile caps, gowns, masks and gloves by surgeons and nurses. Surgery performed under these conditions of extreme cleanliness is called *aseptic surgery.*

Completion Questions

1. Bacteria belong to the group of plants called _____.
2. Rod-shaped bacteria are called _____.
3. For growth, bacteria need darkness, oxygen, moisture and _____.
4. Bacteria which obtain their oxygen from the air are known as _____.
5. A bacterium can endure unfavorable conditions for a time by forming a (an) _____.
6. The _____ is the material on which bacteria are grown in the laboratory.
7. A (an) _____ is a growth of bacteria visible to the unaided eye.
8. Bacteria are _____ to permit a more detailed study.
9. The Germ Theory of Disease was first proposed by _____.
10. The man who introduced the use of solid media was _____.

Multiple-Choice Questions

1. Bacteriologists refer to a round bacterium as (1) spirillum (2) bacillus (3) coccus.
2. Bacteria do not have (1) a cell wall (2) nuclear material (3) chlorophyll (4) a cell membrane.
3. A method of destroying harmful bacteria by heat is known as (1) distillation (2) culturing (3) sterilization (4) fumigation.
4. Properly canned foods do not spoil because they have been (1) homogenized (2) incubated (3) pasteurized (4) sterilized.
5. Of the following, the condition not desirable for bacterial growth is (1) food (2) moisture (3) sunlight (4) warmth.

6. Bacteria reproduce by (1) spore formation (2) binary fission (3) conjugation (4) culturing.
7. A colony of bacteria in which only one type of bacterium is found is known as a (1) slide (2) pure culture (3) stain (4) Petri dish.
8. When milk is pasteurized (1) most bacteria become dormant (2) the bacteria are strained out (3) all bacteria are killed (4) most disease-producing bacteria are killed.
9. Our modern hospitals owe their cleanliness to the pioneer work of (1) Hooke (2) Lister (3) Mendel (4) Leeuwenhoek.
10. The bacterium that causes tuberculosis was discovered by (1) Mendel (2) Lister (3) Pasteur (4) Koch.

Essay Questions

1. A boy without a microscope wants to find out if there are bacteria on his fingers.
   a. What is a culture medium and how is it sterilized?
   b. List two important steps in his experiment after he has sterilized the medium.
   c. What would indicate the probable presence of bacteria?
2. Consider an imaginary situation—a world without bacteria.
   a. State and explain one way in which the food supply would be affected.
   b. List four conditions bacteria require for growth.
   c. Describe the materials used and the methods employed for the growth of colonies of bacteria.
3. Give a biological explanation of each of the following:
   a. An unopened bottle of pasteurized milk turned sour, while an unopened can of evaporated milk beside it on the shelf did not.
   b. Living bacteria may be cultured from dust found in a vacant house.
   c. Bacteria are essential in certain industries.

Chapter XXIV

DISEASES OF MAN

COMMUNICABLE DISEASES

What Is a Disease? A disease is a condition in which any of the normal functions of the body are disturbed or interfered with for a prolonged period of time.

What Is a Communicable Disease? Diseases that can be transmitted from person to person are called *communicable* or *infectious* diseases. Infectious diseases are caused by living organisms, popularly called *germs, microbes* or *microorganisms*. Those germs that cause disease are known biologically as *pathogenic* organisms. Disease-producing germs are of several types: bacteria, viruses, protozoa, molds, worms, rickettsiae and spirochaetes.

How Germs Are Spread. The transmission of a communicable disease involves the transfer of some of the germs causing the disease from the infected person to another person. This transfer of germs may be accomplished in several ways, as follows:

1. *Direct Contact.* Germs may be transferred from an infected person to another person during any direct contact, such as by kissing or by shaking hands. Tuberculosis may be spread in this manner.

2. *Indirect Contact.* Germs may be picked up from objects which have been in contact with the infected person. Such objects might be food, clothing, towels, drinking cups, utensils, etc. Ringworm is commonly transmitted by indirect contact.

3. *Droplet Infection.* As a person talks, coughs or sneezes, a spray of fine droplets is discharged from the nose and mouth. If droplets containing germs of an infected person are breathed in by another person, he too may become infected with the disease. The common cold is spread in this manner.

4. *Animal Carriers.* A lower animal, usually an insect, may transfer germs from an infected person to another person. For example, mosquitoes are known to carry the germs of yellow fever.

5. *Human Carriers.* Carriers are healthy individuals who carry large numbers of disease-producing germs in their bodies. These individuals spread the germs although they themselves have *not* had

the disease. A carrier may also be a person who recovered from an infectious disease but still harbors the germs. Dysentery, a disease of the intestines, may be spread by a carrier.

6. *Water.* Human wastes pollute drinking water. If this water is not treated, it may spread typhoid fever.

Body Defenses Against Germs. The body defends itself against germs in several ways, as follows:

1. *Skin.* The skin is a germ-proof layer of tissue covering the body. As long as the skin remains unbroken, germs are unable to get into the body through the skin.

2. *Mucous Membranes.* These are soft lining tissues, such as those which line the nose and throat. A slimy secretion, *mucus,* is produced by the mucous membranes. Mucus catches germ-bearing dust particles and prevents their entrance into the body.

3. *White Blood Corpuscles.* The white blood corpuscles are ameboid cells which seek out germs and engulf them. This activity is described on page 149.

4. *Body Secretions.* Various secretions, such as the tears and the hydrochloric acid in the stomach, are able to destroy certain germs.

5. *Antibodies.* Antibodies are chemical substances which destroy germs and neutralize germ toxins. Different antibodies are produced by the body to counteract different germs. For example, *lysins* dissolve bacteria. *Agglutinins* clump bacteria, thus making them easier for the white blood corpuscles to destroy.

Immunity. Some individuals are able to contract a given disease, while others never contract the disease even after repeated exposure. The ability to contract a certain disease is called *susceptibility;* the ability to resist a disease is called *immunity.* Immunity is of two types, as follows:

1. *Natural Immunity.* Natural immunity is an inherited ability to resist a disease. Diphtheria, for example, is a common disease to which some people are immune at birth.

2. *Acquired Immunity.* Acquired immunity is an immunity established, or acquired, during a person's lifetime. There are two types of acquired immunity:

a. *Active Acquired Immunity.* In this type of immunity, the body produces its own antibodies. They may remain in the system for a short time, or a long time, perhaps even for life. Active immunity to a disease may result from having recovered from the disease. For example, when a person has smallpox, his body manufactures antibodies to combat the disease. These antibodies stay in the blood and destroy any smallpox germs which may gain entrance into the body in the future.

Active immunity may be acquired by being inoculated with dead germs or weakened germs, or with weakened toxins. When a person is immunized against typhoid fever, he receives an injection of dead typhoid germs. His body, in response to these germs, produces antibodies which remain in the blood to counteract any typhoid germs which may invade his body in years to come.

b. Passive Acquired Immunity. This type of immunity results from injections of antibodies produced in the body of another person or animal. For example, serum containing diphtheria antitoxin can be prepared from the blood of the horse, as explained on page 301. After having been extracted and purified, the serum is injected into a person having diphtheria. Passive immunity is established quickly, but lasts only a short time.

ACTIVE AND PASSIVE IMMUNITY COMPARED

Active Acquired Immunity	*Passive Acquired Immunity*
1. Treatment given to individual before contraction of disease.	1. Treatment given when patient has disease.
2. Individual produces own antibodies.	2. Individual receives antibodies produced in the body of another person or animal.
3. Immunity lasts a long period of time.	3. Immunity lasts a short period of time.

Drugs Help to Fight Disease. The German scientist, *Paul Ehrlich* (1854-1915), developed the drug *salvarsan* (also called "606"). Salvarsan, a compound of arsenic, proved effective in the treatment of syphilis. Salvarsan was the *first* drug found to be able to cure a specific disease. Today, medical science has many different drugs which are used to cure many different diseases. Certain recently discovered drugs have proved to be amazingly effective in treating diseases.

Such medicines, popularly called "wonder drugs," include the following:

1. *Sulfa Drugs.* The sulfa drugs are derived from coal tar. These drugs are used to treat various bacterial infections. The sulfa drugs include sulfanilamide and sulfadiazine.

2. *Antibiotics.* The antibiotics are drugs which are derived from living organisms, such as molds. When taken into the body, the antibiotics stop the growth and reproduction of certain germs. This gives the natural antibodies of the body a chance to destroy the germs. The antibiotics are effective against many bacteria and a few viruses.

The most common antibiotic is *penicillin.* Penicillin was first extracted from the blue-green mold, penicillium, by the British scientist, *Sir Alexander Fleming.* Other antibiotics include streptomycin (isolated by the American scientist, *Selman Waksman*), aureomycin and terramycin.

DISEASES CAUSED BY BACTERIA

Bacteria Cause Disease. Pathogenic bacteria enter the body through a break in the skin, or with air, water or food. Once in the body, bacteria may cause disease by: (1) digesting the living tissues of the host, or (2) releasing poisonous wastes called *toxins.*

Koch's Postulates. One of Robert Koch's many contributions to the field of bacteriology is the technique which he developed in order to prove that a certain germ causes a particular disease. The steps in the process are:

1. The organism thought to cause the disease must be found in all individuals having the disease.

2. This organism must be grown on artificial food in the laboratory, making sure that no other organisms are present.

3. A healthy animal must be inoculated with some of these organisms.

4. The healthy animal must contract the particular disease. In addition, the suspected organism must be isolated from the diseased animal and grown in pure culture in the laboratory.

If the healthy animal does contract the disease each time the experiment is repeated, the suspected organism is definitely the cause of the disease.

Tuberculosis

CAUSE. Tuberculosis (TB) is caused by the *tubercle bacillus*. This germ was discovered by Robert Koch in 1882.

SUSCEPTIBILITY. Negroes are highly susceptible to tuberculosis. Caucasians are less susceptible.

IMMUNIZATION. There is no immunization against tuberculosis. A vaccine, called *BCG*, made from weakened tubercle organisms, is now in limited use. It is given to children who have been exposed to tuberculosis. Although it may not completely prevent the disease, it has been found to reduce the severity of the disease.

TRANSMISSION. The germs of tuberculosis are spread by coughing and sneezing (droplet infection). The germs may also be carried on dust particles, foods and insects.

EFFECT ON BODY. Tuberculosis germs invade various tissues of the body, especially the lungs. The lung tissues attempt to "wall off" the invading organisms by surrounding the germs with a hard covering of calcium, called a *tubercle*. The patient coughs, lacks energy, runs a slight fever, and may cough up blood.

DIAGNOSIS. Tuberculosis is diagnosed chiefly by means of an X-ray of the chest, which reveals the presence of the tubercles. Also, the sputum may be examined for tuberculosis germs. The *tuberculin test* is used to detect the presence of the tubercle bacillus in the body of young children. A small amount of bacterial toxin is placed on the skin or is injected under the skin. The appearance of a small red spot in the area of the injected toxin indicates the presence of the organism in the body.

TREATMENT. As yet, there is no known medicine which will cure tuberculosis. The best treatment is good food and rest in bed, preferably in the open air in sunshine. This treatment was devised by *Dr. Edward L. Trudeau* at Saranac Lake in the Adirondacks. Sometimes it is necessary to collapse the lung, a process called *pneumothorax*, so that the lung may rest and have a chance to heal. This is often done by introducing air into the chest cavity. One of the antibiotics, dihydrostreptomycin, is now being used in the treatment of the disease with reasonable success.

Diphtheria

CAUSE. Diphtheria is caused by the *diphtheria bacillus*.

SUSCEPTIBILITY. Not everyone is susceptible to diphtheria. To determine whether or not an individual is susceptible, the *Schick test* is used. A small amount of bacterial toxin is injected under the skin. The appearance of a small red spot in the area of the injected toxin indicates that the individual is susceptible to the disease. A course of prevention must be undertaken.

IMMUNIZATION. Several preparations are used to establish immunity to diphtheria, as follows:

1. *Antitoxin.* Antitoxin is used to provide temporary immunity in an individual who has been exposed to diphtheria. The antitoxin is prepared in the following manner: An animal, usually a horse, is inoculated with some diphtheria toxin. The animal's cells react rapidly. Soon the animal's blood contains a great amount of powerful *antitoxin*, a chemical substance capable of rendering the toxin harmless. A serum prepared from the animal's blood is used for immunization. The antitoxin is also used in treating diphtheria.

2. *Toxin-antitoxin.* If the antitoxin obtained from the horse is mixed with bacterial toxin, the resulting product is called *toxin-antitoxin*. This is used as a vaccine to build up active acquired immunity. When injected, the toxin stimulates the body to produce its own antitoxin, while the antitoxin prevents the toxin from causing any harm to the body.

3. *Toxoid.* Toxoid is a preparation of toxin weakened by certain chemicals. A toxoid stimulates the body to manufacture its own antitoxin. Toxoids are replacing toxin-antitoxins because fewer injections are required, and they do not produce the undesirable reactions that sometimes result from the use of toxin-antitoxins.

TRANSMISSION. Diphtheria germs are transmitted from an infected person to another person by (1) droplet infection, and (2) articles touched by the patient (indirect contact).

EFFECT ON BODY. Diphtheria causes a general sickness with a very sore throat. These symptoms result from the powerful toxin given off by the diphtheria bacillus.

TREATMENT. Diphtheria may be treated by injections of antitoxin.

Pneumonia

CAUSE. Pneumonia is caused by bacteria. (There is also a virus pneumonia.)

IMMUNIZATION. There is no immunization against pneumonia.

TRANSMISSION. Pneumonia is transmitted from an infected person to another person by discharge from the nose and mouth of the patient (droplet infection).

EFFECT ON BODY. Pneumonia is an infection of the lungs. Congestion of the lungs and respiratory tract, fever and general sickness are characteristic. In severe cases, death may result.

TREATMENT. The sulfa drugs and the antibiotics, especially penicillin, are of great help in the treatment of pneumonia.

Tetanus ("Lockjaw")

CAUSE. Tetanus is caused by the *tetanus bacillus,* an anaerobic bacterium. These germs exist as spores in soil, manure and in tiny crevices, such as those in rusty nails.

IMMUNIZATION. Immunization against tetanus may be brought about by the use of a toxoid.

TRANSMISSION. Tetanus is not caught from one who has the disease. The germs enter the body through breaks in the skin. Being anaerobic, the tetanus bacillus thrives when introduced into the body by a puncture wound or by any cut which closes up and keeps the air out.

EFFECT ON BODY. The tetanus bacillus, when active, liberates a powerful toxin which causes spasms (tightening) of the muscles, particularly those muscles used for closing the jaws.

TREATMENT. Tetanus is treated with tetanus antitoxin. Without this treatment, death usually results.

Typhoid Fever

CAUSE. Typhoid fever is caused by the *typhoid bacillus.*

IMMUNIZATION. Immunity is established by the use of a vaccine containing dead typhoid bacteria. Although dead, these germs cause the body to manufacture antibodies, which make the body immune to typhoid fever.

TRANSMISSION. Typhoid germs are carried by polluted water, milk, flies, oysters, vegetables and human carriers. "Typhoid Mary," a cook to whom several serious outbreaks of typhoid fever were traced, was the most famous human carrier known. Typhoid germs are discharged from the body in the excrement. The germs often find their way to bodies of water. Public health precautions for typhoid fever include proper disposal of sewage, fly control, and examinations of food handlers.

EFFECT ON BODY. Typhoid fever causes general sickness, weakness and fever.

TREATMENT. The treament for typhoid fever includes rest in bed and the use of antibiotics.

DISEASES CAUSED BY VIRUSES

Viruses Cause Disease. The nature of viruses is not well known. Studies indicate that some viruses are little more than molecules of protein. This would mean that the viruses are actually on the borderline between the living and the non-living. Viruses are too small to be seen through the ordinary microscope. Some viruses have been observed through the electron microscope (see page 18). Viruses are so small that they are able to pass through the pores of a filter made of unglazed porcelain. Because of this, they are often called "filterable viruses."

While other pathogenic organisms live *among* the cells of their host, viruses actually *enter* the cells and are usually unable to grow and reproduce elsewhere. For this reason, viruses, unlike bacteria, cannot usually be grown in laboratory dishes. Hence, the study of viruses has been retarded. However, it has recently been found that some viruses can be grown for study in live chick embryos.

Viruses usually enter the body with insect bites, through a break in the skin, or with air, water or food. Viruses cause disease by damaging the cells in which they grow.

The Common Cold

CAUSE. It is believed that colds are due to various viruses. The body is weakened by the virus and is then susceptible to other respiratory diseases of a bacterial nature. The latter disease is called a *secondary infection.*

IMMUNIZATION. There is no immunization against the common cold.

TRANSMISSION. Colds are spread by contact with the infected person and by droplet infection.

EFFECT ON BODY. A cold affects the body in various ways. Some of the symptoms are an inflammation of the nose and throat, closing of the nasal passages, coughing, fever, and a feeling of general sickness. The common cold is not in itself particularly dangerous. It may, however, lower body resistance and lead to sinus infection, pneumonia, and other diseases.

PREVENTION. It is possible that cold-producing organisms are always present in the respiratory passages and become active when the body resistance is reduced, as in periods of exposure and fatigue. Therefore, sufficient rest and healthful living habits are doubtless effective in preventing colds. One of the most important precautions is for an infected person to stay away from others.

TREATMENT. Rest and a light, fluid diet is the best treatment for the common cold.

Poliomyelitis (Polio) or Infantile Paralysis

CAUSE. Polio is caused by a virus. A number of different strains of viruses are known to cause polio.

SUSCEPTIBILITY. Children are more susceptible to polio than adults. This is possibly due to the fact that most adults have become immune to polio by having had the disease perhaps in a form too mild to be recognized.

IMMUNIZATION. A vaccine developed by *Dr. Jonas E. Salk* in 1955 has been proven effective in establishing immunity to polio. *Gamma globulin* (GG), a blood derivative, is given to children who have been exposed to the disease. While gamma globulin does not prevent polio, it may lessen the effects of the disease if one contracts polio.

TRANSMISSION. It is not known how the germs of polio are spread, or how they enter the body. To avoid polio, the following rules should be observed during the epidemic season (late summer): (1) Keep out of crowds. (2) Do not become exhausted or chilled. (3) Keeps hands and food clean. (4) If illness appears, go to bed and call a physician.

EFFECT ON BODY. The first signs of polio include fever, headache, stiff neck and sensitivity to touch. In most cases, the effects of polio are mild. However, the polio virus may damage nerve cells, thereby interfering with breathing or the use of limbs. Permanent paralysis or death results in only a small percentage of cases.

TREATMENT. Polio treatment includes rest in bed, hot baths and hot packs. Sometimes muscles are "reeducated" so that they can be used again.

Smallpox

CAUSE. Smallpox is caused by the *smallpox virus*.

IMMUNIZATION. Smallpox immunization is established by vaccination. This vaccination was first introduced by the English physician, *Edward Jenner* (1749-1823), in the 18th century. The vaccine consists of the material taken from the sores of a cow suffering from *cowpox*, a related but milder disease than smallpox. This material produces immunity to smallpox in humans.

Once a dreaded plague, smallpox has been almost completely wiped out in this country and elsewhere, through vaccination. Compulsory vaccination of school children is a common public health measure.

TRANSMISSION. The germs of smallpox are transmitted from an infected person to another person by direct or indirect contact.

EFFECT ON BODY. Smallpox causes a general sickness, fever, and skin eruptions which leave ugly pock-marks on the body. Smallpox often results in death.

TREATMENT. There is no effective treatment for smallpox.

Yellow Fever

Yellow fever is a tropical disease caused by a virus. The virus of yellow fever is transmitted by the bite of the female *Aëdes* mosquito. Yellow fever is controlled by immunization with weakened virus, and by mosquito control measures. Man's victory over yellow fever is one of the great chapters in medical history. The disease was conquered in Cuba in 1900 by a commission composed of *Doctors Walter Reed, James Carroll, Jesse Lazear* and *Aristides Agramonte*.

Rabies (Hydrophobia)

CAUSE.   Rabies is caused by a virus.

IMMUNIZATION.   A vaccine developed by Pasteur establishes immunity to rabies.

TRANSMISSION.   The germs of rabies are spread by the bite of an infected dog or other animal.

EFFECT ON BODY.   Rabies damages the nervous system. Spasms, thirst and difficulty in swallowing are among the symptoms.

TREATMENT.   The rabies vaccine is given after the patient has been bitten. This vaccine usually wards off the disease. However, no treatment is known to be effective once the disease has developed.

DISEASES CAUSED BY PROTOZOA

Protozoa Cause Disease.   The protozoa are one-celled animals (see page 71). Protozoa may enter the body in food or water, or at the time of an insect bite. Although most protozoa are harmless, some cause disease by damaging the tissues of the host.

Malaria

Malaria is caused by a protozoan called the *Plasmodium malariae.* This germ lives a part of its life in the human bloodstream, where it destroys red blood corpuscles and releases a toxin which causes chills. If the female *Anopheles* mosquito bites a person suffering from malaria, some of these germs are taken into the mosquito. When the mosquito later bites a healthy person, some of the germs are injected into the bloodstream, causing a new case of malaria.

Malaria may be prevented by mosquito control measures, such as draining stagnant water where mosquitoes may breed, or covering the water with a thin layer of oil. The oil prevents the mosquito larvae from obtaining oxygen. Drugs effective in treating malaria include quinine and atabrine.

Amebic Dysentery

This is a serious disease caused by a certain species of protozoa (an ameba) present   (1) on garden vegetables grown in soil contaminated by human wastes, or   (2) in water contaminated by these protozoa. Cleanliness in raising and handling foods is a precaution.

African Sleeping Sickness

This disease is caused by a protozoan carried by the *tsetse* fly. It is a serious disease which causes the victim to fall into a prolonged sleep. The disease can be controlled by destruction of the flies and by screening windows.

DISEASES CAUSED BY MOLDS

Molds Cause Disease. The molds are non-green plants (see p. 42). Molds are usually transmitted in the form of spores. Mold spores may be picked up by the skin, or may enter the body through the nose or mouth. When spores of pathogenic molds reach certain tissues, they start to grow. Molds cause disease by damaging the tissues of the host.

Ringworm and Athlete's Foot

Ringworm is a disease caused by molds, not by worms. Molds infect the skin and often grow in the form of a ring, from which the disease gets its name. Molds often attack the skin between the toes, causing a cracking of the skin with intense burning and itching. This infection of the toes is called *athlete's foot*. The spores of the mold may be picked up by walking barefoot in locker rooms, around swimming pools, etc.

DISEASES CAUSED BY WORMS

Worms Cause Disease. The worms are multicellular animals (see p. 79-82). Parasitic worms gain entrance into the body in various ways, especially as *cysts* in poorly cooked meat. Once inside the body, they reproduce rapidly, using the blood and other tissues of their host for food. Diseases caused by worms are trichinosis, tapeworm, ascaris and hookworm.

DISEASES CAUSED BY RICKETTSIAE

Rickettsiae Cause Disease. Rickettsiae are small organisms whose exact nature is not known. They are considered intermediate between viruses and bacteria. Rickettsiae, like viruses, can grow only in living cells. Rickettsiae are often carried by lice and ticks, and enter the body when these organisms bite. Rickettsiae cause disease by damaging the tissues of their host.

Rocky Mountain Spotted Fever

The rickettsiae which cause this disease are carried by ticks. Hence, the name "tick fever" is sometimes given to this disease. It can be prevented by avoiding regions infested by ticks. The disease is treated with aureomycin.

Typhus Fever

This deadly disease is caused by rickettsiae carried by the human body louse and by rat fleas. Epidemics of typhus can be controlled by the use of *DDT*, an insect-destroying chemical. Aureomycin and chloromycetin have proven effective in the treatment of typhus fever.

DISEASES CAUSED BY SPIROCHAETES

Spirochaetes Cause Disease. Spirochaetes are intermediate in structure between the bacteria and the protozoa. They are usually passed from person to person by contact. Spirochaetes cause disease by damaging the tissues of their host.

Syphilis

The spirochaetes which cause syphilis are transmitted from one person to another by direct contact. The spirochaetes damage the blood and many other tissues of the body, especially the heart and brain. Syphilis is treated with penicillin.

Before obtaining a marriage license in New York and certain other states, a *Wassermann test* to prove the absence of active syphilis is required.

NON-COMMUNICABLE DISEASES

What Is a Non-Communicable Disease? Diseases that are caused by non-living factors are called *non-communicable* or *non-infectious* diseases. These diseases cannot be transmitted from one person to another.

Causes of Non-Communicable Diseases:

1. *Deficiency Diseases.* A lack of any essential nutrient in the diet may cause a specific disease. An example of a deficiency disease

is rickets, caused by a lack of Vitamin D. Vitamin deficiences are discussed on pages 110-111.

2. *Allergies.* An allergy is an unusual sensitivity to a particular substance. Different people are affected by different substances, such as pollen, feathers, dust, eggs and drugs. Contact with the offending substance may produce an itch, a rash, or discomforts similar to those of a cold. Hay fever and poison ivy are examples of allergies.

3. *Endocrine Disorders.* When an endocrine gland fails to function properly, a specific disease results. Diabetes is a disease caused by the improper functioning of the pancreas, an endocrine gland. Endocrine disorders are discussed in Chapter XIV.

4. *Drug Addiction.* When a person uses a drug continually and cannot get along without it, the disease is known as drug addiction. Alcoholism is now recognized as a disease of this nature.

5. *Hereditary Diseases.* Some diseases are due to inherited factors. An example of a heritable disease is hemophilia, discussed on page 150.

6. *Degenerative Diseases.* When an organ or organ system suffers a breakdown, a degenerative disease results. Heart disease, described below, is an example of a degenerative disease.

Heart Disease

Heart disease is the leading cause of death in the United States. There are several types of heart disease. Two of the most common heart ailments are:

CORONARY HEART DISEASE. With advancing age, the walls of the arteries may harden and thicken. This condition is called "hardening of the arteries." The hardening of the arteries reduces their elasticity. The thickening of the arteries reduces the amount of blood that they can carry. As a consequence, the heart must do much more work than normally.

If hardening occurs in the arteries which supply the heart, the heart muscles suffer from a lack of food and oxygen. This is known as coronary heart disease.

CORONARY THROMBOSIS. If a blood clot suddenly blocks one of the arteries supplying the heart, the blood supply to the heart is shut off. The result is a heart attack called coronary thrombosis.

Other heart ailments are known to result from various infectious diseases, including scarlet fever, syphilis and rheumatic fever.

Cancer

NATURE OF CANCER.   Normally, when an individual is fully grown, cell division occurs only for the replacement of injured or worn out cells. However, in some individuals, for unknown reasons, a cell may start a series of divisions resulting in an abnormal growth, or *tumor*. If a tumor is merely a well-defined growth and limited to one area of the body, it is called a *benign tumor*. Such a tumor is harmless. Examples are warts or moles on the body. Benign tumors can be removed and are usually not dangerous. If a tumor is not limited to one area, but continues to grow and spread, it is called a *malignant tumor*, or *cancer*.

A cancer forces its way among healthy cells, surrounding them and interfering with their normal functions. Frequently, the growth invades the cells and destroys them. A cancer often grows away from its source of nourishment. This causes some of the cancer cells to die and, at the same time, to release a poison.

Cancer is not contagious. Neither is cancer inherited, although susceptibility seems to run in some families. Cancer is most common after the age of 40, but it occurs frequently in children, particularly in the form of blood cancer (leukemia). Cancer is the second most common cause of death in the United States.

HOW CANCER SPREADS.   Cancer spreads through the body by:

1. *Growth.*   The original cancer never stops growing. By relentless cell division, cancer invades surrounding organs and destroys them.

2. *Lymph and Blood Distribution.*   Cells break off from the original cancer and are carried by the lymph and blood to other parts of the body where they start new cancers.

DANGER SIGNS OF CANCER.   To be cured, cancer must be detected and treated *in its early stages*. Here are seven signs which may mean cancer:

1. Any sore that does not heal.
2. A lump or thickening in the breast or elsewhere.
3. Unusual bleeding or discharge.
4. Any change in a wart or mole.
5. Persistent indigestion or difficulty in swallowing.
6. Persistent hoarseness or cough.
7. Any change in normal bowel habits.

HOW CANCER IS TREATED:

1. *Surgery.* The cancer can sometimes be removed by a surgical operation.

2. *X-ray.* Cancer cells can be killed by X-ray.

3. *Radium.* Cancer cells can be killed by the radiations given off from radium.

Completion Questions

1. A (an) _____ disease is one which a person can contract from another person.
2. An organism causing a disease is said to be _____.
3. Germs may be transmitted by the spray of a cough or sneeze by a process called _____.
4. The outermost defense of the body against bacteria is the _____.
5. When bacteria invade the body, the _____ move to the infected area to engulf the bacteria.
6. A person who is not susceptible to a certain disease is said to be _____ to that disease.
7. An individual is said to have _____ when his own body produces antibodies against a disease.
8. One of the first drugs made for treating a specific disease was _____.
9. The technique a bacteriologist follows in proving that a particular bacterium causes a disease is known as _____.
10. In the Adirondacks, _____ established the first open-air sanitarium for tubercular patients.
11. If a person is ill with diphtheria, he is usually given _____.
12. A (an) _____, which is used to produce immunity to a particular disease, is a toxin weakened by chemicals.
13. The disease _____ may result from a deep puncture wound.
14. Immunity to typhoid fever may be built up in an individual by giving him injections containing _____.
15. Germs which cause disease and which are too small to be observed through an ordinary microscope are known as _____.
16. Gamma globulin is given to children who have been exposed to _____.
17. The first disease for which a vaccine was made is _____.
18. Atabrine is a drug which is useful in treating the disease _____.

19. African sleeping sickness is a disease spread by an infected _____.

20. _____ is a disease in which there is an abnormal growth of cells.

Multiple-Choice Questions

1. Antibodies are found in (1) plasma (2) red blood corpuscles (3) bacterial cultures (4) blood platelets.
2. An antibody produced by man which dissolves bacteria is (1) a white corpuscle (2) a lysin (3) an antitoxin (4) an agglutinin.
3. Ehrlich's experimental work resulted in improved treatment of (1) cancer (2) scarlet fever (3) Texas fever (4) syphilis.
4. Sulfa drugs are effective against diseases caused by (1) worms (2) vitamin deficiency (3) bacteria (4) glandular upsets.
5. Drugs derived from living organisms such as molds are called (1) sulfa drugs (2) antibiotics (3) hormones (4) viruses.
6. The best general treatment for a victim of tuberculosis is (1) vaccines (2) sulfa drugs (3) surgery (4) rest.
7. The injection of diphtheria antitoxin provides (1) active immunity (2) lasting protection (3) passive immunity (4) a toxoid.
8. Pneumonia is an infection of the (1) lungs (2) skin (3) nervous system (4) blood.
9. Oysters grown in polluted water may spread the agent of infection of (1) measles (2) typhoid fever (3) yellow fever (4) diphtheria.
10. The protein molecules, which are on the borderline of the living and the non-living, are known as (1) bacteria (2) viruses (3) rickettsiae (4) spirochaetes.
11. An example of a disease caused by a virus is (1) tuberculosis (2) tetanus (3) athlete's foot (4) the common cold.
12. The most satisfactory method for preventing the common cold among school pupils is (1) administering antitoxin (2) administering sulfa drugs (3) keeping at home pupils with colds (4) vaccinating all pupils.
13. A disease that is more common in late summer than at other seasons is (1) infantile paralysis (2) measles (3) meningitis (4) tuberculosis.
14. Malaria is carried from one person to another by (1) houseflies (2) human carriers (3) infected patients (4) mosquitoes.

15. The disease for which one well-known method of treatment consists of the use of hot packs and muscle reeducation is (1) goiter (2) pneumonia (3) spinal meningitis (4) poliomyelitis.
16. Athlete's foot is caused by a (1) virus (2) fungus (3) worm (4) vitamin deficiency.
17. The disease hookworm is caused by worms that enter the body (1) in inhaled air (2) in polluted drinking water (3) through the feet (4) in undercooked pork.
18. It is possible to prevent an epidemic of typhus by the use of (1) gamma globulin (2) DDT (3) atabrine (4) vitamins.
19. Syphilis is a disease transmitted by (1) direct contact (2) insects (3) impure food (4) impure water.
20. The most common cause of death is (1) cancer (2) polio (3) heart disease (4) pneumonia.

Modified True-False Questions

1. The transfer of disease germs from one person to another by shaking hands is called *indirect* contact.
2. If large numbers of disease-producing bacteria live in the body of a person who shows no symptoms of the disease, such a person is called a *carrier*.
3. Recovery from smallpox leaves a person with *active* immunity to smallpox.
4. The resistance to a disease present in an individual at birth is called *acquired* immunity.
5. Penicillin was first discovered by the English scientist *Jenner*.
6. The poisons given off by bacteria are known as *toxins*.
7. A chemical substance which neutralizes the poisons given off by bacteria is *a toxin-antitoxin*.
8. Soldiers in the United States Army are protected against tetanus by inoculation with *a toxoid*.
9. *African sleeping sickness* is transmitted by the Aëdes mosquito.
10. Everyone who enters military service is given a Wassermann test to discover whether he has *syphilis*.

Essay Questions

1. *a.* Your body has many defenses against invasion by bacteria. How does each of the following aid in protecting you against disease: skin, cilia, white blood cells, antibodies?

   b. State two differences between active immunization and passive immunization.

   c. Describe a procedure that may be used to determine whether a specific organism causes a certain disease.

2. *a.* Toxin-antitoxin (or toxoid) and antitoxin are used to control diphtheria. Explain briefly what each consists of and the special purpose of each.

   b. For either smallpox or typhoid fever, state each of the following:

     (1) The cause of the disease.

     (2) How the disease is transmitted.

     (3) A public health measure intended to help prevent its spread.

3. *a.* State the cause of infantile paralysis (poliomyelitis) and name a type of tissue affected by the disease.

   b. State two measures by which the spread of rabies can be prevented.

   c. Tell how our knowledge of the breeding and feeding habits of the malarial mosquito helps us to prevent the spread of malaria.

4. Below is a list of diseases:

cholera	pneumonia	tetanus
malaria	smallpox	trichinosis
cancer	syphilis	tuberculosis

   Selecting your answers from this list, name the disease to which each of five of the following descriptive phrases applies:

   a. Prevented by inoculation of antitoxin.

   b. Prevented by inoculation of a related but milder disease germ.

   c. Treated by the use of quinine or atabrine.

   d. Its presence in an individual may be detected by the sputum test.

   e. Transmitted by incompletely cooked meat.

   f. Its cure discovered by Ehrlich.

   g. An abnormal growth of cells.

5. Give a biological explanation of each of the following:

   a. Everyone should have a periodic chest X-ray examination.

   b. A Wassermann test is given to each applicant before marriage.

   c. If bacteria should become extinct, there still would be certain diseases.

   d. Although rickets and smallpox are both diseases, smallpox is contagious, whereas rickets is not.

Chapter XXV

CONSERVATION

What Is Conservation? When the early settlers came to America, they found a land rich in natural resources. The fertile soil had never been cultivated. The supply of timber and the many species of fish and wildlife seemed unlimited. As a result, man cut trees and took fish and game without regard for future supply. In time, it became apparent that something had to be done (1) to control the use of these natural resources, and (2) to replenish our supplies of these resources. The resulting program for the wise use and development of soil, water supply, forests, fish and wildlife is called *conservation*.

In our study of conservation, we shall (1) learn how we can make full use of our natural resources, and (2) at the same time, make certain that a sufficient supply of these necessities will be available for future generations. To begin with, we shall see that conservation is based largely on an understanding of how organisms are related to one another and to their environment.

Ecology. *Ecology* is the science dealing with the relationships existing between living things and their environment. Different environments are inhabited by different species: frogs live in ponds; moles live underground. The animals of a given region are called the *fauna* of that region; the plants of a certain area are called the *flora* of that place. The natural home of any living thing is called its *habitat*.

Adaptations for Different Habitats. Plants and animals have special structures which fit them to live in their own natural environment. These structures are called *adaptations*. Animals are colored to resemble their natural background. This is an adaptation for survival, called *protective coloration*.

Here are some adaptations for particular habitats:

1. The Water. *Water plants*, such as pond weeds and water lilies, usually have small submerged root systems, since in their habitat it is not necessary to penetrate the soil in search of water. Their leaves and flimsy stems have air chambers permitting the water to buoy them up. Thus, the plants are able to float on the water.

315

Water animals, such as the fish, are usually equipped with gills, an adaptation for breathing under water. The webbed foot of the duck is an adaptation for swimming.

2. The Land. *Land plants,* such as the maple, have well-developed root systems for obtaining water and for anchorage. The stems are stiff, an adaptation for holding the leaves up to the light.

Land animals, such as the dog, have lungs for breathing air. Insects have breathing pores.

3. The Desert. *Desert plants,* such as the cactus, have stems and leaves which are thick and fleshy. These are adaptations for storing water. Leaves often take the form of spines, an adaptation to prevent animals from chewing into the plant to obtain water. The root systems of desert plants are very extensive, for moisture is scarce. Most of these plants are protected against excessive loss of water by a covering of wax or hairs on their stems.

Desert animals, such as the horned toad and certain snakes, are adapted to survive on a limited supply of water. They have thick scaly skins for protection against excessive loss of water. Other small desert animals, such as the kangaroo rat, live underground during the day to escape the heat and come out at night to search for food.

4. The Cold Climate. *Polar* (and *alpine*) *plants,* such as reindeer moss and lichens, are low, small and able to survive long periods of snow, wind and cold.

Polar animals, such as the polar bear, often have thick layers of fat, which is an adaptation for surviving the cold.

5. The Tropics. *Jungle plants,* such as the giant tree ferns, rosewood and mahogany, must be able to grow rapidly and reach great heights, for they must compete with the vast growth about them for light.

Jungle animals have special adaptations for obtaining food. The monkey is built for climbing, the lion for springing upon its prey.

Food Chains. In a fresh-water pond there are decaying weeds. The weeds are consumed by bacteria. The bacteria are food for microscopic animals. These tiny animals are food for insect larvae. The larvae are eaten by fishes. The fishes are food for man. This is one example of a *food chain.* A food chain is defined as a series whereby one species is eaten by another species, and that species in turn is eaten by another species, and so forth. Food chains are found in every habitat and serve to maintain the proportion in numbers of one species to another species in that habitat. If one species increases or decreases in number to any appreciable extent, it upsets the entire food chain in which it is a link.

The Balance of Nature. The relative numbers of interdependent species in any area are normally in more or less of an equilibrium. This constantly changing condition is called the *balance of nature.* For example, owls feed upon mice. As the mouse population in a given area increases, owls from adjoining territories move in. In other words, the owl population increases in response to the larger food supply. The greater number of owls devour more mice and, as a result, mice become scarcer. Now the more limited supply of mice reduces the number of owls. One species thus keeps another in check. However, perfect balance is rarely obtained in nature. The balance or relationship between organisms is most frequently upset by man who (1) often destroys the homes of wildlife, (2) kills many organisms, and (3) introduces other species into an area.

Many species which are not particularly destructive in their own habitat often become very destructive when introduced into a new environment. This is often due to the fact that the new environment offers (1) a lack of natural enemies, and (2) the presence of an abundant food supply. Both factors permit the new species to increase in numbers so rapidly that they become destructive pests. Examples of undesirable species introduced from abroad are the Japanese beetle in the United States and the rabbit in Australia.

SOIL

What Is Soil? Such factors as wind and water, acting over a long period of time, break rocks into small particles. The tiny rock particles when mixed with decayed organic material form *soil.* Organic matter in the soil is called *humus.* The uppermost layer of soil is the *topsoil.* This is the soil which normally supports plant life.

Types of Soil. There are three chief types of soil, as follows:

1. *Clay Soil.* This type of soil consists of clay with some humus and other materials. The tiny firm-packing clay particles form a non-porous soil difficult to till and likely to cake. Being non-porous, very little water can be absorbed by the soil. Thus, plant growth is retarded.

2. *Sandy Soil.* This type of soil consists largely of sand with some clay and humus. Sandy soil, being porous, readily admits air and water which are essential to plant growth.

3. *Loam.* The excellent soils classified as loams are composed of sand, clay and humus mixed in proper proportions to maintain healthy plant life. Loam is easily worked and forms only small lumps. Thus, plant growth is encouraged.

The Importance of Fertile Soil. We know that man depends for his food supply on green plants. The quality and quantity of plant life depend on (1) the amount of topsoil available, and (2) the fertility of the topsoil. When soil is lost or becomes unproductive, plant life is meager and food shortages result.

Soil Erosion. The disintegration and removal of rocks and soil is called *erosion.* Since the days of the early settlers, one-third of America's topsoil has been lost by erosion. Water and air cause erosion; man, by his unwise conservation practices, contributes to erosion.

1. *Water.* Water is the chief agent of erosion. Water causes erosion in several ways: (*a*) Streams dislodge and carry great quantities of material from their beds and banks. In this way, the Mississippi River removes hundreds of millions of tons of sediment yearly. (*b*) Rain and ground water dissolve carbon dioxide from the air and from decaying organic matter in the soil. This carbon dioxide unites with water to form carbonic acid, which dissolves limestone. In time, great masses of bedrock are eroded away by this action. (*c*) When water freezes, it expands, exerting great pressure. When this occurs in porous rocks or in rock crevices, rocks are shattered. (*d*) Ocean waves beat relentlessly against the shore, often eroding the land and undermining cliffs. (*e*) Run-off rainfall frequently finds its way into small channels, or *furrows,* in the soil. The constant flow of water deepens these channels, forming *gullies.* Run-off water not only cuts deep depressions in the earth's surface, but also removes large quantities of topsoil.

2. *Air.* Next to water, air is the most common cause of erosion. Air causes erosion as follows: (*a*) Rocks are gradually disintegrated by the chemical action of atmospheric gases, especially oxygen. (*b*) Wind (air in motion), carrying particles of sand, acts as a sandblast, eroding cliffs and carving bedrocks. (*c*) The wind causes dust storms, which carry away valuable topsoil. Wind is the chief agent of erosion in dry regions where the lack of vegetation and

water causes the soil to become loose and easily removed. Situated in the western part of the United States is the "Dust Bowl." This is a region where wind erosion in the form of dust storms has removed topsoil from many farms and orchards and destroyed other farms and orchards by covering them up with sand.

3. *Man.* Man contributes to the process of erosion by such unwise practices as the following: (*a*) By removing forests and other forms of vegetation, man permits wind and water to erode the denuded land. (*b*) By improper planting, man exposes the soil to erosion by wind or water. (*c*) By continuously using topsoil for the growing of only one type of crop, man does not permit the soil to be replenished with minerals.

How Soil Erosion Can Be Controlled. Loss of topsoil by erosion can be controlled in several ways, including the following:

1. *Contour Plowing.* This is a farming method whereby the furrows are plowed around a hill. If the furrows were up and down the hill, rain water would run down the furrows and carry valuable topsoil away. Contour plowing prevents this.

Fig. 115. Contour Plowing

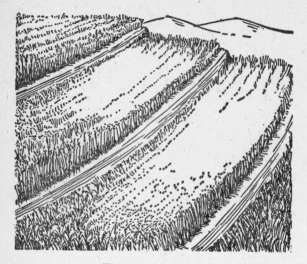

Fig. 116. Terracing

2. *Terracing*. In hilly farmland, step-like terraces are built on a hillside. Crops are planted on the terraces. These terraces retard the run-off of rain water and prevent erosion.

3. *Strip Cropping*. This is a farming method whereby two different crops are planted in alternate strips parallel to each other. A crop such as corn or cotton is planted in rows. Alternating with these rows of crops are the close-growing cover crops, such as rye, hay, clover or alfalfa. The close-growing crops bind the soil together and absorb much run-off rain water, thus preventing erosion.

4. *Cover Crops*. After the crop in a field has been harvested, a cover crop is sometimes planted in the field. The roots of the cover crop hold the soil particles together and prevent erosion during the winter when there is no regular crop.

Fig. 117. Strip Cropping

How Soil Depletion Can Be Prevented. As we have seen, plants take certain substances from the soil. Therefore, if crops are planted in the same soil year after year, this soil becomes *depleted* (exhausted). Soil depletion can be avoided as follows:

1. *Crop Rotation.* To maintain the nitrates in the soil, the process of crop rotation is employed. A leguminous crop, such as clover, alfalfa or soybeans, is alternated with a productive crop. The nitrogen-fixing bacteria living in the nodules of the roots of the legumes convert the nitrogen of the air into nitrates which are then restored to the soil. Thus, the soil fertility is maintained.

2. *Use of Fertilizers.* The minerals which are removed from the soil by crops are replaced by the use of proper fertilizers. Two types of fertilizers are essential: (1) commercial fertilizers restore lost minerals to the soil, and (2) organic fertilizers restore the humus content of the soil. The chief organic fertilizers are manure and decomposing plants.

Plowing under a crop of clover adds valuable nitrates to the soil by bacterial action. (See pages 53-54.)

WATER SUPPLY

The Importance of Water. Water is indispensable to life. Without water, plants could not grow and animal life could not exist. Furthermore, water is the habitat of innumerable species of plants and animals. An adequate water supply is also essential for household use and industrial operations. Finally, water provides man with recreation, such as boating, bathing and fishing.

The Water Cycle. Water vapor is given to the atmosphere (1) by evaporation that occurs at the surface of all bodies of water, and (2) as a waste product of respiration in all plants and animals. The water vapor becomes a part of the air and may be carried to high elevations. There the low temperature causes condensation into clouds, and eventually into larger droplets which fall to earth as precipitation (rain, hail, snow, sleet). Eventually, the water finds its way into the ground and then (1) to be taken in by plants and animals, or (2) to flow to an ocean, lake or stream. This completes the *water cycle.*

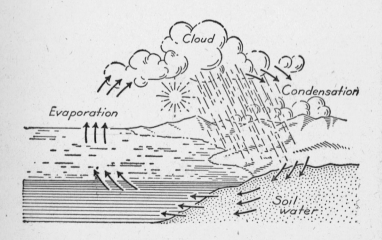

Fig. 118. The Water Cycle

Water Is Often Wasted. Water is frequently wasted or made unfit for use as follows:

1. *Run-off of Rainfall.* Rainfall which runs into streams and eventually finds its way to a lake or sea is lost to the soil. This run-off may be due to: (*a*) removal of vegetation from hillsides, (*b*) plowing up and down a hillside rather than on the contour, (*c*) allowing gullies to form on farmlands, and (*d*) failure to install dams in streams that carry great quantities of water.

2. *Pollution.* Emptying harmful waste materials into bodies of water is called *pollution.* Water may be polluted by sewage, garbage and various industrial wastes. Such substances destroy fish life and make the water unfit for human consumption.

Methods of Conserving Water:

1. *Preventing the Run-off of Rainfall.* The run-off of rainfall may be checked by: (*a*) *Hillside plantings.* Cities often plant evergreen trees on the hills surrounding the lakes which are their sources of water. The porous floor of an evergreen forest acts like a sponge in holding rain water. This prevents wasteful run-off. (*b*) *Contour plowing and terracing.* These farming methods prevent excessive run-off, as explained on 319-320. (*c*) *Sodding of areas subject to gullying.* By preventing excessive run-off, this practice not only saves water, but saves soil as well. (*d*) *Building dams.* Dams hold back rain water which would otherwise be lost. The bodies of water formed by dams are useful for water supply, fishing and boating. Beavers sometimes help by building dams.

2. *Preventing Pollution.* The pollution of public waters can be prevented by (*a*) laws which prohibit the dumping of wastes into the waters, and (*b*) educating the public to the dangers of water pollution.

FORESTS

The Value of Forests. The spongy forest floor absorbs rain water and gives it up only very slowly. This minimizes soil erosion and prevents floods. The sub-surface water, called *ground water,* replenishes springs and wells, which are the sources of man's drinking water. In addition to conserving water and soil, forests furnish many useful products: lumber, paper, rayon, cellophane, plastics, turpentine and alcohol. Furthermore, the forests provide homes for wildlife, and give man opportunities for recreation and employment. Because of the great value of trees, the federal government and the state governments provide us with free tree seedlings for planting.

Forest Enemies. There are many enemies of the forest, including the following: (1) *Tree diseases.* These are often caused by fungi, such as the Dutch elm disease and white pine blister rust. (2) *Insects.* Trees are damaged by many insects, including the tent caterpillar, the wood-boring beetle and the bark beetle. (3) *Wind.* Strong winds blow down trees and create an impenetrable mass of brush difficult to extinguish if it gets on fire. (4) *Fire.* A forest fire, once started, causes extensive damage before it can be brought under control. As a fire-prevention measure, the forests are usually closed to public use during a dry season. (5) *Man.* By far the worst enemy of the forest is man. He destroys the woods by improper lumbering, and starts many forest fires by sheer carelessness.

Forest Management. Today forest trees are rightly recognized as a crop. Forest trees are (1) harvested at the right time—that is, when they are fully mature, and (2) replaced by the planting of young trees. This *reforestation* program insures a constant supply of trees.

Other procedures of good forest management include: (1) removing dead or diseased trees, (2) introducing birds to control harmful insects, (3) organizing fire control, including look-out towers and modern fire-fighting equipment, and (4) educating the public in fire prevention, such as never discarding a lighted match or cigarette, never leaving a campfire untended and always extinguishing a campfire by smothering it with dirt.

FISH AND WILDLIFE

The Values of Fish and Wildlife:

1. *Hunting and Fishing.* Sportsmen find recreation in hunting and fishing. In addition to deer and rabbit, the species commonly hunted include grouse, pheasant and duck. Among the species of fish commonly caught are the trout, bass, pickerel and perch. Aside from their value in providing the sports of hunting and fishing, the fish and game are important foods. Commercial fishing in the United States is a large industry and provides the country not only with food, but also with oils and fertilizers.

2. *Trapping.* Professional trappers and country boys alike earn considerable money by trapping animals and selling the fur. Among

the valuable fur-bearing species are the muskrat, mink, otter and beaver.

Fishes. Most bodies of water can be made to yield a continuous supply of fish. To this end, the states conduct biological surveys of their waters. The biologists secure data on water temperatures, available oxygen, pollution, natural fish food present, parasites of fishes, fish diseases, etc. This information is necessary in determining (1) what fishes, if any, should be stocked in a given body of water, and (2) how to maintain or increase the fishing.

Birds. Birds are valuable because they eat insects and weed seeds. Hawks and owls, although they occasionally feed on chickens, render a great service by destroying mice. Bird conservation includes (1) maintaining feeding stations during the winter months when natural food is scarce, (2) turning stray cats over to the proper authorities, (3) helping to interest the public in conserving bird life, and (4) leaving rows of shrubs or trees to serve as shelters for birds and small mammals.

Vanishing Species. Because of a lack of game management, the auk, heath hen and passenger pigeon are now extinct. The buffalo, or bison, was once abundant on the Western plains, but is now limited to a few small herds in protected areas. Other species, including the elk, moose and antelope, are now threatened with extinction. Limited numbers of these vanishing species find refuge in our national and state parks. Some plants, too, are in need of protection. These include the flowering dogwood, mountain laurel and trailing arbutus.

Game Laws. The harvest of the crop of fish and game is controlled by laws. These laws are designed to insure that some individuals will be left to serve as breeders. Natural breeding lessens the need for artificial stocking. Conservation laws that protect fish and game are:

1. *Closed Season.* A closed season is a period of time during which a species may not be taken. The closed season usually includes the time at which reproduction occurs.

2. *Methods of Capture.* The law forbids the taking of fish and game by methods which would result in too large a catch. For example, taking fish by the use of nets is carefully regulated.

3. *Legal Size.* The law requires that a species be of a certain minimum size. For example, in New York State, a bass under ten inches may not be taken.

4. *Legal Limit.* The legal limit is the maximum number of individuals of a given species of fish or game which one person may take in a given period of time. For example, in New York State, no person may take more than six bass in one day.

Completion Questions

1. The program which is concerned with the proper use and preservation of our natural resources is called _____.
2. The science that studies the relationships between organisms and their environment is known as _____.
3. Fauna refers to the _____ inhabiting a region.
4. The place where an organism lives is known as its _____.
5. An adaptation in which organisms are colored to blend in with their environment is called _____.
6. The structures found in fish which are adaptations for breathing under water are the _____.
7. The stems of desert plants are protected against loss of water by _____.
8. The upper layer of the soil in which plant life will grow is the _____.
9. The three main types of soil are clay soil, sandy soil and _____.
10. The process by which the rocks of the earth are decomposed and removed is called _____.

Multiple-Choice Questions

1. The chief agent of erosion is (1) air (2) running water (3) man (4) animals.
2. The removal of valuable topsoil in dry regions may result in (1) enriched topsoil (2) Dust Bowl areas (3) gullies (4) furrows.
3. Soil erosion on hilly land can be reduced by (1) frequent plowing (2) growing corn (3) removing trees (4) terracing.
4. One method employed to restore nitrates to the soil is (1) contour plowing (2) gullying (3) terracing (4) planting a leguminous crop.
5. The humus content of the soil can be restored by the use of (1) alfalfa (2) rye (3) manure (4) soybeans.
6. Reforestation results in an increase in (1) floods (2) run-off (3) soil erosion (4) water in the ground.

7. One way of preventing floods is by (1) reforestation (2) gullying (3) allowing run-off (4) using fertilizers.
8. An extinct species is the (1) bison (2) elk (3) passenger pigeon (4) antelope.
9. Hawks are valuable because they (1) carry messages (2) feed on chickens (3) destroy mice (4) are used for sport.
10. The most destructive enemy of the forest is (1) wind (2) fire (3) man (4) insects.

Modified True-False Questions

1. The balance of nature is most frequently upset by *man*.
2. The absence of natural enemies in an area may result in the *decrease* in the number of a particular species.
3. Contour plowing *increases* the rate of soil erosion.
4. The planting of two different crops in alternate parallel strips is known as *strip cropping*.
5. The water absorbed by the earth is known as *ground water*.

Essay Questions

1. *a.* What is the meaning of the term conservation?
   b. Explain the reason for each of the following conservation practices:
      (1) distribution of free tree seedlings by State Conservation Departments
      (2) closing the forests during dry seasons
      (3) placing beavers along streams
      (4) forbidding the dumping of garbage or sewage in certain streams and rivers.
2. Explain the meaning of each of the following terms and tell how it is related to conservation: reforestation, contour plowing, forest management, rotation of crops, cover crops.
3. *a.* What is the relation of forests to flood control?
   b. Explain three ways by which man can make better use of forests.
4. Animals and plants that are not especially destructive in their natural environments often become destructive when introduced into a new environment.
   a. Give two good reasons to account for this fact.
   b. Give two examples in proof of the above statement.
   c. Name one method of combatting each pest you have mentioned.

SOME IMPORTANT BIOLOGISTS

Agassiz, Louis. (1807-1873). Swiss-American. Studied fossil fishes and advanced the science of taxonomy.

Andrews, Roy Chapman. (1884-   ). American. Directed many expeditions for the American Museum of Natural History. Famous for his expeditions to the Gobi Desert, where he excavated the remains of ancient animals and uncovered the first dinosaur eggs ever found.

Aristotle. (384-322 B.C.). Greek. Known as the "father of biology." He organized the science of biology of his time and made many important contributions, including a method of classification.

Banting, Frederick G. (1891-1941). Canadian. Discovered the hormone insulin, used in treating diabetes. (Shared Nobel Prize 1923.)

Brown, Robert. (1773-1858). Scotch. Discovered the nucleus of the cell.

Burbank, Luther. (1849-1926). American. Experimented with plant breeding and developed many new and improved varieties, including the Burbank potato, Shasta daisy and spineless cactus.

Carrel, Alexis. (1873-1944). French. Developed a technique for keeping animal tissues alive outside the body. (Nobel Prize 1912.)

Correns, Karl. (1864-1933). German. Studied heredity and rediscovered Mendel's laws in 1900 almost simultaneously with DeVries and Tschermak.

Cuvier, Georges. (1769-1832). French. Founded the science of comparative anatomy.

Darwin, Charles. (1809-1882). English. Wrote *The Origin of Species* (1859) in which he proposed the theory of evolution stressing natural selection, or survival of the fittest.

Davenport, Charles. (1866-1944). American. Studied human inheritance and served as director of the Eugenics Record Office at Cold Spring Harbor, N. Y.

DeVries, Hugo. (1848-1935). Dutch. Pointed out the importance of Mendel's work. He presented a theory of evolution by mutation.

Dujardin, Felix. (1801-1860). French. Discovered that one-celled animals are composed of protoplasm, although he did not call this material protoplasm.

Ehrlich, Paul. (1854-1915). German. Developed salvarsan ("606"), an arsenic compound, which was the first effective drug used in the treatment of syphilis. (Shared Nobel Prize 1908.)

Fleming, Alexander. (1881-1955). English. Prepared the antibiotic penicillin from the green bread mold, *Penicillium notatum*. (Shared Nobel Prize 1945.)

Funk, Casimir. (1884-   ). Polish. Discovered vitamins.

Galton, Francis. (1822-1911). English. Studied human inheritance and founded the science of eugenics.

Goldberger, Joseph. (1874-1929). American. Proved that pellagra is due to a vitamin deficiency.

Harvey, William. (1578-1657). English. Discovered the circulation of blood.

Hooke, Robert. (1635-1703). English. Discovered and named the *cell*, when he studied thin slices of cork under the microscope.

Jenner, Edward. (1749-1823). English. Developed the vaccination for smallpox and laid the foundation for the scientific understanding of vaccination.

Koch, Robert. (1843-1910). German. Discovered the *tubercle bacillus* and several other pathogenic bacteria. He perfected the method of culturing bacteria on a nutrient gelatin. (Nobel Prize 1905.)

Lamarck, Jean. (1744-1829). French. Formulated a theory of evolution emphasizing use and disuse (also known as the theory of the inheritance of acquired characters).

Leeuwenhoek, Anton van. (1632-1723). Dutch. Improved the microscope and discovered many microorganisms as well as capillaries, blood corpuscles and sperms.

Linnaeus, Carolus. (1707-1778). Swedish. Developed the binomial system of classification, which is still in use today with some improvements.

Lister, Joseph. (1827-1912). English. Developed antiseptic surgery.

Mendel, Gregor. (1822-1884). Austrian. Discovered the basic laws of heredity by his work on garden peas, thus founding the science of genetics.

Metchnikoff, Ilya. (1845-1916). Russian. Discovered that certain white blood cells, called phagocytes, destroy germs. (Shared Nobel Prize 1908.)

Morgan, Thomas Hunt. (1866-1945). American. Developed modern genetics by studies of the fruit fly, *Drosophila*. Formulated the gene theory. (Nobel Prize 1933.)

Muller, Hermann J. (1890-   ). American. Discovered that mutations could be produced in fruit flies by exposure to X-rays. (Nobel Prize 1947.)

Pasteur, Louis. (1822-1895). French. Disproved spontaneous generation and first demonstrated the role of bacteria in fermentation, food preservation and disease. Devised a treatment for rabies.

Pavlov, Ivan. (1849-1936). Russian. Experimented with the conditioned reflex. (Nobel Prize 1904.)

Purkinje, Johannes. (1787-1869). Czech. First used the word *protoplasm* to describe the living matter in animal embryos.

Redi, Francesco. (1626-1697). Italian. Was the first to disprove the theory of spontaneous generation by demonstrating that maggots do not appear on meat unless flies have laid eggs on it.

Reed, Walter. (1851-1902). American. Proved that yellow fever is carried by the Aëdes mosquito. This discovery led to control of the disease.

Schleiden, Matthias. (1804-1881). German. Discovered that all plants are composed of cells.

Schultze, Max. (1825-1874). German. Proved that protoplasm is similar in plants and animals.

Schwann, Theodor. (1810-1882). German. Discovered that all animals are composed of cells.

Trudeau, Edward L. (1848-1915). American. Discovered the use of fresh air and healthful surroundings in treating tuberculosis.

Von Mohl, Hugo. (1805-1872). German. First applied the name protoplasm to the living matter in plant cells.

Waksman, Selman. (1888-   ). Discovered several antibiotics, including streptomycin. (Nobel Prize 1952.)

Wallace, Alfred. (1823-1913). English. Formulated a theory of evolution by natural selection similar to that of Darwin.

Weismann, August. (1834-1914). German. Proved that acquired characters are not inherited. He formulated the theory of the continuity of the germplasm.

Wilson, Edmund B. (1856-1939). American. Advanced the study of the cell, particularly the relation of chromosomes to heredity.

BIOLOGY—JUNE 1961 (1)

Part I

Answer all questions in this part.

Directions (1-70): Write on the line at the right of *each* statement or question the *number* preceding the word or expression that, of those given, best completes the statement or answers the question. [70]

1. The basic inorganic raw materials for photosynthesis are (1) water and oxygen (2) water and carbon dioxide (3) oxygen and carbon dioxide (4) sugar and carbon dioxide

2. Passage of materials through the membrane of a cell is called (1) assimilation (2) diffusion (3) circulation (4) transpiration

3. The largest portion of the iron which is supplied to the body by foods is used by the body in the (1) growth of hard bones and teeth (2) manufacture of insulin (3) development of respiratory enzymes (4) formation of hemoglobin

4. The small structures growing on the roots of a legume are called (1) lenticels (2) nodules (3) bulbs (4) tubers

5. A test tube containing a molasses solution and yeast is kept in a warm place overnight. The gas collected from this mixture would (1) turn limewater milky (2) burst into flame when ignited (3) cause a glowing splint to burst into flame (4) cause red litmus paper to turn blue

6. Sperm and egg cells have the haploid number of chromosomes as a result of (1) reduction division (2) mitotic division (3) cleavage division (4) fertilization

7. A new drug for treatment of tuberculosis was being tested in a hospital. Patients in Group A actually received doses of the new drug; those in Group B were given only sugar pills. Group B represents (1) a scientific experiment (2) a scientific method (3) an experimental error (4) an experimental control

8. Which is most closely associated with the process of transpiration? (1) spiracles of a grasshopper (2) root of a geranium (3) leaf of a maple (4) gills of a fish

9. Which term includes the others? (1) organ (2) tissue (3) system (4) organism

10. Fraternal twins develop from (1) one fertilized egg (2) two fertilized eggs (3) one egg fertilized by two sperms (4) two eggs fertilized by the same sperm

11. When several drops of pasteurized milk were placed in a petri dish containing sterilized nutrient agar, many colonies developed. This experiment shows that the milk (1) contained some bacteria

(2) contained harmful germs   (3) should have been sterilized
(4) was incorrectly stamped "Pasteurized"

12. If many tall pea plants were crossed, which result would be *least*
probable?   (1) 100% pure tall   (2) 50% pure tall, 50% hybrid
tall   (3) 50% tall, 50% short   (4) 75% tall, 25% short

13. Which plant tissues are mostly concerned with storage?   (1)
phloem and xylem   (2) phloem and cambium   (3) palisade
cells and epidermis   (4) pith and spongy cells

14. Amphibians which usually hibernate during the winter by burying
themselves in the mud at the bottom of a pond or stream are able
to survive because   (1) the temperature of the mud is always
above their body temperature   (2) sufficient oxygen can be absorbed through their moist skin   (3) they do not need energy
during this time   (4) the mud serves as insulation to protect
them from the cold

15. Which reagent should be used in the urine test for diabetes?
(1) iodine   (2) nitric acid   (3) ammonia   (4) Benedict's
solution

16. Which sequence correctly illustrates a food chain?   (1) algae—
insect larvae—fish—man   (2) algae—fish—insect larvae—man   (3)
insect larvae—algae—fish—man   (4) fish—insect larvae—algae—
man

17. Which generalization concerning sex determination is true?   (1)
The female determines the sex of the offspring.   (2) The XY
chromosomes are found in the male.   (3) The sex of the offspring
is first determined during maturation.   (4) There is a greater
chance of getting female offspring than male offspring.

18. The great fear of snakes that many humans have is an illustration
of   (1) instinct   (2) inherited behavior   (3) conditioned
behavior   (4) simple reflex

19. What was the weak point of Darwin's theory that De Vries' discovery of mutations helped to explain?   (1) overproduction   (2)
natural selection   (3) survival of the fittest   (4) variations

20. A pollen grain contains a nucleus which is most similar in function
to the nucleus of   (1) an egg   (2) a seed   (3) a sperm   (4)
a spore

21. The removal for microscopic examination of a small bit of living
tissue from a patient is called   (1) biopsy   (2) dissection
(3) surgery   (4) therapy

22. The presence of which substance is most important for all cell

activity?   (1) light   (2) water   (3) carbon dioxide   (4) chlorophyl

23. All life depends directly or indirectly for food, energy and oxygen upon   (1) parasitic organisms   (2) green plants   (3) fungi (4) animals

24. The end products of digestion that enter the lacteals are   (1) glucose   (2) minerals   (3) amino acids   (4) fatty acids

25. A student in the laboratory tossed 2 pennies from a container 100 times and recorded these results: both heads, 25; one head and one tail, 47; both tails, 28. Which cross between plants would result in approximately the same ratio?   (1) $Aa \times AA$ (2) $Aa \times Aa$ (3) $AA \times aa$ (4) $Aa \times aa$

26. A pupil would have the best chance of discovering a mutant if he worked with   (1) cattle   (2) garden peas   (3) fruitflies (4) guinea pigs

27. The growth of green plants toward light is related most specifically to the distribution in the plant of   (1) minerals   (2) enzymes (3) auxins   (4) amino acids

28. Production of Salk vaccine against polio depended upon discovery of a method for   (1) growing the polio virus outside the human body   (2) killing the polio virus   (3) observing the polio virus in the human body   (4) producing a polio antitoxin

29. The four-chambered heart is found in   (1) fish and mammals (2) birds and mammals   (3) amphibia and birds   (4) amphibia and reptiles

30. A decrease in the number of red corpuscles would result in a corresponding decrease in the blood's ability to   (1) transport oxygen   (2) destroy disease germs   (3) form fibrinogen   (4) absorb glucose

31. To determine whether an unknown black guinea pig is pure or hybrid black, it should be crossed with   (1) a white   (2) a hybrid black   (3) a pure black   (4) another unknown

32. Fossils found in the lowest rock layers are those of organisms which were   (1) completely different from the fossils found in the upper layers   (2) the same as fossils found in the upper layers   (3) more complex than today's organisms   (4) simpler than today's organisms

33. Two areas in plants where growth occurs most rapidly by mitosis are the   (1) root tip and cambium   (2) cortex and cambium (3) cortex and pith   (4) epidermis and fibrovascular bundle

34. After being in a small, poorly ventilated room for an hour with eleven other persons, a student noticed that his rate of breathing

had increased. The most probable reason for this increase is that the (1) air in the room had become hot (2) carbon dioxide concentration in his blood had increased (3) oxygen concentration in his blood had increased (4) excess water in his body needed to be eliminated

35. The principal way in which forests help to prevent soil erosion is that the (1) trees provide homes for wildlife (2) leaves of the trees manufacture food (3) forest floors absorb water (4) forest shields the soil from the sun's heat

36. Which factor in the environment of an organism causes it to react? (1) a stimulus (2) a response (3) a reflex (4) an impulse

37. A breeder wanted to develop a strain of beef cattle with good meat and the ability to thrive in a hot, dry climate. Which is the best way to accomplish this? (1) continued selection among the members of a prize herd (2) crossbreeding followed by selection (3) inbreeding to bring out desirable hidden traits (4) inbreeding followed by selection

38. The selection of algae as a possible source of additional food for man is based primarily on their ability to carry on (1) fermentation (2) digestion (3) photosynthesis (4) oxidation

39. The main reason why a new antibiotic is thoroughly tested on rats before it is used by doctors is that (1) anything that will kill a human will kill a rat (2) anything that is harmful to rats is harmful to humans (3) a drug that injures one animal is likely to injure other animals (4) a drug that cannot cure a rat cannot cure people

40. Birds and bats are both flying, warmblooded vertebrates. Yet they are *not* considered closely related because of the difference in their (1) brain structure (2) manner of feeding their young (3) ability to see (4) ability to hear

41. If a person suffered from a too rapid pulse and was nervous and irritable, the doctor might ask him to have a (1) Schick test (2) basal metabolism test (3) Wassermann test (4) Widal test

42. Which structures are *not* related to the function of excretion? (1) lungs (2) kidneys (3) salivary glands (4) sweat glands

43. Knowledge of the nucleus is important to the theory of evolution primarily because (1) all cells have nuclei (2) the sperm cell is mainly a nucleus (3) the nucleus controls cell growth (4) the nucleus contains the genes

44. As a result of crossing two hybrid yellow garden peas, 120 offspring are produced. According to the laws of chance, the most

probable number of yellow offspring is (1) 30 (2) 60 (3) 90 (4) 120

45. Food substances are made soluble in the process of (1) absorption (2) assimilation (3) digestion (4) diffusion

46. An increase in the number of rabbits in an area can affect the number of plants, insects, mice and birds. The biological principle best represented by this illustration is (1) the balance of nature (2) symbiosis (3) evolution (4) cooperation

47. Which of these would be expected to grow from a plum scion grafted to an apricot tree? (1) plums (2) apricots (3) plumcots (4) both plums and apricots

48. What is the process by which amino acids are converted into compounds useful in the repair of tissue? (1) digestion (2) secretion (3) absorption (4) assimilation

49. The primary reason why fungi are often found growing abundantly in the depths of the forest is that there (1) it is drier (2) it is cooler (3) they have an abundant supply of organic matter (4) they have little exposure to sunlight for photosynthesis

50. On the basis of structure, the members of which pair of organisms are *least* related? (1) jellyfish and tuna (2) whale and shark (3) horse and cow (4) lion and tiger

51. The carbon dioxide—oxygen cycle best shows the (1) importance of natural enemies (2) ill effects of polluting water (3) independence of green plants (4) interdependence of plants and animals

52. Four elements that make up the greatest percentage of the weight of protoplasm are hydrogen, nitrogen, oxygen and (1) carbon (2) iron (3) manganese (4) sodium

53. Scientists follow the movement of chemicals through plants by the use of (1) antibiotics (2) auxins (3) radioactive tracers (4) X-rays

54. Man's use of biological resources in such a way that future generations may continue to enjoy their benefits is called (1) conservation (2) eugenics (3) plant and animal breeding (4) specialization

55. When a parasite is in the adult stage, which function is most likely to be lost? (1) reproduction (2) assimilation (3) excretion (4) locomotion

56. The live polio vaccine which can be taken by mouth was developed by (1) Albert Sabin (2) Edward Jenner (3) Jonas Salk (4) Selman Waksman

57. Fertilization in mammals normally occurs in the   (1) uterus
(2) stomach   (3) ovary   (4) oviduct
58. The composition of lymph is similar to that of plasma, but lymph
contains more   (1) dissolved glucose   (2) red blood cells
(3) waste products from the tissues   (4) platelets
59. Which is an example of instinctive behavior?   (1) the spinning
of a spider web   (2) the knee jerk of man   (3) pulling the
hand away from a hot object   (4) the solving of a maze by a rat
60. A condition that *least* influences the succession of plants in an
area is a change in the   (1) amount of sunlight   (2) amount
of humus in the soil   (3) water content of the soil   (4) nitrogen
content of the air
61. Which nutrients are most likely to be affected by food processing
and storage?   (1) proteins   (2) carbohydrates   (3) vitamins
(4) fats
62. The genetic makeup of a person who cannot taste a certain chemical is *tt*, while that of a taster may be *TT* or *Tt*. What was the
genetic makeup of the parents if the offspring are 50% tasters and
50% nontasters?   (1) *TT* × *TT*   (2) *TT* × *tt*   (3) *tt* × *tt*   (4)
Tt × *tt*
63. Even though penicillin is used against the *Staphylococcus aureus*
germ, infections caused by it have become a serious problem in
hospitals, primarily because   (1) the hospital environment is
favorable   (2) the germ is brought in by visitors of the patients
(3) a strain of *Staphylococcus* more resistant to penicillin has
evolved   (4) many patients are allergic to penicillin
64. When a gene changes so that a new character appears in the
species, the change is called   (1) blending   (2) dominance
(3) mutation   (4) segregation
65. If the cerebellum of a pigeon were destroyed, the bird would *not*
be able to   (1) fly   (2) breathe   (3) digest food   (4)
oxidize food
66. Which is an example of a sex-linked trait?   (1) eye color   (2)
hemophilia   (3) anemia   (4) height
67. Urea is a waste product in the metabolism of   (1) fats   (2)
glucose   (3) minerals   (4) proteins
68. Bacteria of decay are   (1) parasites   (2) saprophytes   (3)
symbionts   (4) independent plants

Directions (69-70): Base your answers to items 69 and 70 on the
following information:

Equal quantities of broth were placed in three flasks and further
treated as follows:

Flask A: The broth was boiled and the flask was left open to the air.
Flask B: The broth was boiled and the flask was sealed by closing off the neck.
Flask C: The broth was not boiled, but the flask was sealed.

69. Which is the most probable observation that could be made after a few days? (1) all three flasks turbid (2) flasks A and B turbid; flask C clear (3) flasks B and C turbid; flask A clear (4) flasks A and C turbid; flask B clear

70. As a result of this experiment, which conclusion would be most nearly correct? (1) Oxygen is necessary for microbial growth. (2) Boiling prevents future growth of microbes in a medium. (3) Air contains microbes. (4) Microbes cannot live in a sealed flask.

Part II

Answer three questions from this part. Be sure that you answer all parts of each question selected.

1. Answer *a-j* with reference to the following paragraph: [10]
   Several bean seeds planted in a pot of soil were moistened regularly with distilled water and kept on a well-lighted window sill. Within three days the embryonic plants started to grow. Four weeks later the seedlings were six inches tall and the stems were bent toward the window.
   a. The germination of the seeds began as a result of (1) mineral absorption (2) water absorption (3) light absorption (4) photosynthesis
   b. The energy for the early growth of the embryonic plants came from the (1) water in the soil (2) food stored in the cotyledons (3) light energy (4) soil minerals
   c. The most important factors in the germination of the seeds were moisture and (1) light (2) darkness (3) warmth (4) nitrates
   d. Which life activity was responsible for the turning of the leaves toward the light? (1) irritability (2) transpiration (3) oxidation (4) assimilation
   e. Respiration in green plants takes place (1) in the light only (2) in the dark only (3) intermittently both in the light and in the dark (4) continuously both in the light and in the dark
   f. The bean seedling became independent only after it formed

(1) colchicine   (2) chlorophyl   (3) gibberellic acid   (4) amino acid

g. In seedlings, which class of substances converts complex carbohydrates to simpler forms?   (1) vitamins   (2) hormones   (3) enzymes   (4) minerals

h. If one of the bean seedlings were kept in complete darkness, its stem would grow upward. This illustrates   (1) positive phototropism   (2) negative phototropism   (3) negative geotropism   (4) positive geotropism

i. One of the germinating seeds was ground in a mortar, treated with Fehling's solution and heated. Immediately after heating, the color of the mixture was   (1) yellow   (2) purple   (3) blue   (4) red

j. If salt water were used instead of distilled water, the seedlings would probably die because their cells would lose   (1) water   (2) minerals   (3) carbon dioxide   (4) nitrogen

2. In *some* of the following statements the italicized term makes the statement incorrect. For each *incorrect* statement, write on the line at the right the term that must be substituted for the italicized term to make the statement correct. For each *correct* statement, write the word *true* on the line at the right.   [10]

a. The tissue in the human body with the least ability to regenerate itself is *nerve* tissue.

b. The tiny openings in the lower epidermis of a leaf are called *chloroplasts*.

c. The class of nutrients that releases the largest number of calories per gram when oxidized is *carbohydrates*.

d. The gradual change in living organisms that produces a new species is called *regeneration*.

e. Simple plants such as bacteria, yeasts and molds are classified as *algae*.

f. Protein digestion is completed in the *stomach*.

g. Fossil evidence indicates that modern birds have descended most directly from the class of animals called *amphibians*.

h. That acquired traits were not inherited was shown by *Weismann*.

i. Sensitivity to ragweed pollen is called a(an) *allergy*.

j. The sum of all the body activities, including the building up and breaking down processes, is called *anabolism*.

3. On the line at the right of each preventative or remedy in column B, write the *number* preceding the name of the disease in column

A to which that preventative or remedy is most closely related.
[10]

Column A	Column B
(1) anemia	a. Taking quinine or atabrine
(2) trichinosis	b. Immunization with toxoid
(3) rabies	c. Adding foods containing thiamin to the diet
(4) bubonic plague	d. Pasteur treatment
(5) cancer	e. Wearing shoes
(6) hemophilia	f. Eating iodized salt
(7) malaria	g. Restricting carbohydrate content of diet
(8) diabetes	h. Eating foods rich in iron
(9) beriberi	i. Cooking pork thoroughly
(10) hookworm	j. X-ray and surgery
(11) simple goiter	
(12) typhoid fever	
(13) diphtheria	
(14) smallpox	

4. *a.* Column A lists some commonly accepted evidences of evolution. In column B are some statements about some of those evidences. On the line at the right of *each* statement in column B, write the *number* preceding the evidence in column A which is most closely associated with it. [5]

Column A	Column B
(1) vestigial	a. Gill slits occur in the life history of mammals.
(2) geographical distribution	b. Similar bones are present in the arm of man and the wing of the bird.
(3) fossil	c. Kangaroos and the duckbill platypus are found almost exclusively in Australia.
(4) morphology	
(5) embryology	d. Dogs can move their ears, but humans with the same set of muscles cannot do so.
(6) breeding	
	e. Rust-resistant wheat and some late-ripening fruits are now grown in a variety of climates.

b. Below is a list of four organisms. On the line at the right of *each* statement concerning reproduction, write the *number* preceding the organism, *chosen from the list below,* with which that statement is most closely associated. [A number may be used more than once.] [5]

Organisms: (1) Frog (2) Dog (3) Ameba (4) Robin
   a. Fertilized eggs develop completely within the parent's body.
   b. With parental care, fertilized eggs develop chiefly outside the parent's body.
   c. With no parental care, fertilized eggs develop chiefly outside the parent's body.
   d. The parent produces no eggs.
   e. Embryonic development occurs chiefly in the uterus.

5. *a.* In column *B* are listed materials which *enter* the blood stream as they pass through certain structures in the body. Column *A* lists the structures in which this change occurs. On the line at the right of *each* material in column *B*, write the *number* preceding the name of the body structure in column *A* where that material enters the blood stream. [5]

Column A	Column B
(1) capillaries of the lungs	*a.* Amino acids
(2) capillaries of the villi	*b.* Red corpuscles
(3) lacteals of the villi	*c.* Oxygen
(4) pituitary	*d.* ACTH
(5) adrenals	*e.* Insulin
(6) bone marrow	
(7) Islands of Langerhans	

   b. The following schematic diagram represents a reflex arc.

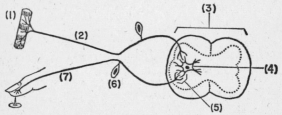

On the line at the right of *each* phrase, write the *number* from the diagram that indicates the part of the reflex arc described by the phrase. [5]
   a. The part which transmits an impulse to the cell body
   b. The neuron which transfers an impulse from the sensory neuron to the motor neuron
   c. The part which receives an impulse from the motor nerve
   d. The part of a neuron which is found in a motor nerve
   e. A synapse

BIOLOGY—JANUARY 1962 (1)

Part I

Answer all questions in this part.

Directions (1-60): For *each* statement or question, write on the separate answer sheet the *number* preceding the word or expression that, of those given, best completes the statement or answers the question. [60]

1. Which organ of higher animals is most similar in function to the contractile vacuole of protozoa? (1) stomach (2) lungs (3) kidneys (4) intestines

2. In an ameba, which characteristic of living protoplasm is most likely to be directly observed under the microscope? (1) digestion (2) movement (3) respiration (4) absorption

3. Which cell substance would one normally associate with wood? (1) cellulose (2) cytoplasm (3) plastid (4) A.T.P.

4. The life functions which the virus apparently performs are (1) respiration and reproduction (2) reproduction and locomotion (3) locomotion and respiration (4) excretion and digestion

5. The most complex substance found in cells is (1) starch (2) fat (3) protein (4) sugar

6. A cell placed in a strong salt solution will shrink because (1) the cytoplasm will decompose (2) mineral salts will break the cell wall (3) salt will enter the cell (4) water will leave by osmosis

7. Which function is *least* likely to be understood through the study of pores in cell membranes? (1) differential absorption (2) osmotic pressure (3) excretion of cell wastes (4) assimilation

8. The chemical substances that make foods soluble are called (1) hormones (2) auxins (3) antacids (4) enzymes

9. If the apparatus shown is placed in a moderately warm location, within a few hours the

   (1) molasses solution will flow into the beaker

   (2) molasses solution will turn brown

   (3) limewater will turn milky

   (4) limewater will flow into the flask

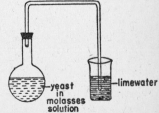
yeast in molasses solution — limewater

10. Which organisms generally make their own food?   (1) algae
    (2) bacteria   (3) molds   (4) protozoa

11. Two plants which possess xylem and phloem tissue are ferns and
    (1) algae   (2) mosses   (3) roses   (4) mushrooms

12. The only pouched mammal native to the United States is the
    (1) kangaroo   (2) armadillo   (3) opossum   (4) raccoon

13. The air immediately over a large forest on a bright summer day
    is different from the air over a large city. The most obvious dif-
    ference is that the air over a forest, compared with the air over
    a city, contains   (1) more oxygen and less carbon dioxide
    (2) more oxygen and less moisture   (3) less oxygen and
    more carbon dioxide   (4) less oxygen and more moisture

14. Which would be the best procedure for an overweight teenager
    who wanted to reduce?   (1) fast completely one day a week
    but drink plenty of water   (2) continue to eat all foods ex-
    cept desserts and bread   (3) use a completely balanced 900-
    calorie liquid diet until the desired weight is reached; then re-
    turn to her usual eating habits   (4) consult a physician to
    obtain a balanced diet

15. A plant that was placed in a totally dark box for 24 hours grew
    upright. A second plant was placed for 24 hours in a dark box
    with a hole which allowed light to enter on one side. The second
    plant grew toward the hole. The most valid conclusion from this
    experiment is that   (1) a plant responds positively to light
    (2) a plant needs light for photosynthesis   (3) auxins are nec-
    essary for plant tropisms to occur   (4) sunlight encourages
    plant growth

16. Which is a waste product of protein metabolism?   (1) urea
    (2) lymph   (3) bile   (4) glucose

17. The results of burning one ounce each of protein, carbohydrate
    and fat in a calorimeter were:

Protein	147 calories
Fat	271 calories
Carbohydrate	152 calories

    On the basis of this evidence, the correct conclusion would be
    that   (1) An ounce of fat contains approximately twice as
    many calories as an ounce of protein   (2) a protein is a better
    energy food than a carbohydrate   (3) carbohydrates, fats and
    proteins all yield approximately the same number of calories per
    unit of weight   (4) proteins and carbohydrates are the best
    source of calories in a diet

18. If two coins were flipped simultaneously a great number of times, the expected results would be   (1) two heads—50%; two tails —50%   (2) two heads—25%; one head, one tail—50%; two tails —25%   (3) two heads—25%; two tails—75%   (4) two heads—50%; one head, one tail—50%

19. If circulation of the lymph were blocked, which would most likely occur?   (1) Fat would not be digested.   (2) Glucose would continue to pass into the lacteals of the villi.   (3) Complete digestion of fats would occur in the stomach.   (4) Cells would not receive an adequate supply of food.

20. Which group of activities will be most affected by coating the under side of a geranium leaf with vaseline?   (1) irritability, photosynthesis, digestion   (2) osmosis, assimilation, excretion (3) secretion, phototropism, respiration.   (4) transpiration, respiration, photosynthesis

21. If a healthy plant whose leaves contain starch is placed in the dark for several days and then examined, the starch will be absent. The most reasonable explanation for this is that a plant (1) uses up its own starch   (2) needs oxygen for starch making   (3) needs carbon dioxide for starch making   (4) gives off oxygen during photosynthesis

22. Bean seedlings, nearly white when they first emerge from the soil, are completely green in a day or two. The green color is due to chlorophyl which was not present when the plant first appeared. This chlorophyl is   (1) extracted from green molds in the soil   (2) absorbed by the plant from the soil with the aid of sunlight   (3) synthesized by the tissues of the seedlings (4) formed as a result of photosynthesis

23. Hormones of the body pass directly from the endocrine glands into the   (1) digestive system   (2) circulatory system (3) excretory system   (4) respiratory system

24. A light stimulus which has been converted to a nerve impulse is interpreted by the   (1) cerebrum   (2) cerebellum   (3) medulla   (4) spinal cord

25. Inbreeding is used by dairymen primarily to   (1) produce larger animals   (2) produce more mutations   (3) maintain a desired quality   (4) introduce new traits

26. The sex of the mammalian offspring is determined   (1) at the time of fertilization   (2) at the time of birth   (3) before fertilization   (4) during cleavage

27. Mutations can be valuable to plant breeders because   (1) harmful mutations can be weeded out   (2) useful hereditary

traits may appear   (3) most mutations are harmful   (4) mutations usually produce hybrids

28. No white guinea pigs resulted from a cross between two hybrid black guinea pigs. Two hybrid black guinea pigs from the first filial generation were then crossed and again no white pigs resulted. The most reasonable explanation is that   (1) the genes for white color were somehow destroyed   (2) the crosses resulted in incomplete dominance   (3) the Law of Dominance was modified in this case   (4) the recessive genes for white failed to combine

29. In genetics, *crossing over* refers to the   (1) exchange of genes between two chromosomes of a pair during meiosis   (2) movement of chromosomes to the poles during mitosis   (3) movement of chromosomes from eggs to sperms during fertilization   (4) movement of genes along a chromosome

30. If two individuals who have hereditary feeblemindedness marry, how many of their offspring would most probably be feebleminded?   (1) all of them   (2) only half of them   (3) only the boys   (4) none of them

31. If two brown-eyed parents have a blue-eyed child, the genetic makeup of the parents must be   (1) *Bb* and *Bb*   (2) *Bb* and *BB*   (3) *BB* and *BB*   (4) *BB* and *bb*

32. A trait appeared in five out of six boys in a family but in none of the three girls. The trait was most likely   (1) dominant   (2) incompletely dominant   (3) recessive   (4) sex-linked

33. The member of the vertebrate group that produces the largest number of eggs is the   (1) bird   (2) fish   (3) reptile   (4) mammal

34. Probably the most likely reason why dinosaurs became extinct was that they   (1) were killed by erupting volcanoes   (2) were eaten by the advancing mammalian groups   (3) failed to adapt to a changing environment·   (4) killed each other in combat

35. Artificial selection by breeders resembles natural selection because, in both instances,·   (1) asexual reproduction can be used   (2) the number of offspring is controlled   (3) many unfit are eliminated   (4) use and disuse is involved

36. Occasionally a black mutant occurs among arctic foxes of the polar region. Such a mutant usually does not survive long because the black coat   (1) absorbs too much sunlight   (2) is linked with a lethal gene   (3) lacks the insulating effect of white   (4) interferes with the capture of food

37. The classes of vertebrates are believed to have had common ancestry mainly because   (1) all life arises only from preexisting life   (2) some members of each class are aquatic   (3) there are marked similarities between the embryos of each class   (4) warmbloodedness developed among these classes of vertebrates

38. Many types of marsupials populate the continent of Australia because it   (1) has a greater temperature range than other continents   (2) is geographically isolated from other continents   (3) is in the Southern Hemisphere   (4) has a greater variation of altitude than other countries

39. The best explanation of evolutionary changes in plants and animals is a combination of the theories of DeVries and   (1) Darwin   (2) Lamarck   (3) Linnaeus   (4) Weismann

40. Nitrogen is a constituent of   (1) fats   (2) sugars   (3) starches   (4) proteins

41. Which plants, when present in large numbers, are most likely to cause a lake gradually to become filled in?   (1) lichens   (2) elodea   (3) duckweed   (4) water lilies

42. Leaves, stems and other plant parts decay and form   (1) subsoil   (2) soil flora   (3) humus   (4) loam

43. Seed dispersal is of great value to many species of plants because it   (1) usually results in a larger number of adults   (2) can be carried out by wind or water   (3) may occur both during the day and at night   (4) is an inherited dominant characteristic

44. Which plant crop would be most likely to deplete the soil of its nitrates?   (1) clover   (2) corn   (3) alfalfa   (4) soybeans

45. The nutritional relationship between mushrooms and humus is known as   (1) parasitism   (2) saprophytism   (3) symbiosis   (4) synthesis

46. Various species of plants inhabiting the same natural community will usually be found to have similar   (1) flower structures   (2) numbers of seeds   (3) chromosome numbers   (4) environmental requirements

47. Why do the densest populations of most organisms that live in the ocean occur near the surface?   (1) The surface water is less polluted.   (2) The bottom contains radioactive materials.   (3) Salt water has more minerals than fresh.   (4) The intensity of light that reaches ocean organisms decreases as depth increases.

48. The study of the interrelationships of plants and animals with each other and with their environment is known as (1) ecology (2) morphology (3) geology (4) histology

49. An important advantage of using highly inbred strains of mice in cancer research is that (1) such mice are more resistant to cancer (2) the variable factors in an experiment are reduced (3) control groups become unnecessary (4) the number of chromosomes in the cells of mice is very small

50. What has probably been the most important reason for the great increase in the average length of life since the 18th century? (1) reduction of deaths from infectious diseases (2) conquest of cancer and heart disease (3) improvement in methods of food production (4) general improvement in housing

51. Children may be protected by the injection of "quadruple antigen" against (1) diphtheria, smallpox, tetanus and leukemia (2) diphtheria, measles, leukemia and typhoid (3) diphtheria, whooping cough, tetanus and polio (4) diphtheria, smallpox, measles and tuberculosis

52. Several years ago, the Board of Health of a city conquered a small typhoid epidemic in a certain area of that city. Of the facts found in its investigation, the one which was most important in helping to stop the spread of the disease was that, in that area, (1) a defective sewage pipe in a store leaked sewage on food (2) nests of insects were found around water pipes (3) garbage trucks had been slow in collecting garbage (4) a great number of mosquitoes were found

53. An outbreak of bubonic plague can best be prevented by (1) adding thiamin to the diet (2) destroying rats (3) destroying roaches (4) preventing the breeding of houseflies

54. DDT spray is effective in the eradication of malaria because it (1) kills the tsetse fly (2) kills mosquitoes (3) kills the malarial protozoan in the blood (4) sterilizes the home in which it is used

55. A pure culture must contain only (1) nutrient agar (2) harmless bacteria (3) lifeless matter (4) one kind of living thing

56. After a vaccination, the body builds up (1) toxins (2) antibodies (3) lymph (4) plasma

57. The most frequent cause of death of children between 5 and 14 years of age is (1) leukemia (2) pneumonia (3) influenza (4) accidents

58. Experiments with radioactive carbon can provide valuable infor-

mation mainly in connection with the process of   (1) photosynthesis   (2) transpiration   (3) evaporation   (4) condensation

59. Which substance has recently received widespread attention in investigations concerning heart and blood vessel diseases?   (1) glycerol   (2) lipase   (3) cholesterol   (4) protein

60. A suggested procedure for providing both food and oxygen on long-distance space flights is to maintain, on the rocket ship, cultures of   (1) algae   (2) molds   (3) yeasts   (4) protozoa

Part II

This part consists of six groups, each containing ten questions. Choose four of these six groups. Be sure that you answer all questions in each group chosen. Write the answers to these questions on the separate answer sheet.

Group 1

Directions (61-65). Write the word or expression that best completes *each* statement.   [5]

61. Epithelial tissue is to protection as muscle tissue is to . . . .
62. The nucleus is to reproduction as the chloroplasts are to . . . .
63. Cells are to tissues as genes are to
64. A structure that stains readily with a solution of iodine in both plant and animal cells is the
65. A structure that would show a cell to be a plant cell is the . . . .

Directions (66-70): Write the *number* preceding the system from column *B* that is most significantly associated with *each* item in column *A*.   [5]

Column A	Column B
66. Alveoli	(1) endocrine
67. Meninges	(2) reproductive
68. Islands of Langerhans	(3) digestive
69. Fibrinogen	(4) skeletal
70. Ptyalin	(5) nervous
	(6) circulatory
	(7) respiratory

Group 2

Directions (71-75): Write the *number* of the phrase from column *B* that is most closely associated with *each* plant group in column *A*. [5]

Column A	Column B
71. Bacteria	(1) are the simplest of the chlorophyl-bearing plants
72. Algae	
73. Flowering plants	(2) have cells containing centrosomes
74. Ferns	(3) have seeds enclosed in fruit
75. Conifers	(4) are nongreen plants that generally reproduce by fission
	(5) live only on organic materials
	(6) usually have needle-like leaves
	(7) are nonseed bearers with true roots, stems and leaves

Directions (78-80): Column *A* lists possible explanations for the reduction in the number of toes in the ancestry of the horse. Column *B* lists names of scientists who have contributed significant ideas in the development of the modern concept of the theory of evolution. Write the *number* preceding the name of the scientist from column *B* whose work is most closely associated with the ideas expressed in *each* explanation in column *A*.   [5]

Column A	Column B
76. Eohippus, in running swiftly, put more weight on the toe that became larger and less on those that disappeared.	(1) Darwin
	(2) DeVries
	(3) Lamarck
77. The fittest variation is one which, by mutation, arises spontaneously and happens to be an improvement.	(4) Mendel
	(5) Morgan
	(6) Muller
78. Every hereditary trait is caused by a pair of determiners, one dominant and one recessive, working independently of other traits.	(7) Weismann
79. Fleetness of foot helped to determine which of the descendants of Eohippus became the ancestor of the modern horse.	
80. Environment can change the body but not the heredity which lies in the germplasm.	

Group 3

Directions (81-85): Write the *number* of the leaf part in the diagram that is best identified by *each* phrase below. [A number may be used more than once.]   [5]

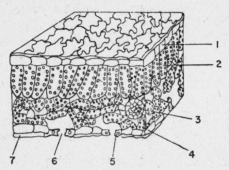

81. Principal region of food manufacture
82. Place where oxygen leaves the leaf
83. Tissue which conducts water to the leaf
84. Part that regulates the size of the stomatal openings
85. Place where carbon dioxide is given off from the leaf

Directions (86-90): Answer questions 86-90 on the basis of the information below and your knowledge of biology. Write the *number* preceding the word or expression that best completes the statement or answers the question.   [5]

A doctor examined several patients and observed the following symptoms:

   A   Overweight
   B   Metabolism above normal (rapid)
   C   Sugar in the urine
   D   Calcium content in the blood—low
   E   Stiff joints
   F   Emotional instability
   G   Beginning of tetany

86. What gland must be treated to alleviate symptom *B*?   (1) thyroid   (2) parathyroid   (3) pancreas   (4) adrenal
87. Which symptom is *least* likely to be found in a patient who complains of symptom *B*?   (1) *A*   (2) *F*   (3) *C*   (4) *D*

88. Which gland is probably malfunctioning to cause symptom *C*?
    (1) thyroid   (2) parathyroid   (3) pancreas   (4) adrenal
89. Which symptom is probably responsible for symptom *G*?   (1)
    A   (2) *B*   (3) *C*   (4) *D*
90. Symptom *E* will probably be alleviated by treatment with the
    combination of cortisone and   (1) thyroxin   (2) ACTH
    (3) adrenin   (4) pituitrin

Group 4

Directions (91-95): Write the *number* of the biological principle in
column *B* that is most closely associated with *each* statement in column *A*.   [5]

Column A	Column B
91. A mule is superior in many ways to either of its two parents.	(1) inbreeding
92. Breeders are constantly on the lookout for the sudden appearance of new traits.	(2) selection
	(3) hybridization
93. Mating members of the same litter may result in establishing pure lines for desirable traits.	(4) vegetative propagation
	(5) backcross
	(6) mutations
94. Man has commonly picked the fastest horses for breeding.	
95. Mating with a recessive will determine if an animal with a dominant trait is pure or hybrid.	

Directions (96-100): Answer questions 96-100 on the basis of the
diagram below and your knowledge of biology. Write the word or expression that, when inserted in the blank, will correctly complete *each*
statement.   [5]

96. The cell indicated by letter *A* is a (an) . . . .
97. The process which results in the formation of the cell indicated
    by letter *C* is . . . .

98. The cell shown by letter *B* is manufactured in an organ called the . . . .
99. The chromosome number in cells *A* and *B* is produced by the process known as . . . .
100. The cell shown by letter *C* will immediately begin to undergo a process called . . . .

Group 5

Directions (101-105): Write the *number* of the disease in column *B* that is most closely associated with *each* statement in column A. [5]

Column A	*Column B*
101. Known to be caused by irritation from stone dust	(1) diphtheria
102. Prevented by a toxoid	(2) cretinism
103. Treated with radioactive iodine	(3) dysentery
104. Development prevented by the Pasteur treatment	(4) cancer
105. Prevented by proper sewage disposal	(5) silicosis
	(6) rabies
	(7) poliomyelitis

Directions (106-110): Write the *number* of the term in column *B* that is most closely associated with *each* statement in column A. [5]

Column A	*Column B*
106. Some organisms, such as the crocodile and the crocodile bird, live in mutually beneficial partnership.	(1) symbiosis
107. Some minnows which feed on algae are important to larger fish which provide energy for man.	(2) climax organism
108. An increase in the number of rabbits in an area can affect the number of plants, insects, mice and birds.	(3) succession
109. On a field successive crops of peas, wheat, clover and wheat are planted.	(4) crop rotation
110. An area in which aquatic plants flourish gradually becomes populated with cattails; later grasses and other plants appear, followed by shrubs.	(5) sandy beach community
	(6) balance of nature
	(7) food chain

BIOLOGY—JANUARY 1962 (12)

Group 6

Directions (111-120): In *some* of the following statements the ital
icized term makes the statement incorrect. For each *incorrect* state
ment, write the term that must be substituted for the italicized term to
make the statement correct. For each *correct* statement, write the word
true.   [10]

111. The brightly colored petals of many flowers can be important to
the survival of the *species.*

112. The fossilized remains of the saber-toothed tiger have been found
preserved in *amber.*

113. The fact that reptiles and birds show many structural resem-
blances can be explained on the basis of similar *environment*

114. The useless remnants of organs which were functional in the
ancestor of a present-day animal are called *fossils.*

115. Flora and fauna in geographic locations which are isolated for
long periods of geologic time generally have species which are
quite *similar.*

116. The *Sabin* vaccine for polio is administered by injection.

117. The element in radioactive fallout which is most dangerous because it concentrates in bone tissue is *iodine.*

118. The essential constituent of a virus is *DNA.*

119. The ability to resist disease is called *susceptibility.*

120. The antibiotic most effective in treating tuberculosis is *penicillin.*

BIOLOGY—JUNE 1962 (1)

Part I

Answer all questions in this part.

Directions (1-60): For *each* statement or question, write on the separate answer sheet the *number* preceding the word or expression that, of those given, best completes the statement or answers the question. [60]

1. All living cells, regardless of origin, contain (1) a plasma membrane and cytoplasm (2) a nucleus and vacuoles (3) a centrosome and mitochondria (4) a cell wall and chloroplasts

2. The fact which best supports the position that viruses are living is that viruses (1) are made of common chemicals (2) duplicate themselves (3) cause disease (4) penetrate cell membranes

3. A boy examining his finger under a microscope could detect no epidermal cells because (1) these cells are located under the skin (2) a finger consists of living tissue (3) a finger is about one-half inch thick (4) each single cell is larger than the area of the microscope field

4. A trace element is an element that (1) is radioactive and can be traced with a Geiger counter (2) is present in very minute amounts in protoplasm (3) draws other elements out of protoplasm (4) was one of the first to be discovered in protoplasm

5. Catabolism, the destructive phase of metabolism, includes (1) protein synthesis (2) A.T.P. production (3) hormone production (4) fat digestion

6. If the body of an ameba is punctured, its cytoplasm will cover the opening with a (1) cell wall (2) tissue (3) pseudo-podium (4) cell membrane

7. Which two structures are present in plant cells? (1) a centrosome and a nucleus (2) a chloroplast and an oral groove (3) the cytoplasm and cilia (4) the cell wall and vacuoles

8. A piece of wilted celery becomes crisp when placed in tap water because it (1) loses water (2) absorbs water (3) loses solutes (4) absorbs solutes

9. Cells are to tissues as organs are to (1) cells (2) tissues (3) systems (4) genes

10. The first complete animal body to be formed on earth most likely resembled that of the present-day (1) paramecium (2) sponge (3) ameba (4) spirogyra

11. An earthworm is more like a fly than it is a small snake in that both the earthworm and the fly (1) are invertebrates (2) eat decaying food (3) excrete wastes (4) are small

12. Which statement concerning all coldblooded animals is true? (1) Their bodies are cold to the touch. (2) Their body fluid has no constant temperature. (3) They thrive in cold places. (4) They are carnivorous.

13. To test the urine of a suspected diabetic, one would use a test tube, a bunsen flame and (1) nitric acid (2) ammonium hydroxide (3) iodine solution (4) Benedict's solution

14. The acquired ability of an animal to perform certain acts is an example of (1) an instinct (2) an autonomic response (3) a simple reflex (4) a learned habit pattern

15. Which is represented in the demonstration shown in the diagram?

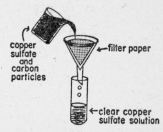

(1) separation of urea from blood in the kidneys

(2) action of capillaries connecting arteries and veins

(3) formation of antibodies in the blood

(4) reclaiming of hemoglobin by the liver

16. A chemical that retards blood clotting would be most useful in the treatment of (1) hemophilia (2) anemia (3) leukemia (4) coronary thrombosis

17. The materials that would be most useful in demonstrating that germinating seeds give off carbon dioxide are a glass bottle, glass tubing, (1) limewater, a rubber stopper, lima beans (2) colchicine, test tubes, wheat (3) a rubber stopper, beaker, lima beans (4) a battery jar, limewater, sawdust

18. Which factor is *least* related to the fact that blood flows at different rates in different blood bessels? (1) force of the heartbeat (2) diameter of the blood vessels (3) amount of oxyhemoglobin present in the red blood cells (4) contraction of the walls of the vessels

19. Blue cobalt paper becomes pink when moist. Pieces of blue cobalt paper are attached to both the upper and lower surfaces of

a geranium plant leaf. A third piece of blue cobalt paper is placed on the window sill beside the plant. After about a half hour, one would expect that the piece of cobalt paper on the (1) under side of the leaf would become pink, and the others would not change (2) upper side of the leaf would become pink, and the others would not change (3) window sill would turn pink, and the others would not change (4) window sill would remain blue, and the others would turn pink

20. Which part of the central nervous system is concerned with the same function as the semicircular canals of the inner ear? (1) cerebrum (2) medulla (3) cerebellum (4) spinal cord

21. The rate of the heartbeat is controlled by the (1) cerebrum (2) cerebellum (3) medulla (4) spinal cord

Directions (22-24): Answer questions 22 through 24 on the basis of the statement below and on your knowledge of biology.

> A student examined a microscope slide of cells that had been removed from a root and noted these three types:
> Cell No. 1—very thin walls
> Cell No. 2—thick heavy walls, cell dead
> Cell No. 3—mitotic division taking place

22. Cell No. 1 was most likely a (1) root hair cell (2) cell in the growing region (3) root cap cell (4) palisade cell

23. Cell No. 2 was most likely a (1) root hair cell (2) cell in the growing region (3) root cap cell (4) palisade cell

24. Cell No. 3 was most likely a (1) root hair cell (2) cell in the growing region (3) root cap cell (4) palisade cell

25. A chemical called P.T.C. tastes bitter to about 75% of the people. The other 25% do not detect any taste in P.T.C. The ability to taste P.T.C. has been traced to a single pair of genes which follow the Mendelian Law of Dominance. What inference can most reasonably be drawn from this description of the action of P.T.C.? (1) The nontasters of P.T.C. are probably pure recessives. (2) The nontasters of P.T.C. probably do not taste other chemicals well either. (3) The tasters of P.T.C. are probably all pure homozygous types. (4) The tasters of P.T.C. probably have inherited an ability to learn the taste of P.T.C.

26. The correct explanation for the fact that offspring result from the crossing of animals of the same or closely related species is that

the egg and sperm of the same or related species   (1) are most closely related with respect to size   (2) contain the same number of chromosomes   (3) have the same number of molecules (4) have fewer mutations

27. The number of functional egg cells usually produced by each primary sex cell during oogenesis is   (1) 1   (2) 2   (3) 3 (4) 4

28. Inbreeding among humans is generally considered unwise because of the greater possibility that an undesirable trait, such as feeble-mindedness, may appear. Which is the best explanation for this? (1) When inbreeding occurs, the undesirable trait becomes stronger and shows up in the offspring.   (2) When parents are closely related, undesirable dominant traits are more likely to be created.   (3) Inbreeding leads to a higher probability of combination of recessive genes of the undesirable trait from normal parents.   (4) There is a chemical incompatibility between genes of closely related parents which results in the appearance of an undesirable trait.

29. Bacteriologists frequently dip a sterile needle into a tube containing live bacteria and streak the needle across the surface of solid agar on which the bacteria will grow. The purpose of this technique is to   (1) make a bacterial count   (2) isolate a single strain of bacteria   (3) put bacteria into the agar so that they can absorb food better   (4) digest the agar so that the food is available in liquid form

30. A dog breeder can determine that a "hairless" dog is a mutation if the dog   (1) is still "hairless" after 5 years   (2) shows no change in the "hairless" condition after its diet is changed   (3) develops other conspicuous differences from the parent   (4) is bred and the trait is capable of being inherited

31. Artificial parthenogenesis is achieved by the development of an egg which   (1) has been fertilized before treatment with chemicals   (2) has been fertilized after treatment with chemicals (3) is unfertilized but has been treated by chemical or physical methods   (4) has been fertilized and kept at proper temperature before and after treatment with chemicals

32. The germ plasm from both parents is combined at the time of (1) reduction division   (2) mitosis   (3) segregation   (4) fertilization

33. After the sperm nucleus and the egg nucleus fuse, the resulting embryo develops by the process called   (1) cleavage   (2) fertilization   (3) reproduction   (4) specialization

34. Evolution is going on at the present time. This is best shown by the   (1) continuous formation of sedimentary rock   (2) development of new organisms   (3) increase of environmental changes   (4) preservation of plants and animals by man

35. There is little likelihood of reaching complete agreement on the biological classification of organisms because many forms exist which are   (1) intermediate between two diverse groups   (2) known only by their fossils   (3) the result of human selection and cultivation   (4) restricted to a small environmental area

36. The suggestion that all vertebrates probably have a stock of genes in common with one another is supported most strongly by the   (1) hard-shelled eggs of birds and reptiles   (2) two-chambered hearts of fish   (3) observance of structural similarities   (4) theory of mutation

37. Fish are considered more primitive than reptiles because many structures of the   (1) adult fish also occur in the adult reptile   (2) adult fish occur only in the embryo of the reptile   (3) embryo fish occur in the adult reptile   (4) adult reptile are found in the embryo of the fish

38. Although Madagascar is separated from Africa only by a narrow strait, many plants and animals common on the mainland are unknown on the island. This fact illustrates the principle of   (1) incomplete dominance   (2) evolutionary equilibrium   (3) evolution in isolated populations   (4) succession

39. Which scientist first stressed the importance of survival of the fittest?   (1) Darwin   (2) Beadle   (3) De Vries   (4) Weismann

40. All food chains include   (1) parasites   (2) independent plants   (3) aquatic birds   (4) lichens

41. Respiration of all living things contributes to green plants a supply of   (1) carbon dioxide   (2) oxygen   (3) water   (4) nitrogen

42. Which group represents the most probable order of succession of plants in a barren, rocky area?   (1) mosses, grasses, shrubs, trees   (2) lichens, mosses, grasses, shrubs   (3) lichens, grasses, shrubs, mosses   (4) grasses, shrubs, trees, mosses

43. When the ecological factors of the environment change rather drastically, the organisms must die, migrate or   (1) reproduce   (2) readapt   (3) rejuvenate   (4) hibernate

44. The methods of agriculture used by humans have created serious insect problems primarily because these methods   (1) increase soil erosion   (2) provide concentrated areas of food for insects

(3) increase the effectiveness of insecticides over a long period of time   (4) grow crops in former desert areas

45. Which is an example of an ecological community?   (1) the lawn outside your school   (2) an oak tree   (3) all the people in your town or city   (4) all the whales in the world

46. Which does *not* reduce the content of nitrogen compounds in the soil?   (1) leaching   (2) erosion   (3) growing crops   (4) adding green manure

47. Under natural conditions large quantities of organic matter decay after each year's plant growth has been completed. As a result of such conditions   (1) many animals are deprived of adequate food supplies   (2) soils maintain their fertility   (3) soils soon become exhausted if not fertilized   (4) soil erosion is accelerated

48. Parasitic organisms may be considered beneficial to man when the host organism is   (1) beneficial to man   (2) more numerous than the parasite   (3) harmful to man   (4) unharmed by the parasite

49. A drop of anti-A blood typing serum was placed on the left side of a slide and a drop of anti-B serum on the right side. Then a drop of blood was mixed into the serum on the left and another drop into the serum on the right. If the blood was type A, the red blood cells would be clumped on   (1) the right side only   (2) the left side only   (3) both sides   (4) neither side

50. Radioactive isotopes are likely to be most useful in treating certain types of   (1) cancer   (2) heart disease   (3) infection   (4) high blood pressure

51. The people most likely to check the daily reports of pollen counts are those who are interested in   (1) allergies   (2) cross-pollinating plants   (3) self-pollinating plants   (4) new types of plants

52. The parasitic animals that cause malaria live in and bring about great destruction of the red blood cells of the victim. This may result in   (1) severe anemia   (2) weight gain   (3) increased energy   (4) increased hemoglobin content

53. In a trial of the Salk vaccine involving 1,830,000 school children, only 440,000 of these children actually received the vaccine. The remainder were *not* given the vaccine because they   (1) had a natural immunity   (2) had an acquired immunity   (3) had had polio   (4) served as a control

54. Animals fed vitamin B_{12} show increased growth. Pure vitamin B_{12} is extracted from waste materials left in vats in which antibiotics

are made. Animals fed rations that include wastes from the anti-biotic vats grow faster than those fed only pure vitamin B₁₂. It is probable that (1) waste from the antibiotic vats contains a growth promoter other than vitamin B₁₂ (2) pure vitamin B₁₂ is not a growth promoter at all (3) the waste material in the vats contains vitamin B₁₂ which the process does not extract (4) antibiotics are better growth promoters than vitamin B₁₂

55. Which disease is associated with eating uncooked pork? (1) tetanus (2) hookworm disease (3) lockjaw (4) trichinosis

56. In the emergency situation during an operation in which the rate of heartbeat decreases, a doctor would be most likely to administer an injection of (1) insulin (2) ACTH (3) adrenalin (4) thyroxin

57. A study of the death rates of policy holders of a large life insurance company showed the following:

	Deaths per 100,000	
	1911	1957
Tuberculosis	224.6	6.7
Communicable Diseases of Childhood	58.9	.1
Cancer	69.3	136.2
Heart Disease	156.4	256.2

The study shows most clearly that (1) cancer of the lungs is increasing (2) people are living longer (3) children are safer from communicable diseases (4) better housing can reduce deaths from tuberculosis

58. A substance named calvacin which prevents the growth of certain types of tumors has been extracted from a species of giant puff-ball mushroom. The most probable *immediate* use of this substance would be as a (1) supplement to the diet of cancer patients (2) basis for new cancer experiments (3) new method of treating cancer (4) new method of destroying unwanted growths in both plants and animals

59. In the United States the death rate from a certain form of cancer has declined 40% in the last 25 years. The reason generally given is that this decline is the result primarily of (1) increased resistance to the disease (2) the discovery of a definite cure for cancer (3) earlier diagnosis and treatment (4) greater availability of more radioactive isotopes

60. The number of chromosomes in a human somatic (body) cell is now generally agreed to be   (1) 48   (2) 46   (3) 24   (4) 23

Part II

This part consists of six groups, each containing ten questions. Choose four of these six groups. Be sure that you answer all questions in each group chosen. Write the answers to these questions on the separate answer sheet.

Group 1

Directions (61-65): For *each* description in column *A* write the *number* of the structure in the drawing in column *B* that best fits that description.   [5]

Column A	Column B
	Cell

61. The structure with semipermeable action in selecting those substances which can enter and leave the cell
62. A semipermeable membrane that disappears during mitosis but reappears after the cell has divided
63. A structure that stores water
64. The structure that contains the determiners of heritable characteristics
65. The structure which acts as the controlling center of cellular activities

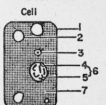

Directions (66-70): For *each* description in column *A* write the *number* of the scientist in column *B* best identified by that description.   [5]

Column A

66. First saw and named cells in cork
67. Found that X-rays caused important changes in the molecular structure
68. First recognized that all cells have nuclei and named the structure
69. First published the theory that all parts of all plants are made of cells
70. First postulated the existence of genes

Column B

(1) Brown
(2) Schleiden
(3) Von Mohl
(4) Darwin
(5) Morgan
(6) Hooke
(7) Muller

Group 2

Directions (71-75): For *each* phrase in column A, write the *number* of the animal group in column B which is best described by that phrase. [A number may be used more than once.]   [5]

Column A	Column B
71. Lay eggs with a calcareous shell	(1) fish and
72. Lay eggs with a leathery shell	amphibia
73. Usually have external fertilization and external development	(2) insects
	(3) reptiles
74. Produce young that are warm-blooded	(4) birds
75. Produce young with an external skeleton	

Directions (76-80): For *each* biological fact write the *number* of the biological generalization from the list below which best explains that fact. [A number may be used more than once.]   [5]

Biological Generalizations

(1) Plants and animals are interrelated.
(2) Plants and animals have changed over long periods of time.
(3) Plants and animals that are similar share similar gene pools.
(4) Plants and animals are adapted to their environment.

Biological Facts

76. Cactus plants have leaves modified into spines.
77. The python has vestigial hind legs.
78. A fish in a sealed aquarium dies if the plants are removed.
79. A walking stick insect is difficult to see in its habitat.
80. Archaeopteryx was the link between reptiles and birds.

Group 3

Directions (81-85): Answer questions 81 through 85 on the basis of the following selection from the work of an early scientist and on your knowledge of biology, by writing the word or expression that best completes *each* statement.   [5]

A sprig of a nettle plant was put in a jar full of
air fouled by breathing so as to extinguish a candle;
it was placed in a room during the whole night; the
next morning the air was found to be as bad as before. At 9 o'clock in the morning the jar was put in
the sunshine and in the space of two hours the air
was so much corrected that it was found to be
nearly as good as common air.

81. The "jar full of air fouled by breathing" probably contained an
excess of the gas . . . .
82. The fact that "the air was found to be as bad as before" was due
to the process of . . . taking place in the plant.
83. The plant performed the process of . . . to produce air nearly as
good as "common air."
84. The gas produced by the plant in the process which improved the
air in the jar is called . . . .
85. The gas which was produced by the plant in the dark is
called . . . .

Directions (86-90): For *each* substance in column A, write the
number of the part of the body in column B from which that substance enters the circulatory system.   [5]

Column A	Column B
86. Cortisone	(1) lungs
87. Amino acids	(2) liver
88. New red corpuscles	(3) skin
89. Oxygen	(4) adrenals
90. Fatty acids	(5) thoracic duct
	(6) bone marrow
	(7) small intestine

Group 4

Directions (91-95): For *each* statement in column A write the
number of the biologic principle from column B that is most closely
associated with that statement.   [5]

Column A

91. When crossed, two tall pea plants produced 25% short plants.
92. The gene for colorblindness is carried on the X-chromosome.
93. All the F₁ offspring of a cross between black and white guinea pigs were black.
94. The blue Andalusian fowl does not resemble either parent.
95. A Neurospora culture (mold) loses its ability to synthesize a certain vitamin.

Column B

(1) linkage
(2) backcross
(3) segregation
(4) dominance
(5) blending inheritance
(6) crossing over
(7) mutation

Directions (96-100): Write the term (*decreases, increases, remains the same*) that, when inserted in the blank, will correctly complete the statement.   [5]

96. As a result of outbreeding, the chance of getting recessive traits to appear . . . .
97. As the amount of parental care provided for the young increases, the number of eggs produced . . . .
98. The ratio of mutations produced in a wild population of fruitflies from generation to generation . . . .
99. As a result of sporulation, the chance for an organism to survive unfavorable conditions . . . .
100. As a result of exposure to radiation, the mutation rate . . . .

Group 5

Directions (101-105): For *each* disease in column A, write the *number* of the word from column B which best describes or classifies that disease.   [5]

Column A

101. Malaria
102. Diabetes
103. Tuberculosis
104. Poliomyelitis
105. Beriberi

Column B

(1) bacterial
(2) virus
(3) hereditary
(4) protozoan
(5) nutritional deficiency
(6) endocrine
(7) fungus

Directions (106-110): Write the word or expression that, when inserted in the blank, will correctly complete *each* statement. [5]

106. When the hydrogen in foods is oxidized, the compound . . . is formed.
107. A series of organisms in which each in turn serves as food for the next organism is known as a (an) . . . .
108. Plants that live on the dead bodies of plants or animals are called . . . .
109. The plants that assume final control in a plant community are known ecologically as the . . . plants.
110. Soil is a mixture of decomposed rock and organic products called . . . .

Group 6

Directions (111-120): In *some* of the following statements the term in italics makes the statement incorrect. For each *incorrect* statement, write the term that must be substituted for the italicized term to make the statement correct. For each *correct* statement write the word *true*. [10]

111. The ratio of *Carbon 14* to lead is used to determine the age of a mineral in a rock.
112. The area of the brain that became dominant in the evolution of the mammals was the *cerebellum*.
113. A young girl, 8 feet 2 inches tall, is still growing. This condition is probably due to an abnormality of the *thyroid* gland.
114. An antibiotic used in the treatment of syphilis is *penicillin*.
115. The actual bending of a plant stem toward the window is due to the accumulation of auxins on the side of the stem *away from* the window.
116. A rise in the concentration of carbon dioxide in the blood will stimulate the *cerebellum* to increase the rate of breathing.
117. The liquid portion of whole blood which remains after clotting is called *plasma*.
118. The digestive enzyme pepsin is secreted by glands in the *small intestine*.
119. Infectious hepatitis is a disease caused by a (an) *virus*.
120. Two substances useful in promoting blood clotting are fibrinogen and *vitamin C*.

INDEX

1

AMSCO SCHOOL PUBLICATIONS

SCIENCE

General Science, Health, Biology, Chemistry, Physics
Workbooks and Laboratory Manuals—Chemistry, Physics

MATHEMATICS

Mathematics (7th and 8th Years)
Elementary Algebra (9th Year)
Intermediate Algebra
Plane Geometry
Tenth Year Mathematics
Eleventh Year Mathematics
Trigonometry

HISTORY

Social Studies   *American History*   *World History*

FOREIGN LANGUAGES

Latin—First Year, Two Years, Three Years
French—First Year, Two Years, Three Years
Spanish—First Year, Two Years, Three Years
Workbook in French—First Year, Two Years
Workbook in Spanish—First Year, Two Years

ENGLISH

Comprehensive English (Three and Four Years)
Review Text in English Language Arts—Preliminary
Lessons in Reading Comprehension
Adventures With Words—Book I, Book II, Book III
Drill for Skill   *Grammar at Work*
Corrective English   *Grammar for Today*
Essentials of English   *Words at Work*

COMMERCIAL

Typewriting